Failure Mode and Effect Analysis

Also available from ASQC Quality Press

Weibull Analysis
Bryan T. Dodson

Volume 15: How to Determine Sample Size and Estimate Failure Rate in Life Testing
Eduardo C. Moura

Reliability: Management, Methods, and Mathematics, Second Edition
David K. Lloyd and Myron Lipow

To request a complimentary catalog of publications,
call 800-248-1946.

Failure Mode and Effect Analysis
FMEA from Theory to Execution

D. H. Stamatis

ASQC Quality Press
Milwaukee, Wisconsin

Failure Mode and Effect Analysis: FMEA from Theory to Execution
D. H. Stamatis

Library of Congress Cataloging-in-Publication Data

Stamatis, D. H., 1947–
Failure mode and effect analysis: FMEA from theory to execution /
D. H. Stamatis.
p. cm.
Includes bibliographical references (p.). and index.
ISBN 0-87389-300-X
1. Reliability (Engineering) 2. Quality control. I. Title.
TS175.S7517 1994
620'.00452—dc20 94-32121
CIP

10 9 8 7 6 5 4 3

ISBN 0-87389-300-X

Acquisitions Editor: Susan Westergard
Project Editor: Jeanne W. Bohn
Production Editor: Annette Wall
Marketing Administrator: Mark Olson
Set in Garamond and Futura by Pecatonica Publishing Services.
Cover design by D. H. Stamatis.
Printed and bound by BookCrafters, Inc.

ASQC Mission: To facilitate continuous improvement and increase customer satisfacion by identifying, communicating, and promoting the use of quality principles, concepts, and technologies; and thereby be recognized through the world as the leading authority on, and champion for, quality.

For a free copy of the ASQC Quality Press Publications Catalog, including ASQC membership information, call 800-248-1946.

Printed in the United States of America

Printed on acid-free recycled paper

ASQC
Quality Press
611 East Wisconsin Avenue
Milwaukee, Wisconsin 53202

To my wonderful wife Carla Jeanne,
daughter Christine, and
sons Cary, Stephen, and Timothy

Contents

List of FMEA Samples

All samples are real and represent a variety of different industries. Due to their proprietary nature, changes were made to eliminate company identification. Some of the FMEAs are still being developed and do not have all the columns filled or are only partly presented.

List of Figures

Figures

List of Tables

Tables

Preface

It was late 1987 when I first started using the concepts of failure mode and effect analysis (FMEA). Up to that point my familiarity with the topic was strictly from an academic and reliability engineering point of view.

It was a contractual agreement between Ford Motor Company and Eastern Michigan University that led me to apply the FMEA in industrial environments. Easy application and the many benefits gained through FMEAs with Ford Motor Company and their supplier base impressed me so much that since then I have devoted a tremendous amount of my time training and consulting in FMEA throughout the United States, Europe, and Southeast Asia.

The fundamental cornerstone of FMEA is the need to improve. It is this need that becomes the impetus for change. Change in this case may be modifications, improvements, and/or a complete change. The idea that the FMEA proposes is not revolutionary; it is a simple yet systematic methodology used to approach problems, concerns, challenges, errors, and failures, to seek answers for improvement.

This book results from my efforts to document the concept and implementation of the FMEA. It may be the first full-length book on reliability that establishes the legal need for an FMEA, contributes to the theory of FMEA, and offers a practical rationale and step-by-step approach to carrying out an FMEA. It explains the process of conducting an FMEA and gives the rationale for doing so. Specifically, it addresses issues such as: What is an FMEA? How is it used? What are some other tools (if any) that we may use instead of, or with, an FMEA? What is the specific methodology of conducting an FMEA? Is the FMEA applicable to all industries? How does the FMEA relate to service? Does the FMEA apply to the ISO 9000 series standards and the product liability directive?

Acknowledgments

In any endeavor, more than one person is responsible for carrying the task to completion. The efforts resulting in this book are no exception. Many people have contributed to the production of this book, either directly or indirectly.

I want to thank Prentice Hall for giving me permission to use some of the material from *Reliability Engineering Handbook* (volumes 1 and 2) by Dimitri Kececioglu, and *Logistics Engineering and Management,* 3rd edition, by Benjamin S. Blanchard.

I want to thank the SAE and Dr. Alvin S. Weinstein for giving me permission to use and summarize some of the materials on product liability from the seminar material given by SAE under the title *Product Liability and the Engineer,* SAE publication #82002.

I also want to thank Shepard's/McGraw-Hill Inc. for allowing me to use some data from *Products Liability: Design and Manufacturing Defects* by Lewis Bass.

Furthermore, I want to thank Mr. D. Lazor and Mr. B. Schwartz Jr. from Ford Motor Company for giving me the opportunity to work on an FMEA; and the corporate quality department at Ford for their permission to use some of the early data on FMEA.

Thanks to the Motorola Company for permitting use of some failures found in the semiconductor industry from *Reliability and Quality Handbook,* 1992 edition.

A thank you to Aspen Publication for giving me permission to summarize some of the chapters dealing with Law of Reliability from *Legal Aspects of Health Care Administration* by G. Pozgar.

I also want to thank Mr. H. Cardenas from Texas Instruments for discussing issues and concerns in that industry.

Thanks also go to J. Baker from LifeScan Company, Mr. S. Hall from Hewlett Packard, E. J. Dammeyer from Sandoz Pharmaceuticals, and M. G. Peterson from Ford Motor Company for discussing issues that deal with specific trouble spots in utilizing an FMEA.

Special thanks go to judges J. Kandrevas and T. Chionos and attorney M. Golematis for reviewing and helping in the compilation of the reliability section and the legal references.

To all the participants of my public seminars over the years, I owe a large thank you for offering suggestions and specific failures, causes, and effects. I have included as many as possible. Without the participants' comments and input, this book would not have been possible.

I also want to thank Mr. R. Munro and editors of this book for reviewing and offering suggestions for improvement.

Introduction

In the past 100 years or so, the United States has been the envy of the world. This country has been the leader in almost every major innovation people have made. The historical trend has been positive indeed. But what about the future? Should the status quo be retained? Is there anything to worry about? Can the leadership for tomorrow be guaranteed by following past successes?

Yes, indeed the United States wants to be among the leaders; it wants to be better; its citizens want to work smart and be efficient. But with leadership and general betterment comes change—change in behavior and technology. The old ways served workers well but not anymore. The following saying describes the situation best.

> If you always do what you always did, you will always get what you always got.

What the United States has is not good enough anymore as world competition increases. The United States must improve or it will be left behind to those who will pursue technological and quality improvements for their products and/or services. Stated in simple terms: This country must change.

As with any transformation, this change brings uncertainty and risk. The recognition that all well-managed companies are interested in preventing or at least minimizing risk in their operations is the concept of risk management analysis. Bass (1986) showed this concern of risk in Figure I.1. The requirements for performing such analysis may be

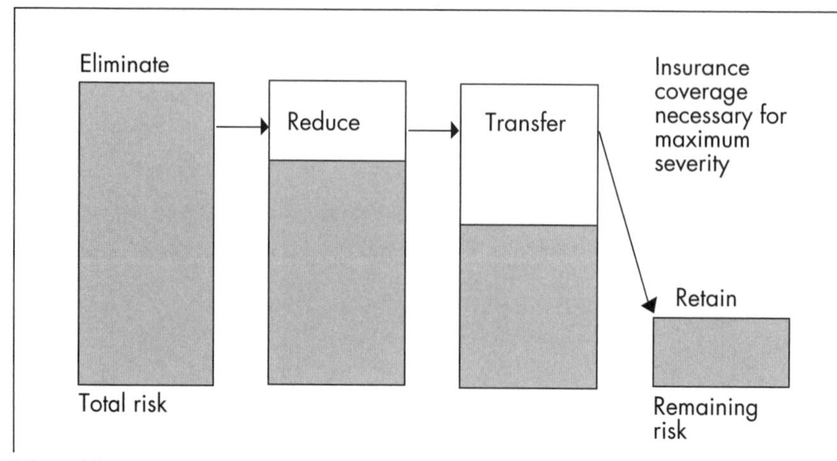

Adopted from Bass, L. 1986. *Products Liability: Design and Manufacturing Defects*. Colorado Springs, Colo.: Shepard's/McGraw-Hill. Used with permission. Modifications were made by author.

Figure I.1 Loss control sequence.

extensive and demanding. The elimination, control, or reduction of risk is a total commitment by the entire organization, and it is more often than not the responsibility of the engineering department.

The focus of identifying and/or analyzing the risks may be due to a variety of reasons, such as customer requests, continual improvement philosophy, and competition. This is shown in Figure I.2.

The risk analysis has a fundamental purpose of answering the following two questions (Stamatis 1989, 1991, 1992).

1. What can go wrong?
2. If something does go wrong, what is the probability of it happening, and what is (are) the consequence(s)?

To answer these questions, problems used to be examined. Of course, by focusing on problems it was assumed that somebody was to blame, and action was taken.

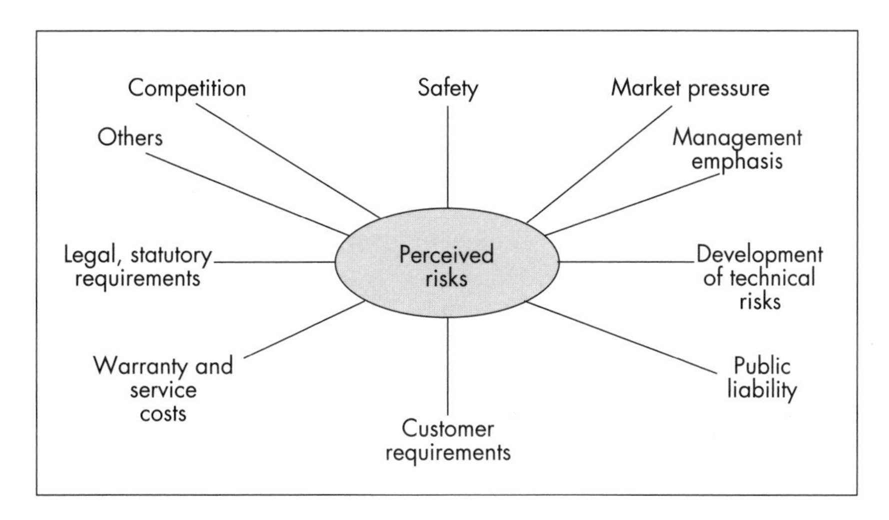

Figure I.2 Pressures leading to overall perception of risks.

Today, that paradigm has changed. The focus is on prevention. A comparison of the shift in thinking follows.

Old way	New way
Solution of problems	Prevention of problems
Monitoring of waste	Elimination of waste
Quantification of reliability	Reduction of unreliability

This book addresses the issue of risk elimination by focusing on the failure mode and effect analysis (FMEA). FMEA is a specific methodology to evaluate a system, design, process, or service for possible ways in which failures (problems, errors, risks, concerns) can occur.

For each of the failures identified (whether known or potential), an estimate is made of its occurrence, severity, and detection. At that point, an evaluation is made of the necessary action to be taken, planned, or ignored. The emphasis is to minimize the probability of failure or to minimize the effect of failure.

This simple but straightforward approach can be technical (quantitative) or nontechnical (qualitative). In either case, the focus is on the risk one is willing to take. By definition, the FMEA becomes a systematic technique using engineering knowledge, reliability, and organizational development techniques; in other words, teams to optimize the system, design, process, product, and/or service (Stamatis 1991a).

The complication of the approach always depends on the complexity of the problem as defined by the following (Juran and Gryna 1980):

1. *Safety*—Injury is the most serious of all failure effects. In fact, in some cases it is of unquestionable priority. At this point it must be handled either with a hazard analysis and/or failure mode and critical analysis (FMCA).
2. *Effects on downtime*—What problems are affecting yield? How is that effect being monitored? What type of testing is available? Is the testing appropriate? How are repairs made? Are the repairs appropriate? Is preventive maintenance part of quality planning? Can the repairs be made while the machine is off-line or should they be made while the machine is operating? Is corrective action actively pursued?
3. *Repair planning*—Repair time; maintainability; repair costs; repair tools; recommendation(s) for changes in specifications in fit, form, and function. The Shingo (Poka-Yoke) approach, design of experiments (DOE), or design for manufacturability (DFM) may be considered for this problem.
4. *Access*—What hardware items must be removed to gain access to the failed component? This area will be of great importance as environmental laws and regulations are introduced and/or changed to reflect world conditions for disassembly, removal, and disposal.

To carry this methodology to its proper conclusion there are at least four prerequisites that must be understood and followed.

1. *All problems are not the same.* Not all problems are equally important. This is perhaps the most fundamental concept in the entire FMEA methodology. Unless a priority of problems (as a con-

cept) is recognized, workers are likely to be contenders for chasing fires. They will respond to the loudest request and/or the problem of the moment. (In other words, they will manage by emergency.) In no uncertain terms, workers must recognize and believe in the principle of the vital few as opposed to the trivial many (Pareto principle). The FMEA will help identify this priority.

2. *The customer must be known.* Before one undertakes the responsibility of conducting an FMEA it is imperative that the customer be defined. Traditionally, the definition of *customer* is thought of as the end user. That, however, may be a simplified approach; indeed a definition that may not apply to the problem. A customer also may be viewed as the subsequent or downstream operation as well as a service operation (Ford 1992). In some cases, the customer may be the operation itself.

This is important because when using the term *customer* from an FMEA perspective, the definition plays a major role in addressing problems and their solutions. For example, as a general rule, in the design FMEA the customer is viewed as the end user, but in the process FMEA the customer is viewed as the next operation in line.

This next operation may be the end user, but it does not have to be. After the customer has been defined as external, intermediate, internal or self, it cannot be changed (at least for the problem at hand) without some surprise ramifications. Those ramifications will affect the definition and consequences of the problem.

3. *The function must be known.* It is imperative that the function, purpose, and objective of what is to be accomplished be known. Otherwise the result is wasting time, and the effort is focused on redefining the problem based on situations. If necessary, the extra time must be taken to ensure that everyone concerned understands the function, purpose, and objective of what is to be accomplished.

4. *One must be prevention oriented.* Unless continual improvement is the force that drives the FMEA, the efforts of conducting an FMEA will be static. The FMEA will be conducted only to satisfy customers and/or market requirements to the letter rather than the spirit of the requirements. (Unfortunately, this is a common

problem in implementation of an FMEA program). This is a myopic perspective and as such the spirit of improvement will be lost. The emphasis will be on speed—"Let us get it done, as soon as possible and move to the next one." Remember, there is a correlation between time and quality. The following diagram shows the relationship.

Fast <——————————> Cheap

Quality

The moral of the diagram is that it is impossible to have all three factors at the same time. A company must decide which type of product it wants. After the decision is made, it develops that niche in the market. The television commercial for Paul Masson's wines exemplifies the notion of quality versus time versus price: "We will sell no wine before its time."

The push for this continual improvement makes the FMEA a dynamic document, changing as the system, design, process, product, and/or service changes with the intent always to make a better system, design, process, product, and/or service.

Why Conduct FMEAs?

The propensity of managers and engineers to minimize the risk in a particular system, design, process, and/or service has forced an examination of reliability engineering, not only to minimize the risk, but also to define that risk whenever possible. Some of the forces for defining risks were shown in Figure I.2.

These risks can be measured by reliability engineering and/or statistical analysis. Because of their complexity, however, the FMEA has extracted the basic principles without the technical mathematics. (See Appendix A for specific formulae and techniques.) It also has provided a tool that anybody committed to continual improvement can utilize.

Statistical process control (SPC) is another tool that provides the impetus for implementation of an FMEA, especially for a process and service FMEA. SPC provides information about the process in regard to changes. These changes are called common and special causes. From an FMEA perspective, the common causes may be considered as failures that are the result of inherent failure mechanisms; as such, they can affect the entire population. In this case, the common cause may raise additional questions and/or concerns so that further examination of the system or design may be in order (Denson 1992).

Conversely, special causes are considered as failures that result from part defects and/or manufacturing problems; they can affect a relatively small population. In this case, there is cause for examining the process (Denson 1992).

Customer requisition strongly influences the motivation to perform an FMEA. For example, all major automobile companies in their supplier certification standards (such as, Ford-Q101, General Motors–Targets for Excellence, Chrysler–Pentastar) require an FMEA program for their suppliers (Chrysler 1986; Ford 1992; General Motors 1988). The same is true with other industries (such as semiconductor, computer, government, and medical device). Through product liability, courts may also require some substantiation as to what level of reliability products and/or services perform (Bass 1986).

International standards such as the ISO 9000 series may define the program of documentation in design (Stamatis 1992). For example, the product liability directive of the EC 1985 stipulates that manufacturers of a product will be held liable, regardless of fault or negligence, if a person is harmed or an object is damaged by a faulty or defective product. (This includes exporters into the European Union [EU] market.) This liability directive essentially reverses the burden of proof of fault from the injured to the producer. For more details see chapters 12 and 13. (Hagigh 1992; Kolka, Link, and Scott 1992; Kolka and Scott 1992; Linville 1992).

Other benefits of conducting an FMEA include the following:

- Helps define the most significant opportunity for achieving fundamental differentiation (Peters 1992). After all, there is only one organization that can distinguish itself as the cheapest in town. The rest have to depend on other attributes.
- Improves the quality, reliability, and safety of the products or service. (Table I.1 shows that even 99.9 percent is not good enough in certain situations.)

Table I.1 Quality today.

99.9% quality in the United States would mean	
• One hour of unsafe drinking water per day	• 12 babies given to the wrong parents each day
• Two unsafe landings at O'Hare Airport per day	• 291 incorrect pacemaker operations per year
• 16,000 lost pieces of mail per hour	• 107 incorrect medical procedures performed daily
• 20,000 incorrect drug prescriptions per year	• 268,500 defective tires shipped per year
• 500 incorrect surgical operations performed each week	• Two million documents lost by the IRS per year
• 19,000 newborn babies dropped at birth by doctors each year	• 880,000 credit card magnetic strips with wrong information
• 22,000 checks deducted from the wrong account each hour	• 5,517,200 cases of flat soft drinks produced per year
• Your heart fails to beat 32,000 times per year	• 14,208 defective personal computers shipped per year

- Improves the company's image and competitiveness.
- Helps increase customer satisfaction.
- Reduces product development time and costs.
- Helps select the optimal system design.
- Helps determine the redundancy of the system.
- Helps identify diagnostic procedures.
- Establishes a priority for design improvement actions.
- Helps identify critical and/or significant characteristics.
- Helps in the analysis of new manufacturing and/or assembly processes.
- Helps in the analysis of tasks, sequence, and/or service.
- Helps establish the forum for defect prevention.
- Helps error identification and prevention.
- Helps define the corrective action.

- Helps select alternatives (in system, design, process, and service) with high reliability and high safety potential during the early phases (Blanchard 1986).
- Ensures that all conceivable failures and their effects on operational success have been considered.
- Lists potential failures and identifies the relative magnitude of their effects.
- Provides the basis for the test program during development and final validation of the system, design, process, or service.
- Develops early criteria for manufacturing, process, assembly, and service (Kececioglu 1991).
- Provides historical documentation for future reference to aid in the analysis of field failures and consideration of design, process, and service changes.
- Provides a forum for recommending and tracking risk-reducing actions.

The most important reason for conducting an FMEA is the need to improve. To receive all or some of the benefits of an FMEA program, the need to improve must be ingrained in the organization's culture. If not, the FMEA program will not to succeed.

References

Bass, L. 1986. Products liability: *Design and manufacturing defects.* Colorado Springs, Colo.: Shepard's/McGraw-Hill.

Blanchard, B. S. 1986. *Logistics engineering and management.* 3d ed. Englewood Cliffs, N.J.: Prentice Hall.

Chrysler Motors. 1986. Design feasibility and reliability assurance. In *FMEA.* Highland Park, Mich.: Chrysler Motors Engineering Office.

Denson, W. K. 1992. The use of failure mode distributions in reliability analyses. *RAC Newsletter* (Reliability Analysis Center, a Department of Defense Information Analysis Center) (spring): 1–3.

Ford Motor Company. 1992. *FMEA handbook.* Dearborn, Mich.: Ford Motor Company, Engineering Materials and Standards.

General Motors. 1988. *FMEA reference manual.* Detroit, Mich.: General Motors Corporation, Reliability and Technology Department.

Hagigh, S. 1992. Obtaining EC product approvals after 1992: What American manufacturers need to know. *Business America,* 24 February.

Juran, J. M., and F. M. Gryna, Jr. 1980. *Quality planning and analysis.* New York: McGraw-Hill.

Kececioglu, D. 1991. *Reliability engineering handbook.* Vols. 1 and 2. Englewood Cliffs, N.J.: Prentice Hall.

Kolka, J. W., D. M. Link, and G. G. Scott. 1992. *Medical device directives: Certification, quality assurance, and liability.* Fairfax, Va.: CEEM Information Services.

Kolka, J. W., and G. G. Scott. 1992. *Product liability and product safety directives.* Fairfax, Va.: CEEM Information Services.

Linville, D. 1992. Exporting to the European Community. *Business America,* 24 February.

Peters, T. 1992. *Liberation management.* New York: Alfred A. Knopf.

Stamatis, D. H. 1989, 1991, 1992. *FMEA training manual.* Southgate, Mich.: Contemporary Consultants.

———. 1992. ISO 9000 standards: Are they for real? *Technology* (Engineering Society of Detroit) (August): 13–17.

Chapter 1
Legal Approach to Liability

This chapter addresses the fundamentals of product liability, theories of recovery, and defenses and bars to recovery. The intent is to give the engineer some understanding of law and establish the need for FMEA. This is not an attempt to exhaust the topic, or to offer legal advice.

A Legal Approach to Liability

Product liability laws are complex and continue to cover the products and services that enter commerce. By addressing the fundamentals of the legal ramifications of product liability and examining other basic issues regarding liability, the need for conducting an FMEA should be quite obvious.

Who Is Responsible for Safe Products?

Product liability applies to those in the business of manufacturing products that enter the stream of commerce—placing the product in the marketing cycle (*Armstrong Rubber Co. v Urquidez,* 570 SW2d 3741 [Texas 1978]). Liability includes demonstration, lease, a free sample, or sale of the product. (A product under construction or for internal use is not considered to be in the stream of commerce).

Special note: The intent of this chapter is not to interpret the law of liability but to establish the rationale and need to perform the FMEA.

Specifically, product liability (negligence or strict liability) may be considered in the following industries (Bass 1986, 1991; Pozgar 1993).

- All services, because negligence principles are applicable.
- Software, because there is the potential for personal injury, property damage or business loss. From a liability perspective the primary issue is not whether software is liable, but whether or not it is a service or a product. If it proves that it is a service, the principles of negligence will apply. If it is considered as a product, the strict liability will apply.
- Engineers and architects, because they provide a service (*La Rosa v Scientific Design Co.,* 402 F2d 937 [3d Cir 1968]).
- Medical products and drugs; depending on how the court views the usage of the product, it may be considered either as a strict liability (*Johnson v Sears, Roebuck and Co.,* 355 F Supp 1065 [ED Wis 1973]) or negligence (*Carmichael v Reitz,* 17 Cal App 3d 958, 95 Cal Rptr 381 [1971]).
- Component suppliers, because they are held liable under the theories of strict liability, warranty, and negligence (*City of Franklin v Badger Ford Truck Sales, Inc.,* 58 Wis 2d 641, 207 NW2d 866 [1973]).
- Insurance companies, because they have been found liable for negligent inspections performed by their loss control engineers. This may involve, furnaces, utilities, buildings, or machinery (*Evans v Liberty Mutual Insurance Co.,* 398 F2d 665 [3d Cir 1968]).
- Testing laboratories, because they have been found liable for negligent tests performed at their facilities (*Hemstead v General Fire Extinguisher Corp.,* 269 F Supp 109 [D Del 1967]).
- Franchisors or trademark licensors may be held for strict liability if they have extended strict tort liability to franchisors or trademark licensors who sell the right to use their trade name, or even processes, to others who actually supply the product (*Connelly v Uniroyal, Inc.,* 75 Ill 2d 393, 389 NE2d 155 [1979], revg 55 Ill App 3d 530, 13 Ill Dec 162, 370 Ne2d 1189 [1977]).

- Bailors and lessors of goods; strict liability may be extended to bailors and lessors of goods as well as those who sell goods (*Price v Shell Oil Co.,* 2 Cal 3d 245, 466 P2d 722, 85 Cal Rptr 178 [1970]).
- Sellers of used products, because they have been found liable for negligence, warranty, and strict liability (*Turner v International Harvester Co.,* 133 NJ Super 277, 336 A2d 62, 69 [1975]).
- Landlords, because they have been found liable under negligence (*Sargent v Ross,* 113 NH 388, 308 A 2d 528 [1973]).
- Engineers, because they have been found liable under negligence. Engineers are held responsible, however, when it can be proved that their negligence resulted in the plaintiff's injury (*Gagre v Bertran,* 43 Cal 2d 481 [1954]).
- Rebuilders, because they have been found liable under strict liability, just as with manufacturers of complete machines (*Michalko v Cooke Color & Chemical Corp.,* 91 NJ 386, 451 A2d 179 [1982]).

Although this list is not exhaustive, the message should be clear that everything one (individual or organization) does (product or service) can be an issue of liability and negligence. By performing the FMEA at the appropriate stage, the liability and negligence may be minimized, and if punitive damages are not completely eliminated, they will be minimized.

What Is Product Liability?

The term *product liability* often stands for a variety of meanings; however, the term in law is defined as the liability of a seller or manufacturer for damages caused by its allegedly defective product. Product liability action can be based on a number of legal theories, including negligence, strict liability, fraud, misrepresentation, warranty, and so on. To more fully understand the legal concepts, one must familiarize oneself with some of the basic theories.

Theories of Recovery

Although several legal theories may be used in a product's liability action, the three most commonly used are: negligence, warranties, and strict liability in tort.

Negligence Action. Negligence law (failing to act as a reasonable and prudent person would in like or similar circumstances) was developed approximately 200 years ago. Before that, all wrongdoers had to pay for any damages that they directly caused. Consequently, a type of no-fault concept would hold the person directly causing the harm to be liable for such harm. Negligence law developed as a protection for the defendant and required more than proof of a mere direct injury. Negligence includes the concept that an individual may not be liable for the direct or indirect harm he or she causes unless he or she has acted unreasonably. The modern view of negligence consists of the following four elements.

1. Duty
2. Breach
3. Causation
4. Damages

An individual who is harmed by someone must be able to show all four elements. If any one is missing, there is no case.

The duty element of negligence requires that a person owes to another to conduct him or herself in a particular manner. A person may owe a duty that is created by statute or a local ordinance. For example, a person must drive according to the motor vehicle laws, or construct safe buildings, or build certain items with specific codes so as not to create dangerous conditions to the public.

Duty may be established by the courts, such as exercising reasonable care to protect and warn persons of dangers on one's property. For example, in medicine, doctors have a duty to practice within the accepted standard of care; engineers have a duty to design and manufacture a safe product.

Duty is measured by the reasonable person under like or similar circumstances and can be created in many different ways based on the facts of a particular case. Therefore, the objective hypothetical reasonable person is the standard by which the law measures the duty of all defendants in a negligence action. If no duty is found, the negligence issue fails and the defendant will not be liable even if he or she caused the damages to the injured party (called the *plaintiff*).

If a duty is found to exist, then the plaintiff must also show that the defendant breached that duty. In other words, one asks whether the defendant fulfilled the duty to act or not to act in a reasonable manner. Breach of duty is the failure (any failure) to perform or conduct oneself in a particular manner when one is obligated to do so.

The negligent conduct must have been a cause of the injury, and the injury is a natural and probable result of the negligent conduct. "Did the negligent conduct cause the injury to another?" This is the fundamental question of causation and, as such, it has become one of the most philosophical areas of negligence. Because this is a tricky area of defense, defendants will argue that the injured party also was negligent and may have been 40 percent responsible for his or her own injury.

Causation can be divided into two basic elements: (1) the but for test, and (2) proximate or legal cause test. The but for test merely asks the question: "But for the defendant's conduct, would the accident or injury have occurred?" Obviously, the but for test is very broad and cannot be used alone to sufficiently narrow the possibilities to find responsible parties to an action. For example, but for Joe and Jane the defendant would not have been born; thus, almost all responsibility could be attributed to some past, direct happenings. Negligence law includes only those causes that have been a proximate or legal cause in producing the damage to the plaintiff. Proximate cause is measured by the *substantial factor test,* which includes only causes that have been a substantial factor in producing the plaintiff's damages. What constitutes a substantial factor will vary from case to case, but such flexibility is necessary because of the wide variety of situations brought as negligence actions.

Generally, damages are determined by asking how has the injured party suffered physically, mentally, financially, or otherwise. (Many forget this piece of the puzzle.) If there is a suit for negligent acts of another, the plaintiff must be able to demonstrate in court that harm has occurred. If a person was hurt by a product, run over by a truck, slipped and fell, used a defective product, or received improper care from a physician, or wrong instructions in the course of using a product, it may be that there was clear negligent conduct. The person suing must show that he or she was harmed even if the wrongdoer admits his or her negligence.

If the defendant has breached his or her duty, and this breach caused the harm or damages, then he or she *may* be found liable. Engineers who work with exactitude may have some difficulty with apparent vagueness of the elements of negligence; however, this vagueness is necessary because *negligence law covers almost any conceivable situation.* No one correct answer is possible when one considers the almost infinite variety of situations that occur in day-to-day activities. The variable conduct of human beings, however, by observance of social norms, can be considered either reasonable or unreasonable. This is the essence of negligence.

Warranties. Warranty law, a hybrid of both contract and tort law, developed before negligence. Warranties can be either expressed or implied. Thus, if the seller of a product states that the product will perform in a certain manner, and the product fails to live up to those expressed representations, then the seller may be found liable. Through custom, it gradually became common for certain products to be expected to perform in a certain manner, and if the product failed to do so, the user was deprived of his or her reasonable expectations. Under these conditions, the seller could be found liable for warranties, which by implication accompanied the product. The warranty types of actions have now been codified in almost all jurisdictions (states and territories), and can be found in the Uniform Commercial Code (UCC). The UCC generally involves commercial situations; however, it also may be used in personal injury actions. The expressed warranty is found in UCC S2-316, whereas the implied warranties are found in UCC S2-314 (implied warranty of merchantability), and UCC S2-315 (implied warranty of fitness for a particular purpose).

Strict Liability in Tort. As negligence law developed, the concept of no-fault method of recovery retained some vitality. Negligence law developed as a protection for the defendant, especially newly developing industries and railroads at the time of the industrial revolution. Thus, if the defendant caused injury to the plaintiff, but acted reasonably, he or she was not liable. There were certain types of conduct, however, that the law considered so hazardous or unsafe that the older no-fault concept law was retained to establish liability. Thus, one who used dynamite (no matter how reasonably) was held liable for the injury caused by the dynamite. In addition, food that was unwholesome or deleterious was considered a product to which negligence should not apply. The restaurant that served unwholesome food was strictly liable for the damages caused by such food. This type of liability was called strict liability, absolute liability, or no-fault liability because, no matter how reasonably he or she acted, the defendant could be held liable if his or her deleterious food or dynamite caused injury.

As negligence law developed and the industrial revolution moved into the twentieth century, the production and marketing of all products began to expand and involve more complex situations. In the nineteenth century the sale and exchange of goods and products was, more or less, on a one-to-one basis. In this instance the buyer or user, familiar with the product, would inspect the product for defects. Furthermore, the nineteenth century exchange of goods did not involve mass advertising and extremely complicated products. Therefore, it was assumed and expected that a buyer could and would inspect for defects and accept or reject the product upon delivery. This may have been acceptable practice for products such as the rake, plow, or saddle; however, with the advent of mass production, complicated machinery, and Madison Avenue advertising, a modern consumer was neither capable of nor expected to inspect products such as his or her automobile, blender, or combine. In addition, the manner of production changed to such an extent that it became impossible for a plaintiff to prove negligence.

Although nineteenth century buyers could show with some reasonable certainty that the cobbler's conduct was unreasonable when he failed to properly nail shoes, it was almost impossible for the twentieth century consumers to discover the exact point in the chain of production where the vehicle or product became defective and how the defendant's conduct was unreasonable. With greater public reliance upon products being reasonably safe, without inspection, the almost impossible problems of proving who was responsible for unreasonable conduct, and what conduct in the manufacturing process was unreasonable, resulted in more injured consumers not being recompensed for injuries that truly were caused by defective products.

In recognition of the serious problems caused by the requirements of negligence law, the courts began to allow recovery under a theory of strict liability in tort. Beginning in 1963 in California with *Greenman v Yuba Power Products, Inc.*, 59 Cal 2d 57, 377 P2d 897, 27 Cal Rptr 697 (1963), the courts allowed recovery without showing a defect was caused by unreasonable conduct. The requirement changed. Now, the plaintiff must show that the product was defective, and that the defect caused him or her injury. Thus, the emphasis changed from the showing of unreasonable conduct that created the defect to one of merely showing a defect, regardless of how or what caused the defect in the product. If the plaintiff could show that the product left the manufacturer's or seller's hands in a defective condition, and that the defect caused the plaintiff injury, he or she could recover.

From 1963 until the present, almost all jurisdictions in the United States have adopted strict liability in product liability actions. The generally accepted version of strict liability is found in the American Law Institute's Restatement (Second) of Torts S402A (1965) which states

(1) One who sells any product in a defective condition unreasonably dangerous to the user or consumer or to his or her property is subject to liability for physical harm thereby caused to the ultimate user or consumer, or to his property, if:

(a) the seller is engaged in the business of selling such a product, and

(b) it is expected to and does reach the user or consumer without substantial change in the condition in which it is sold.

(2) The rule stated in Subsection (1) applies although

(a) the seller has exercised all possible care in the preparation and sale of his or her product, and

(b) the user or consumer has not bought the product from or entered into any contractual relation with the seller.

Although one can examine in detail the language of S402A, the major elements consist of

1. A defect/unreasonably dangerous
2. Causation
3. Damages

What Is a Product?

Historically a product was a chattel, defined as an article of personal property which was not land. The courts, however, recently have allowed recovery under a product liability theory for homes, rental apartments, and sometimes, condominiums. The term *product* also can include the product's packaging or container; some courts have included electricity as a product.

Because the product definition by the courts is so broad, one may wonder, how can the court define the defect and what are some of the conditions that will indeed define the defect (if in fact, there is such a requirement)?

In order to understand the defect requirement one must understand how the legal system defines defects, how it views the types of defects, and whether or not there is a difference between design, manufacturing, and service.

Defects

In the scientific and realistic sense, nothing is perfect (Bass 1986, 1991). All products and/or services have flaws. From a legal perspective, defects are defined based on user expectation, manufacturer representation, and foreseeability. The test for defect is safe performance under foreseeable conditions of use.

The law generally agrees that perfect safety usually is not technologically possible or if it is possible, it costs too much. Therefore, a defect is more likely to be discussed under a customer expectation test or a risk-benefit test (Bass 1986, 1991).

Types of Defects

A product presents a reasonable risk and is not defective when

- The product meets the ordinary customer's expectations
- Risks are reduced to the greatest extent possible by design or safety features (Peters 1992)
- The product contains adequate warnings that a risk is associated with the product
- The user is given enough information to decide whether or not to accept the risk
- The benefits cannot be obtained in a less risky way
- It is not economically feasible to reduce the severity
- Evaluating the product as a whole, the benefits outweigh the risks

Products may be defined as defective because they

- Deviate from the intended condition by the manufacturer
- Are unsafe, due to design defects, even though they are produced perfectly
- Are incapable of meeting their implied or expressed claims of performance
- Are dangerous because they lack adequate warnings and instructions

Design Defects

A design defect is a defect that affects an entire line of products (Bass 1986; Omdahl 1988; ASQC 1983). It may be a result of trade-off analysis, cost-benefit analysis, and/or customer's requirements. A design defect occurs when a product does not adequately protect against risks of injury, fails to perform intended functions safely, does not protect adequately against the danger against which it was supposed to guard, creates unreasonably dangerous side effects, or fails to minimize avoidable consequences in the event of an accident.

Manufacturing Defects

A manufacturing defect exists when the product does not meet the manufacturer's own specifications (Bass 1986; Omdahl 1988; ASQC 1983). This can be because

- The raw materials or components used in making the product may contain unacceptable flaws.
- There are assembly mistakes.

The major issue in manufacturing defect cases is whether the defect is due to a mistake in design, manufacturing, normal wear, normal tear, or misuse.

Service Defect

A service defect exists when the service does not meet the defined criteria of the design and/or the customer. The FMEA can and does provide the method for analysis of known and potential problems in all of the system, design, process, and service phases. (Remember, although the law describes defects, in modern quality thinking one should substitute the term *nonconformity* in its place.)

The Defect Requirement

The major consideration of S402A is the defect requirement. In fact, negligence, strict liability, and implied warranties all require at least three of the same elements that the plaintiff must prove to sustain his or her case: (1) defect, (2) causation, and (3) damages. The major difference between negligence law and strict liability and warranties is that in negligence the plaintiff must prove unreasonable conduct that causes the defect or injury, whereas in strict liability and implied warranties all the plaintiff has to prove is the existence of the defect itself. In strict liability actions there are three basic types of defects that may render the defendant liable

1. Manufacturing defects
2. Design defects

3. A failure to adequately instruct on usage and a failure to warn of dangers in the product

A manufacturing defect exists when the product comes off the production line in a condition different from what the manufacturer intended. Thus, a rectangular cover plate that was intended to have a total of four holes, one at each corner for bolts, would contain a manufacturing defect if it had only three holes. In other words, the product that has a manufacturing defect is different than the other products that come off the production line.

A design defect is when a product is designed such that there are unreasonable dangers in the product as designed. Thus, a designer might design a rectangular plate with only three holes in the plate where it is to be fixed with bolts, but because of the design, the plate might fail due to lack of sufficient bolts fixing the plate in place. Here it is clear that there is no manufacturing defect because the plate comes off the production line as intended (like all others), but is maldesigned.

If a product is to be used in a specified manner, the manufacturer has the obligation to give sufficient instruction to the person who is to use the product. If the manufacturer fails to give instructions or gives inadequate instructions, and the consumer uses the product in a forbidden manner and is injured, the consumer may recover because of the lack of instructions.

Finally, a product can be perfectly manufactured, have no design defect, and may contain adequate instructions on usage, but still be defective. This is true if the manufacturer fails to warn about the dangers that may be involved in proper usage.

The Parties

Defendant—Seller and Stream of Commerce. It is assumed that the manufacturer of the product may be a defendant in a product liability action. But what about other parties such as assemblers and component part manufacturers? Can they be sellers? In *Suvada v White Motor Co.,* 210 NE 2d 182 (Ill 1965), the defendant Bendix-Westinghouse Automotive Air Brake Company was held liable for a defective brake system installed in a tractor by White Motor Company.

Although White Motor Company did not make a change in the brake system, White also was liable to plaintiff for the defective brake. There are numerous cases where the assembler of a defective component part is liable to the plaintiff even though he or she did nothing to the component part nor could have discovered the defect.

The law has developed in such a way that any party that comes into contact in the commercial stream may be held strictly liable for the defective product. Thus, wholesalers, retailers, and distributors have been held liable and some courts have held used-goods dealers and lessors of defective products liable under a strict liability theory. A famous Indiana case stated the following:

> "Liability under S402A will attach to anyone who places such a product in the stream of commerce by sale, lease, bailment or other means." *Gilbert v Stone City Construction Co.,* 357 NE 2d 738 (Ind Ct App 1976).

The Plaintiff—The User. Recovery will be allowed for the consumer or user of the defective product. Since privity has been eliminated in all but a few commercial cases, it is not necessary that the user be the actual purchaser of the product. The plaintiff may be a neighbor who borrows a lawn mower and is injured by it, or he or she may be the employee using the punch press. What about the bystander or onlooker? Can the person walking on the sidewalk and struck by the rock thrown from an unshielded lawn mower recover? In strict liability actions, all jurisdictions that have discussed the issue allow the bystander or onlooker to recover.

Defenses and Bars to Recovery

There are many factors that may bar a plaintiff even though he or she can show that a defective product caused him or her injury, and there are several defenses or bars to liability that question the elements of defect, duty, or causation. Remember that a plaintiff may bring his or her action based upon multiple theories, and that a valid defense under one theory may not be a defense under another theory. For example, contributory negligence is a defense in negligence actions, but is not a defense in strict liability actions. Thus, one should note the context of which defense or bar to recovery applies to each legal theory.

Privity. Since medieval times, a seller or manufacturer could be held liable for a breach of warranty, but only to the immediate buyer. In the mid-nineteenth century this same concept (called privity) was extended to negligence cases. Thus, a buyer of a defective product could not recover unless he or she could show some type of contractual nexus between him or herself and the seller. In 1916, in the case of *MacPherson v Buick Motor Co.,* 111 NE 1050 (NY 1916), the privity concept was eliminated in negligence actions and within the next 50 years all jurisdictions followed the *MacPherson* rule.

It is now well accepted in negligence and strict liability cases that no privity is required. In some jurisdictions privity may still be required in UCC cases that have their basis in contract law and do not involve personal injuries.

Contributory Negligence. As the nineteenth century common law concept of negligence developed, a complete defense evolved which consisted of the plaintiff's own negligence contributing to his or her injury (called *contributory negligence*). Thus, if the plaintiff was contributorily negligent, and such contributory negligence was a substantial factor in bringing about his or her own harm, the plaintiff was barred from recovery. As a fault concept, this was compatible with nineteenth century logic—a wrongdoer should not recover. Contributory negligence, however, was greatly criticized on many grounds, including the concept that although a person had contributed somewhat (say theoretically 5 percent) to his or her own injury, he or she should not be completely deprived of recovery when the defendant was the major wrongdoer (say 95 percent).

In strict liability actions (including warranty actions), fault of either the defendant or the plaintiff is not a factor. In other words, the unreasonable conduct of the defendant in creating the defective product is not a consideration, nor is the unreasonable conduct of the plaintiff in contributing to his or her own injury. Thus, in strict liability actions, contributory negligence is not a defense *(Farmer v School District,* 171 Wash 278, 17 P 2d 899).

Assumption of Risk. The second major defense in negligence actions is assumption of the risk (sometimes called incurred risk). Assumption of the risk is based upon consent. Consent is measured upon a subjective standard. If the plaintiff consents, either expressly or impliedly, then he or she cannot complain of his or her injury. Consent consists of four major elements

1. Knowledge
2. Understanding
3. Appreciation
4. Voluntariness

Thus, the plaintiff must have actual knowledge (subjective) of the risk, understand the consequences (subjective) of the risk, appreciate the extent (subjective) of the risk, and voluntarily enter said risk. All four elements must be complied with before anyone is said to consent. For example, for something to be done voluntarily, the person making the choice must be given reasonable and viable alternatives or he/she cannot be said to have voluntarily undertaken the risk.

In many situations all four elements of assumption of risk may be met, yet the plaintiff may still have acted reasonably in his or her choice (reasonable assumption of risk). In other situations the plaintiff may have consented to an unreasonable risk; thus, his or her consent becomes unreasonable based upon objective standards (unreasonable assumption of risk).

In negligence law either reasonable or unreasonable assumption of risk is a defense. In strict liability (or warranty) cases, however, only unreasonable assumption of risk is considered a defense.

Misuse. The misuse of a product is said to be a defense or bar to plaintiff's recovery. Misuse has been used interchangeably with abnormal use and unintended use. Misuse was first used in the context of how the manufacturer *subjectively* intended the product to be used. This concept was extremely narrow, however, and misuse was gradually broadened to require the manufacturer to objectively anticipate or foresee greater use of the product. In this expanded, foreseeability concept, the manufacturer was required to *objectively* anticipate the uses of the product in the environment in which the product was placed. Thus, unusual but foreseeable, uses would not be considered a misuse of the product.

Misuse also was considered part of the defense of contributory negligence or assumption of risk. In other instances, misuse was considered a part of the defect requirement or of causation. This chameleon character of misuse proved to be confusing to everyone.

Misuse, if it has independent existence as a bar to plaintiff's recovery, depends upon reasonable foreseeability. If the use of the product is not foreseeable, then such unforeseeable use may bar the plaintiff's recovery. Foreseeability of use, however, is not restricted to the manner of use that a manufacturer desires, but may include all objectively foreseeable uses of a particular product in a particular environment. The ingestion of furniture polish by young children is hardly the intended use of furniture polish. But what would be more reasonably foreseeable than young children consuming bottles of red liquid that look like cherry cola?

Comparative Fault. After heavy criticism of both contributory negligence and assumption of risk as complete bars to recovery, almost all jurisdictions have adopted some form of comparative fault or comparative negligence. In such jurisdictions the contributory negligence and assumption of risk of the plaintiff are weighed against the fault of the defendant, and the plaintiff is allowed recovery based upon a percentage comparison. Sometimes misuse is also included in such percentage comparison. There are three major types of comparative negligence.

1. *49%–51%* In some jurisdictions the plaintiff is allowed to recover as long as his or her fault or negligence is *less* than that of the defendant. If the plaintiff's fault is equal to or greater than that of the defendant, he or she cannot recover.

2. *50%–50%* In some jurisdictions, if the plaintiff's conduct or negligence is equal to or less than the negligence of the defendant, then he or she may recover.

3. *Pure comparative fault* In a growing number of jurisdictions, the plaintiff is allowed to recover, and his or her damages are to be reduced by the proportion of his or her contributory fault, whether it is 1 percent or 99 percent. Thus, a plaintiff who is 65 percent at

fault is still allowed to recover 35 percent of the costs of his or her injury.

In negligence actions, comparative fault seems appropriate, but in strict liability actions, the fault of either party is irrelevant. It would seem that comparative fault would not be appropriate in strict liability cases since this would bring contributory negligence back as a defense. Despite the incompatibility of the theories, a growing number of courts have allowed the comparison of all forms of plaintiff's conduct (contributory negligence and assumption of risk) to apply comparative fault in strict liability actions.

State of the Art. It has been said that *state of the art* is not a defense to liability under any theory of recovery, but is merely an explanation of what is being done by a particular industry at a particular time. In recent years, however, several states have enacted legislation that does have a defense called state of the art. The real problem is defining state of the art.

State of the art has been used to mean many different things. At one end of the spectrum of meanings is custom and practice in the industry; at the other end of the spectrum is that state of the art is the cumulation of all conceivable knowledge relating to a product at any given point in time. The case law has discussed both ends of the spectrum and quite a bit in between.

If used in a legal context, state of the art does not mean the custom or standards of a particular industry. See *Cantu v John Deer Co.,* 24 Wash App701, 603 P2d 839 at 840 (1979).

The generally accepted state of the art definition is: whatever is technologically feasible and economically feasible at the time of either the manufacture of the product or at the time of the accident. Thus, to be in conformance with the state of the art, the manufacturer or seller must consider what is feasible, not what is being done. An entire industry could be acting in a substandard manner in producing a particular product, and it is no defense to say that no one is using a particular guard or safety device as long as it was feasible to include such guard or safety device with the product. The primary reason for the rejection of any particular custom or usage of any industry as a complete defense is the court's lack of trust in self-imposed standards, and the court's recognition that any such self-regulatory standard will probably provide only a minimum of protection and safety for the consumer or user.

State of the art does not mean that the seller must do the impossible or perform the impractical. For instance, a $500 product may not necessarily have to include a $1000 guarding device to make it safer because this would not be economically feasible. A $500 product may have to include a $10 guard, however, if such guard could reduce injuries to the user.

Technological feasibility does not require prescience; however, any technology that could reasonably be incorporated with a product and that could reduce injuries or improve safety may be required. State of the art does not require that a manufacturer use certain safety items; however, if injury or damage results from the lack of such safety items or design, the manufacturer may have to pay for said injuries.

Recently New Jersey decided that state of the art was not an acceptable defense to strict liability in tort. *Beshada v Johns-Manville Products Corp.,* 90 NJ 191, 447 A2d 539 (1982).

The effects of customer satisfaction because of a defect (nonconformance) in design, manufacturing, or service may cause the customer to sue. But what is the legal process to sue? The next section addresses this problem.

The Legal Process

The focus of this section is on the legal process as it relates to design and manufacturing. It is an attempt to give a sense of understanding of the legal process for those who design and manufacture a product. This is not an exhaustive legal review; however, the short summary should establish the ground for the engineer and those around the design, and/or process to take preventive measures to avoid this legal action.

A Cursory View of the Legal Process*

A lawsuit begins when a person (corporations, as well, are considered as persons for legal purposes) whose body or property is injured (or

*This legal review is based on *Product Liability and the Engineer* by J. F. Vargo and A. S. Weinstein, SAE publication #82002. (Warrendale, Penn.: Society of Automotive Engineers.) It is used in here with their permission.

damaged or destroyed) alleges that the injury was caused by the acts of another and files a complaint. The person asserting the complaint is the *plaintiff* and it is brought against the *defendant.*

Implicit in such a complaint must be the existence of *duty* (or responsibility) that would make the defendant liable to the plaintiff, if the plaintiff can prove his or her case. In addition to a duty, the plaintiff also must assert that there is *cause of action* (a legal theory or principle) that would permit the plaintiff to recover *damages* (money, return, or restoration of property, or whatever may be appropriate to restore the plaintiff to the condition existing before the injury).

For example, a product manufacturer has a duty to use reasonable care in the design and manufacture of a product and this duty extends to all persons who can reasonably be expected to use or come in contact with the product. But the law does not impose a legal duty on a stranger to give aid to a person on a street corner who may be suffering a heart attack and requests help.

Although a legal duty may exist, a cause of action may not exist. A person suffering bad dreams after seeing a foreign object in a soft drink bottle, but not consuming the beverage, may not have a cause of action in that the harm suffered (in other words, the bad dreams) may not be legally compensable, even though the bottler has violated a legal duty by inserting foreign objects in the bottles along with the drink.

To avoid stale claims, the plaintiff must file the complaint within the period of the *statute of limitations* (generally between one and six years) after the alleged injury has occurred or after the plaintiff should have known of the injury. After the plaintiff files the complaint, the defendant must answer within a specified time period. The answer, as one might expect, generally denies all of the allegations and will also assert *affirmative defenses.* That is, the defendant will state that if there was an injury it was due to the plaintiff's own behavior which fell short of an appropriate legal standard (for example, *contributory negligence, assumption of the risk, misuse, abuse*). After the paper sparring is completed, the period of *discovery* begins. Each side of the litigation can submit *interrogatories* (questions) to the other attempting to learn facts that can assist in formulating the issues and defenses.

In addition, each party can *depose* the other party's witnesses or other persons who may have information pertaining to the case. The deposition is a legally formal session at which the deponent, under oath, answers questions posed by the attorney or the opposing side. The proceedings are recorded and transcribed. The transcript may be used at trial if the witness cannot be present or to impeach the witness if the testimony at trial differs materially from that given at the deposition.

The plaintiff has the right to request a trial by jury, or may decide to let the judge alone decide the case, in which instance the judge also serves as the jury. The roles of the judge and jury are totally different. The judge (often referred to as "the court") is to decide the issues and points of law and instruct the jury on the legal principles within which the case is to be decided. The jury is to focus on the factual evidence as brought out by the witnesses under questioning by the attorneys and by any physical evidence introduced by both sides. The jury is to weigh this factual evidence and decide whether the plaintiff has proved the allegations within the legal framework described by the judge.

For example, assume that the plaintiff was injured by an exploding soft drink bottle. If the legal principle asserted is that of negligence, the plaintiff must prove that the bottler was at fault in shipping a bottle that either had a flaw in the glass or was overcarbonated and caused the explosion. The plaintiff must therefore prove to the satisfaction of the jury that if the bottler had used reasonable inspection or control procedures the problem would have been discovered. The defendant bottler would counter by attempting to show that there were no reasonable inspection or control techniques that would have uncovered the problem or alternatively, that it was the plaintiff's misuse or abuse of the bottle in handling it that caused it to explode.

The jury is instructed, under a negligence theory, that it must measure the fault of both sides by using a reasonable person standard. That is, the jury decides whether or not a reasonable person, under the same or similar circumstances as the plaintiff and defendant in their respective situations in their case, would have acted in the same way. If the jury finds that the bottler was acting reasonably in not uncovering the problem, then the bottler was not negligent and the plaintiff cannot recover for the injuries suffered. On the other hand, the jury may decide that it was the combination of the negligences of the defendant and the contributory negligence of the plaintiff that caused the injury. Today a significant number of state courts (if not most) ask the jury to compare the relative degree of fault of the plaintiff and defendant and to reduce any award by the percentage of the plaintiff's fault.

The complaining party, the plaintiff, has the *burden of proof* in the trial. That is, the plaintiff, who presents his or her or her case first must introduce sufficient evidence to convince the judge that, if the jury believed all of the evidence to that point, the jury would find the defendant liable. If so, the plaintiff has made out a *prima facie* case and the trial goes on, with the defendant then introducing evidence to refute the plaintiff's contentions as well as the evidence necessary to prove the asserted affirmative defenses.

If the defendant makes a motion, after the plaintiff has rested his or her case (in other words, has introduced all of the evidence supporting the allegations in the complaint), asserting that a prima facie case has not been made out and the judge agrees, the judge will grant a *directed verdict* for the defendant. The trial is ended at that point with the plaintiff losing, because of not having submitted sufficient evidence to make out a case against the defendant.

This first stage of a lawsuit can end even before the trial begins by either party making a motion for *summary judgment* after the complaint and reply have been filed (collectively termed the *pleadings*) together with any supporting affidavits. If the judge agrees with a party making the motion that there is really no dispute over the crucial material facts, that side can prevail as a matter of law. Alternatively, the judge can wait until the very end of the trial, but before the jury retires to consider its verdict, and grant a directed verdict in favor of either party. Further, the judge may believe that all of the evidence (after both plaintiff and defendant have rested their respective cases) so overwhelmingly favors one side or the other that if the jury's verdict does *not* agree with the judge's belief, the judge can *reverse* the jury's verdict through a *JNOV* (that is, a judgment notwithstanding the verdict) and find for the losing side.

After the trial court has made a final judgment as a result of a summary judgment, directed verdict, jury verdict, or JNOV, the losing side has the right to appeal that loss to the appropriate appellate court and is called the *appellant* (or *petitioner*). The appeal asserts that a substantial error(s) of law (not fact) has been made by the judge and that the error(s) resulted in that side losing. If the appellate court agrees, it can order a new trial or can reinstate the original jury verdict if the trial judge had entered a JNOV. Of course, the winning side, the *appellee* (or *respondent*), argues to the appellate court that the trial judge had not made an error or that the error was harmless and the original ruling should stand. The appellate process only involves the submission of the appropriate paperwork and perhaps a brief oral argument by the attorneys in front of a panel of the appellate judges. There is no jury.

A lawsuit of the nature considered here usually is brought in the appropriate court in the plaintiff's state. If there is *diversity of citizenship* (that is, if the plaintiff and defendant are residents of different states), however, the lawsuit can be filed in the appropriate U.S. District Court, a court system established by Congress, having its own trial and appellate courts. A corporation is considered to be a resident of both the state in which it is incorporated and the state in which it principally conducts its business (which could be either the location of corporate management headquarters or the location of the principal manufacturing facilities, if the two are not located in the same state).

The legal theories or principles of law that form the matrix of any lawsuit arise from two sources. First, there are the legislative enactments such as the traffic laws, criminal laws, the UCC, antipollution laws, and so on. Generally separate and distinct from these *statutory laws* is the *common law,* created by the courts as they articulate principles to adjudicate disputes. The common law, developed and expanded over the last 200 years from the English common law, is perhaps more firmly established than statutory enactments which can change because of the view of a new legislature.

The courts, sensitive to the potential disruption of common law that could arbitrarily be altered by one judge in one court, have established the policy of *stare decisis,* which means an adherence to precedent. Once a principle of law has been laid down applicable to a certain set of facts, the court will adhere to that principle and apply it to all future cases involving substantially the same factual setting, unless they later find that the principle is no longer sound social policy.

Finally, the U.S. legal system is premised on the adversary process where the attorney's role is to present his or her client's case in the most favorable light and to cast significant doubt on the believability of the opposing party's evidence. Because the principal evidence is presented orally by witnesses under *direct examination* by the attorney of the party calling that witness, the opposing party's attorney attempts to discredit either the testimony or the witness or both through *cross examination.* Both direct and cross examination are simply the series of questions by the attorneys and answers by the witnesses from which the jury is to judge the believability of the answers and the credibility of the witness. Ultimately, justice is determined by the jury reaching a verdict through secret deliberation of the factual evidence it has heard and seen as applied to the law given by the judge in his or her charge to them.

Legal References

Armstrong Rubber Co. v Urquidez, 570 SW2d 3741 Texas (1978).

Beshada v Johns-Manville Products Corp., 90 NJ 191, 447 A2d 539 (1982).

Cantu v John Deer Co., 24 Wash App701, 603 P2d 839 at 840 (1979).

Carmichael v Reitz, 17 Cal App 3d 958, 95 Cal Rptr 381 (1971).

City of Franklin v Badger Ford Truck Sales, Inc., 58 Wis 2d 641, 207 NW2d 866 (1973).

Connelly v Uniroyal, Inc., 75 Ill 2d 393, 389 NE2d 155 (1979), revg 55 Ill App 3d 530, 13 Ill Dec 162, 370 Ne2d 1189 (1977).

Evans v Liberty Mutual Insurance Co., 398 F2d 665 (3d Cir 1968).

Farmer v School District, 171 Wash 278, 17 P2d 899.

Gagre v Bertran, 43 Cal 2d 481 (1954).

Gilbert v Stone City Construction Co., 357 NE 2d738 (Ind Ct App 1976).

Greenman v Yuba Power Products, Inc., 59 Cal 2d 57, 377 P2d 897, 27 Cal Rptr 697 (1963).

Hemstead v General Fire Extinguisher Corp., 269 F Supp 109 (D Del 1967).

Johnson v Sears, Roebuck and Co., 355 F Supp 1065 (ED Wis 1973).

La Rosa v Scientific Design Co., 402 F2d 937 (3d Cir 1968).

MacPherson v Buick Motor Co., 111 NE 1050 (NY 1916).

Michalko v Cooke Color & Chemical Corp., 91 NJ 386, 451 A2d 179 (1982).

Price v Shell Oil Co., 2 Cal 3d 245, 466 P2d 722, 85 Cal Rptr 178 (1970).

Sargent v Ross, 113 NH 388, 308 A 2d 528 (1973).

Suvada v White Motor Co., 210 NE 2d 182 (Ill 1965).

Turner v International Harvester Co., 133 NJ Super 277, 336 A2d 62, 69 (1975).

Uniform Commercial Code.

References

American Society for Quality Control Statistics Division. 1983. *Glossary and tables for statistical quality control.* 2d. ed. Milwaukee: ASQC Quality Press.

Bass, L. 1986. *Products liability: Design and manufacturing defects.* Colorado Springs, Colo.: Shepard's/McGraw-Hill.

———. 1991. Cumulative supplement to *Products liability: Design and manufacturing defects.* Colorado Springs, Colo.: Shepard's/McGraw-Hill.

Omdahl, T. P., ed. 1988. *Reliability, availability, and maintainability dictionary.* Milwaukee: ASQC Quality Press.

Peters, T. 1992. *Liberation management.* New York: Alfred A. Knopf.

Pozgar, G. D. 1993. Tort laws. In *Legal aspects of health care administration.* Gaithersburg, Md.: Aspen Publishers.

Additional Readings

Additional information on the subject of liability may be found in the following:

Anderson, R. A., and W. A. Kumf. 1972. The law of torts and business; courts and court procedure. In *Business Law.* 9th ed. Cincinnati, Ohio: South-Western Publishing.

Chapter 2

FMEA: A General Overview

A failure mode and effect analysis (FMEA) is an engineering technique used to define, identify, and eliminate known and/or potential failures, problems, errors, and so on from the system, design, process, and/or service before they reach the customer (Omdahl 1988; ASQC 1983).

The analysis of the evaluation may take two courses of action. First, using historical data, there may be analysis of similar data for similar products and/or services, warranty data, customer complaints, and any other appropriate information available, to define failures. Second, inferential statistics, mathematical modeling, simulations, concurrent engineering, and reliability engineering may be used to identify and define the failures (Stamatis 1989, 1991a, 1992).

Using an FMEA does not mean that one approach is better than the other, or that one is more accurate than the other. Both can be efficient, accurate, and correct if done properly and appropriately.

This chapter focuses on generic concerns of what the FMEA is, what it can do, what it means, how it is conducted, and how it compares with other tools available.

Any FMEA conducted properly and appropriately will provide the practitioner with useful information that can reduce the risk (work) load in the system, design, process, and service. This is because it is a logical and progressive potential failure analysis method (technique) that allows the task to be performed more effectively. FMEA is one of the most important early preventive actions in system, design, process, or service which will prevent failures and errors from occurring and reaching the customer (Kececioglu 1991).

This early warning and preventive technique provides the designer with a methodical way of studying the causes and effects of failures before the system, design, process, or service is finalized. In essence, the FMEA provides a systematic method of examining all the ways in which a failure can occur. For each failure, an estimate is made of its effect on the total system, design, process, or service, of its seriousness, of its occurrence (frequency), and its detection.

The FMEA will identify corrective actions required to prevent failures from reaching the customer, thereby assuring the highest durability, quality, and reliability possible in a product or service.

A good FMEA

- Identifies known and potential failure modes
- Identifies the causes and effects of each failure mode
- Prioritizes the identified failure modes according to the risk priority number (RPN)—the product of frequency of occurrence, severity, and detection
- Provides for problem follow-up and corrective action

Critical or Significant Characteristics or Key Indicators

To achieve customer satisfaction, the quality of the products and services must be the number one priority. The mission is to improve customer satisfaction through never-ending improvement (eliminate, reduce failures, errors, cost, mistakes, and so forth) in quality. To support that objective, a company may employ many measures of quality. These measures (sometimes called indicators, critical, or significant characteristics) are numerous and in some cases not widely known. For further explanation see Appendix B, Table B.4.

The key for selecting these characteristics is the ability to detect quality concerns before the product reaches the hands of the customer, or on their ability to measure customer dissatisfaction with the product or service. The ideal place for the identification of these characteristics is the design phase of the project.

The definitions that are used in relation to the FMEA follow:

Critical characteristics—Those characteristics that can affect compliance with governmental regulations or safe product or service operation. These characteristics must be identified in the drawings and/or procedures, as well as on the FMEA form.

Generally, the critical characteristics are defined by (Stamatis 1992)

- The courts—through product liability
- Regulatory agencies—through formal laws and/or regulations
- Industrial standards—through generally accepted practices in the industry
- Customer requisition—through their wants, needs, and expectations
- Internal engineering requirements—through historical data or leading edge technology, or experience with product or service

Significant characteristics—Quality features of a process or product or service on which data should be collected. These characteristics are identified by a consensus of the customer and supplier as well as the FMEA team.

When a supplier's proprietary design is being used, it is imperative that the supplier and customer's quality planning team jointly identify the internal characteristics that will affect quality requirements and customer expectations. In the case of the service FMEA, the customer's voice may be heard through a survey, QFD study, or even benchmarking.

The content of the design FMEA and process FMEA should be used to identify appropriate significant product, process, or service characteristics (Ford 1992). Figure 2.1 shows how Ford Motor Company views the FMEA in relation to the other tools available for an optimum design.

All significant characteristics should be designated and agreed upon during the feasibility stage.

Key characteristics—Measurement indicators that provide rapid feedback to the process and thus provide an opportunity to immediately correct quality issues. They also provide problem definition at the source, as well as quantitative and qualitative measures of customer dissatisfaction with quality issues.

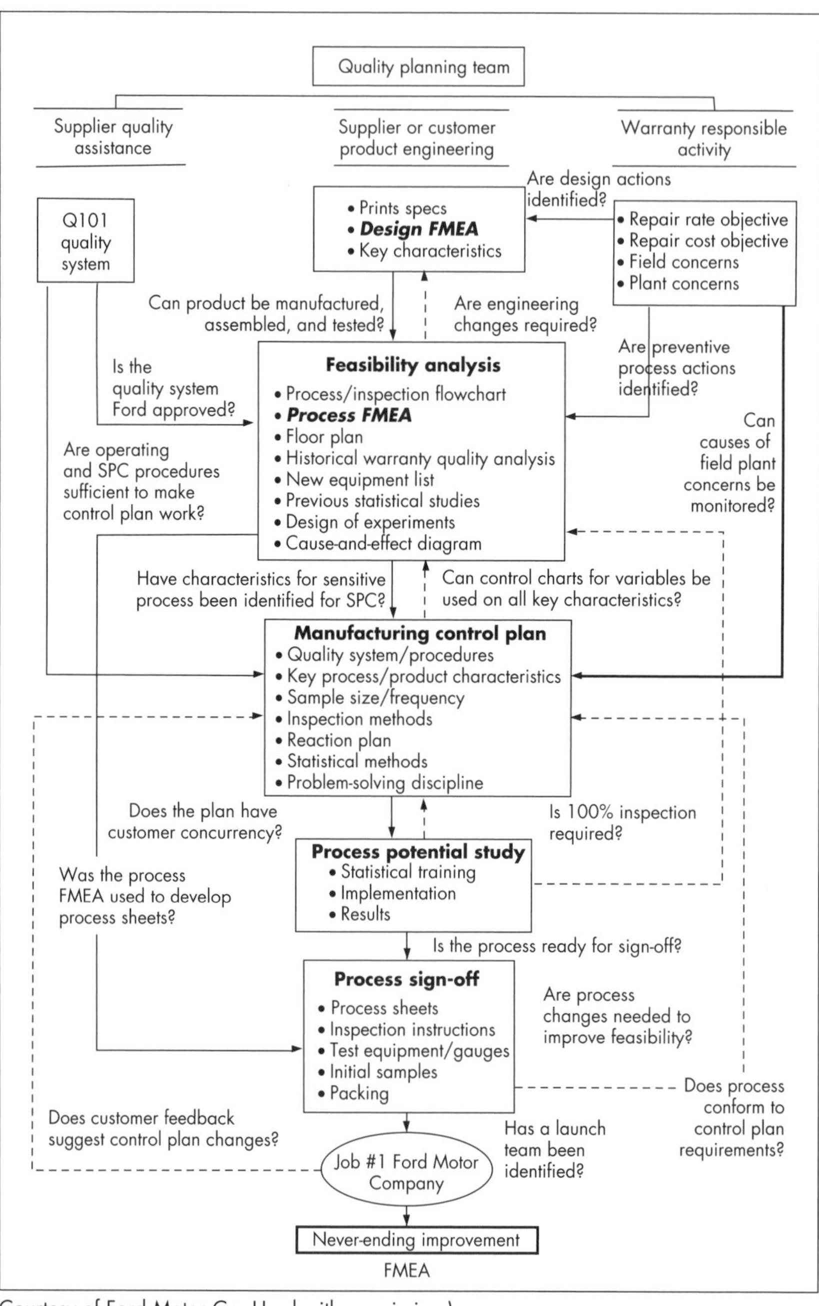

(Courtesy of Ford Motor Co. Used with permission.)

Figure 2.1 FMEA interrelationships.

There are three types of key characteristics used in the FMEA.

1. *Leading characteristic*—A measure of quality that can be assessed and analyzed prior to shipment of product or service to the customer
2. *Intermediate characteristic*—A measure of quality that can be assessed and analyzed after shipment or delivery of the product or service, but prior to placing the product or service in the hands of the customer
3. *Lagging characteristic*—A measure of quality that can be assessed and analyzed to measure customer satisfaction, long after the product or service has been built, and/or delivered

When Is the FMEA Started?

By definition the FMEA is a methodology to maximize the satisfaction of the customer by eliminating and/or reducing known or potential problems. To do this the FMEA must begin as early as possible, even though all the facts and information are not known yet. The FMEA focuses on the motto

Do the best you can, with what you have.

Is there a really best time to start? Yes. One should start an FMEA as soon as some information is known (usually through a QFD). Practitioners should not wait for all the information. If they do, they will never perform an FMEA because they will never have all the data or information. Certainly, with the preliminary information, some system constraints or design definitions may develop. This early notion of preparing the FMEA is illustrated in Figure 2.1.

Specifically, an FMEA program should start

- When new systems, designs, products, processes, or services are designed
- When existing systems, designs, products, processes, or services are about to change regardless of reason
- When new applications are found for the existing conditions of the systems, designs, products, processes, or service

- When improvements are considered for the existing systems, designs, products, processes, or services

Remember that the issue of the FMEA is to help map the road to continual improvement. As such, the FMEA may start at any point between system conception and manufacturing or service delivered. This road map is shown in Figure 2.2.

After the FMEA begins, it becomes a living document and is never really complete. It is a true dynamic tool of improvement (as opposed to static) because regardless of the beginning phase, it will use information to improve the system, design, product, process, or service. It is continually updated as often as necessary. The evolution of design is shown in Figure 2.3.

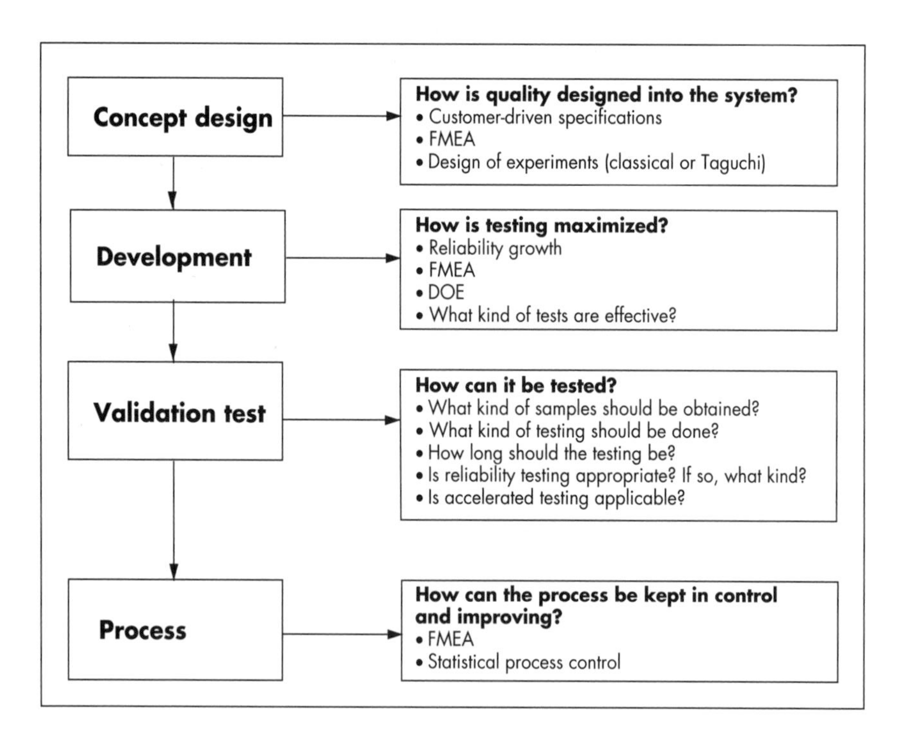

Figure 2.2 The road map of product engineering and FMEA.

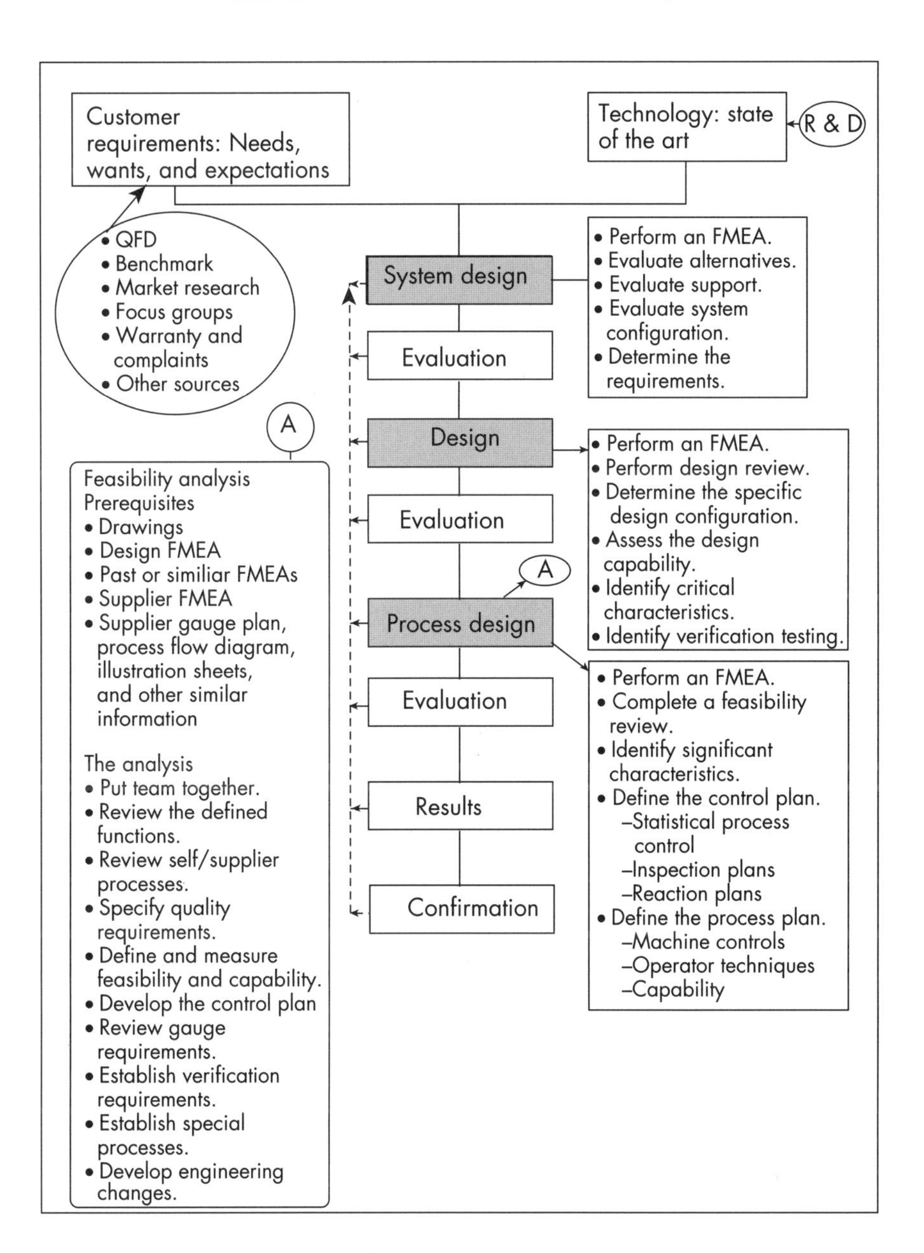

Figure 2.3 Evolution of design.

When Is the FMEA Complete?

Is there a time when the FMEA may be considered finished or complete? Yes. Only when the system, design, product, process, or service is considered complete and/or discontinued.

Specifically, the system FMEA may be considered finished when all the hardware has been defined and the design is declared frozen. The design FMEA may be considered finished when a release date for production has been set. The process FMEA may be considered finished when all operations have been identified and evaluated and all critical and significant characteristics have been addressed in the control plan. The service FMEA may be considered finished when the design of the system and individual tasks have been defined and evaluated, and all critical and significant characteristics have been addressed in the control plan.

It is important to note the following: Even though a finished or completed FMEA is defined as such based on circumstances, at any point it may be opened for a review, evaluation, and/or improvement of the system, design, product, process, or service as long as the system, design, product, process, or service is currently in existence.

Can the FMEA be discarded? If so, how? When? The strict answer to the question is yes. Depending on the relationship between the organization and the customer or supplier, however, different guidelines exist. There are no definite and universal guidelines other than specific rules in specific organizations and industries. For example, in the nuclear industry the retention record is from cradle to grave, but in some automotive guidelines the FMEA should be kept as long as the product is produced. (As a general rule, the FMEA should be available for the entire product life.)

Who Conducts the FMEA?

The FMEA is a team function and cannot be done on an individual basis. The team must be defined as appropriate for a specific project and cannot serve as the universal or company FMEA team. The knowledge that is required for the specific problem is unique to that problem. Therefore, the makeup of the team must be cross-functional and multidisciplined for each FMEA (Stamatis 1991b). For more detailed information see chapter 4.

Under no circumstances should any FMEA be done with a single individual (in other words, design or process engineer). An individual may fill out the FMEA form properly, but there will be built-in biases based on the single perspective of the individual conducting that FMEA.

If time constraints do not allow for a full team discussion, the recommendation (reluctantly) is to allow the leader of the FMEA team to present some of the failures in the team's presence, and follow with a full discussion.

Under no circumstances should the enumeration of failures be done privately by anyone with the expectation that the team will at a later time discuss the discrepancies. That will never happen. The format for such an exercise is shown in Figure 2.4.

Interpretation of the FMEA

The essence of the FMEA is to identify and prevent known and potential problems from reaching the customer. To do that one has made some assumptions, one of which is that problems have different priorities. Thus, finding that priority is important and the thrust of the methodology.

There are three components that help define the priority of failures

- Occurrence (O)
- Severity (S)
- Detection (D)

Occurrence is the frequency of the failure. Severity is the seriousness (effects) of the failure. Detection is the ability to detect the failure before it reaches the customer.

There are many ways to define the value of these components. The usual way is to use numerical scales (called *risk criteria guidelines).* These guidelines can be qualitative and/or quantitative.

If the guideline is qualitative, it must follow theoretical (expected) behavior of the component. For example, in the case of the occurrence the expected behavior is normality. This behavior is expected because frequencies over time behave in a normal fashion. Thus, the guideline should follow the normal distribution. In the case of severity, the

Type of FMEA: ____________ Others involved: ____________ FMEA date: ________

Prepared by: ____________ Responsibility: ____________ Page _____ of____pages

System/ design/ process/ service function	Potential failure mode	Potential effect(s) of failure	∇	Potential cause(s) of failure	Detection method	OCC	SEV	DET	RPN	Recommended action	Responsibility and completion date	Action results				
												Action taken	SEV	OCC	DET	RPN
Engineer				Team							Engineer with selective team					

Figure 2.4 An alternate FMEA construction.*

*Not recommended for general use. Use only when time contraints do not allow full FMEA development.

expected behavior is lognormal. This behavior is expected because the failures that occurred should be of the nuisance category as opposed to critical or catastrophic. Thus, the guideline should follow a distribution that skews to the right (positively skewed). In the case of the detection, the expected behavior is that of a discrete distribution. This is expected because there is more concern if the failure is found by the customer as opposed to finding the failure within the organization. Therefore, there is a discrete outcome (internal organization versus customer) in the detection. Thus, the guideline should follow a distribution with a gap between the values. Figure 2.5 shows these distributions.

If the guideline is quantitative, it must be specific. It must follow actual data, statistical process control data, historical data, and/or similar or surrogate data for the evaluation. The guideline does not have to follow the theoretical behavior. If it does, it is strictly coincidence. Table 2.1 displays some of the guidelines for the selection guideline. Appendix F includes examples of actual evaluation criteria.

The ranking for the criteria can have any value. There is no standard for such value; however, there are two very common rankings used in all industries today. One is the ranking based on 1 to 5 scale and the second, a 1 to 10 scale.

The ranking of 1 to 5 is limited in nature, but offers expediency and ease of interpretation. It does not provide for sensitivity (accuracy) of specific quantification, because it reflects a uniform distribution. The ranking of 1 to 10 is used widely and, in fact, is highly recommended because it provides ease of interpretation, accuracy, and precision in the quantification of the ranking. Examples of both rankings are in Appendix F. Rankings of higher than 1 to 10 scales are not recommended (even though they can be very precise and accurate) because they are difficult to interpret and lose their effectiveness.

The priority of the problems is articulated via the RPN. This number is a product of the occurrence, severity, and detection. The value by itself should be used only to rank order and concerns of the system, design, product, process and service. All RPNs have no other value or meaning (Ford 1992).

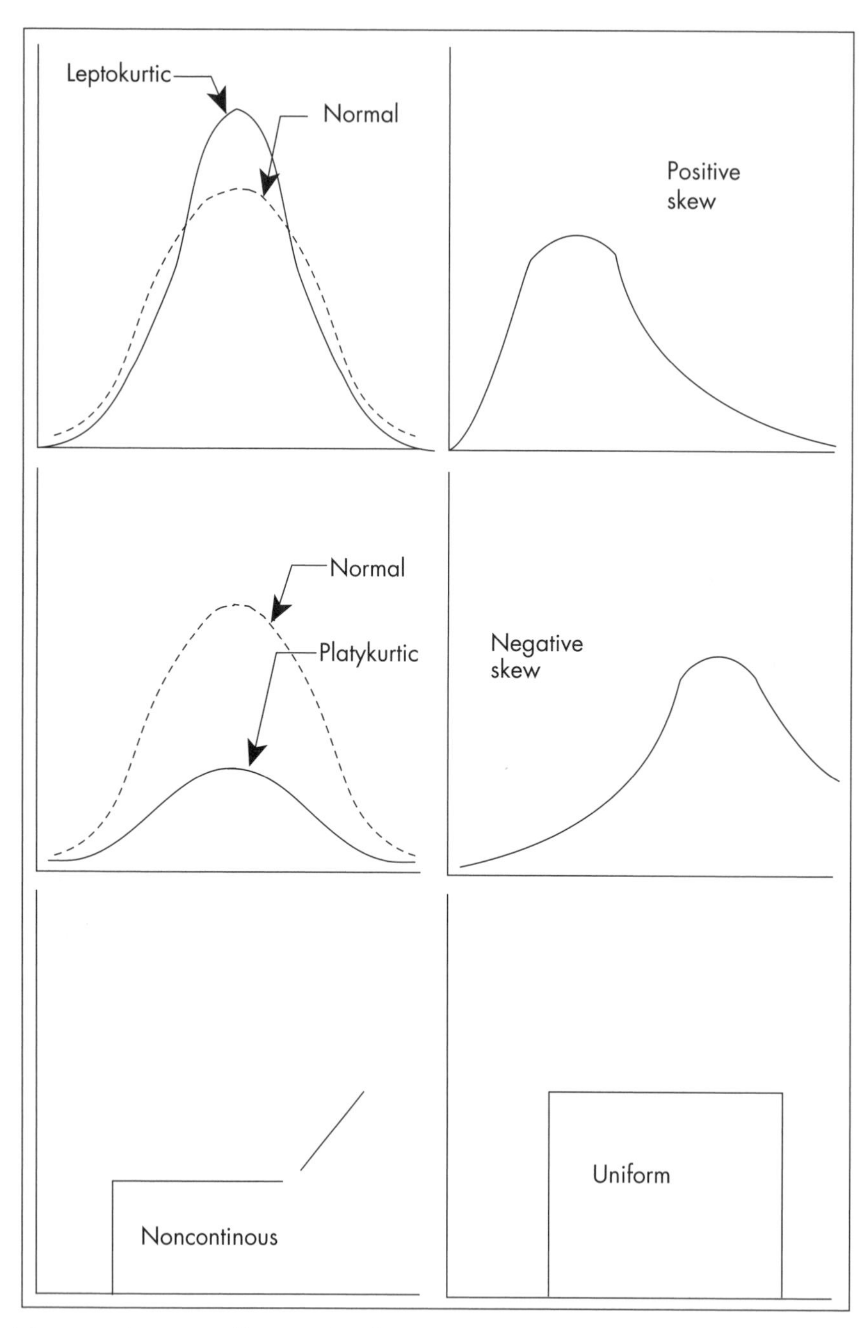

Figure 2.5 Different distributions.

If	Then use	Select
The system is similar to others or historical data exist	Statistical data from either historical or surrogate systems: Reliability data, actual distribution, mathematical modeling, simulation	Actual data and/or CpK
Failure history is available with the system itself or similar, or surrogate parts	Historical data based on reliability, system, actual distributions, mathematical modeling, simulation, cumulative data, and/or fraction defectives.	Actual data and/or cumulative number of failures
The system is new and/or no quantification for any data is available	Team judgment	Subjective criteria. Use team consensus and be conservative.
The design is similar to others or historical data exist	Statistical data from either historical or surrogate systems: Reliability data, actual distribution, mathematical modeling, simulation	Actual data and/or CpK
Failure history is available with the design itself or similar, or surrogate parts	Historical data based on reliability, design, actual distributions, mathematical modeling, simulation cumulative data, and/or fraction defectives.	Actual data and/or cumulative number of failures
The design is new and/or no quantification for any data is available	Team judgment	Subjective criteria. Use team consensus and be conservative.

Table 2.1 Criteria for selecting ratings.

If	Then use	Select
The process is under statistical process control (SPC)	Statistical data: reliability data, process capability, actual distribution, mathematical modeling, simulation	Actual data or CpK
The process is similar to others or historical data exist	Statistical data from either historical or surrogate systems: Reliability data, process capability, actual distribution, mathematical modeling, simulation	Actual data or CpK
Failure history is available with the design itself or similar, or surrogate parts	Historical data based on reliability, process, actual distributions, mathematical modeling, simulation, cumulative data, and/or fraction defectives.	Actual data and/or cumulative number of failures
The process is new and/or no quantification for any data is available	Team judgment	Subjective criteria. Use team consensus and be conservative.
The service is under statistical process control (SPC)	Statistical data: simulation	Actual data or CpK
The service is similar to others or historical data exist	Statistical data from either historical or surrogate systems: reliability data (queue modeling), process capability, actual distribution, mathematical modeling, simulation	Actual data or CpK
Failure history is available with the design itself or similar, or surrogate parts	Historical data based on reliability, process, actual distributions, mathematical modeling, simulation, cumulative data, and/or fraction defectives.	Actual data and/or cumulative number of failures
The service is new and/or no quantification for any data is available	Team judgment	Subjective criteria. Use team consensus and be conservative.

Table 2.1 (continued)

The threshold of pursuing failures/problems is an RPN equal to or greater than 50 based on a 95 percent confidence and a 1 to 10 guideline scale. By no means is this a standard or a universal number. It can and does change with the scale chosen and the statistical confidence the engineer wants. Of course, there is no limit to pursuing all failures, if that is the goal. At that point the order is determined by the magnitude of the RPN for each of the failures. (The high RPN failures are addressed first, then the lower, and so on until all failures have been resolved.) To undertake an analysis of all problems at the same time is not recommended and is contrary to the philosophy of the FMEA.

The threshold can be changed for any given statistical confidence and/or scale. For example, say 99 percent of all failures must be addressed for a very critical system, design, product, process, and/or service on a guideline scale of 1 to 10. What is the threshold? The maximum number possible for the RPN is 1000 (10 × 10 × 10 from occurrence, severity, and detection). Ninety-nine percent of 1000 is 990. Now subtract 1000 – 990 = 10. Therefore, the threshold of examining the failures would be anything equal or greater than a 10 RPN. If the statistical confidence is 90 percent with a scale of 1 to 10, then the threshold becomes 100, and so on.

If the scale is 1 to 5, then the threshold changes accordingly. The method is the same; however, the total number now is 125 instead of 1000. Thus, in a 90 percent, 95 percent, and 99 percent confidence the RPN of concern is 13, 7, and 2, respectively.

After the RPN has been determined, the evaluation begins based on the definition of the risk. Usually this risk is defined by the team as minor, moderate, high, and critical. It may be changed to reflect different situations.

- Under minor risk, no action is taken.
- Under moderate risk, some action may take place.
- Under high risk, definite action will take place. (Selective validation and evaluation may be required.)
- Under critical risk, definite actions will take place and extensive changes are required in the system, design, product, process, and/or service.

If there are more than two failures with the same RPN, then first address the failure with high severity, and then detection. Severity is approached first because it deals with the effects of the failure. Detection is used over the occurrence because it is customer dependent, which is more important than just the frequencies of the failure.

An example of extreme cases when corrective action must be taken is shown in the following design ratings.

Assessment rating			Causes of failure	Action taken
O	S	D		
1	1	1	Ideal situation (goal)	No action (N/A)
1	1	10	Assured mastery	N/A
1	10	1	Failure does not reach user	N/A
1	10	10	Failure reaches user	Yes
10	1	1	Frequent fails, detectable, costly	Yes
10	1	10	Frequent fails, reach the user	Yes
10	10	1	Frequent fails w/ major impact	Yes
10	10	10	Trouble!	Yes, Yes, Yes, Yes

Again, a typical example of actions which will influence the design FMEA risk evaluation follows.

Corrective actions	O	S	D
Redesign the product	Y	Y	Y
Improve current control	N	N	Y
Change material parts	Y	N	Y
Change the application	Y	Y	Y
Change the field environment	Y	Y	Y
Improve reliability program	Y	N	Y
Improve employee training	N	N	Y
Implement FMEA program	Y	Y	Y
Implement SPC program	N	N	N
Improve quality plan	N	N	N

Y = Yes N = No

For a process, extreme cases where corrective action must be taken include the following process ratings.

Assessment rating			Causes of failure	Action taken
O	S	D		
1	1	1	Ideal situation (goal)	No action (N/A)
1	1	10	Assured mastery	N/A
1	10	1	Failure does not reach user	N/A
1	10	10	Failure reaches user	Yes
10	1	1	Frequent fails, detectable, costly	Yes
10	1	10	Frequent fails, reach the user	Yes
10	10	1	Frequent fails w/major impact	Yes
10	10	10	Trouble!	Yes,Yes,Yes,Yes

Another example of actions that will influence the process FMEA risk evaluation follows.

Corrective actions	O	S	D
Redesign the process	Y	M	Y
Redesign the product	M	M	M
Improve current control	N	N	N
Change material parts	M	N	M
Change the application	N	M	M
Change the field environment	N	M	N
Improve reliability program	Y	N	Y
Improve employee training	M	N	Y
Implement FMEA program	Y	Y	Y
Implement SPC program	Y	N	Y
Improve quality plan	Y	N	Y
Y = Yes M = Maybe N = No			

The Process of Conducting an FMEA

To conduct an FMEA effectively one must follow a systematic approach. The recommended approach is an eight-step method that facilitates the system, design, product, process, and service FMEA.

1. *Select the team and brainstorm*—Make sure the appropriate individuals are going to participate. The team must be cross-functional and multidisciplined and the team members must be willing to contribute (Stamatis 1991b).

   After the team has been identified and is in place, the team tries to prioritize the opportunities of improvement. Is the concern in a system, design, product, process, or service? What kind of problems are there and/or what kind are anticipated with a particular situation? Is the customer and/or supplier involved or is continual improvement being pursued independently? If the customer and/or supplier has identified specific failures, then the job is much easier because direction has already been given. On the other hand, if continual improvement is being independently pursued, the brainstorm, affinity diagram, storybook method, and/or a cause-and-effect diagram may prove to be the best tools to identify some direction.

2. *Functional block diagram and/or process flowchart*—For system and design FMEAs the functional block diagram is applicable. For the process and service FMEAs the process flowchart is applicable. The idea is to make sure that everyone is on the same wavelength. Does everyone understand the system, design, process, and/or service? Does everyone understand the problems associated with the system, design, process, and/or service?

   The functional block diagram focuses the discussion on the system and design while the process flowchart focuses the discussion on the process and service. Both of these tools also provide an overview and a working model of the relationships and interactions of the systems, subsystems, components, processes, assemblies, and/or services and help in the understanding of the system, design, product, process, and/or service.

3. *Prioritize*—After the team understands the problem, the actual analysis begins. Frequent questions are: What part is important? Where should the team begin?

   Sometimes, this step is completely bypassed because the prioritization is de facto. The customer has identified the priority, or due to warranty cost or some other input the determination has been made by the management to start at a given point.

4. *Data collection*—This is where the team begins to collect the data of the failures and categorizes them appropriately. At this point the team begins to fill in the FMEA form. The failures identified are the failure modes of the FMEA.

5. *Analysis*—Now the data are utilized for a resolution. Remember, the reason for the data is to gain information that is used to gain knowledge. Ultimately, that knowledge contributes to the decision. This flow can be shown as follows:

Data ——> Information ——> Knowledge ——> Decision
——->>>> Flow >>>>——>

The analysis, may be qualitative or quantitative. The team may use brainstorming, cause-and-effect analysis, QFD, DOE, SPC, another FMEA, mathematical modeling, simulation, reliability analysis, and anything else that team members think is suitable.

Information from this step will be used to fill in the columns of the FMEA form in relationship to the effects of the failure, existing controls, and discussing the estimation of severity, occurrence, and detection.

6. *Results*—The theme here is *data driven.* Based on the analysis, results are derived.

The information from this step will be used to quantify the severity, occurrence, detection, and RPN. The appropriate columns of the FMEA will be completed.

7. *Confirm/evaluate/measure*—After the results have been recorded, it is time to confirm, evaluate, and measure the success or failure. This evaluation takes the form of three basic questions.

- Is the situation better than before?
- Is the situation worse than before?
- Is the situation the same as before?

The information from this step will be used to recommend actions and to see the results of those actions in the corresponding columns of the FMEA form.

8. *Do it all over again*—Regardless of how step 7 is answered, the team must pursue improvement all over again because of the underlying philosophy of FMEA, which is *continual improvement.*

The long-term goal is to completely eliminate every single failure. The short-term goal is to minimize the failures if not eliminate them. Of course, the perseverance for those goals has to be taken into consideration in relationship to the needs of the organization, costs, customers, and competition.

How Long Should the FMEA Be and How Much Time Should It Take?

Conducting an FMEA is a time-consuming exercise, but if one evaluates all alternatives, it is evident that it is worthwhile. Regarding the eight steps, the majority of the time is spent on the first three steps. Identifying the problem, understanding the problem, and prioritizing the analysis accounts for approximately 60 percent to 80 percent of the total time. The remainder of the time is spent in actual analysis.

There are no specific length or time limits for any FMEA. The length and time is defined by the conditions, objectives, and complexity of the project at hand.

An appropriate FMEA may be one-quarter of a page that took only one-half hour to complete. Conversely, an FMEA with 164 pages and six months (five persons meeting twice a week for three hours per meeting) of work does not guarantee completion.

Often an FMEA is performed on commodity items. In these situations, it is acceptable to perform group FMEAs on similar or identical items and then address the out-of-the-ordinary conditions as separate items. Examples of this include washers (fasteners), screws, springs, and O-rings. They all have some inherent common characteristics that can be addressed together; however, they all have some special attributes that should be addressed separately.

What Happens After Completion of the FMEA?

Generally there are seven steps that the team must follow (Stamatis 1993).

1. *Review the FMEA*—Make sure that the function, purpose, and objective have been met. Make sure that all the loose ends have been addressed and the appropriate action has been recommended and/or implemented. Some helpful hints for this review follow.
    - Is the problem identification specific?
    - Was a root cause, an effect, or a symptom identified?
    - Is the corrective action measurable?
    - Is the corrective action proactive?
    - Is the use of terminology current and consistent?

2. *Highlight the high-risk areas*—A visual inspection of the critical column, the severity column, and the RPN column generally will identify the high-risk areas. In the critical column, the high-risk item may be identified as such; in the severity column the high-risk item usually will have a number higher or equal to 7; and in the RPN column usually a number higher or equal to 100 (on a 1 to 10 scale) will indicate that there might be a high-risk item.
3. *Identify the critical, significant, and major characteristics*—Upon completion of the FMEA, a visual check of the RPN and critical columns should identify the critical, significant, and major characteristics. Make sure that there is a direct correlation between the critical column and the effects of the failure and the severity columns. Great care should be taken when reviewing the RPN because these numbers will indicate whether or not action should be taken.
4. *Ensure that a control plan exists and is being followed*—As previously mentioned, the idea of performing an FMEA is to eliminate and/or reduce known and potential failures before they reach the customer. In this step, make sure that all critical, significant, and major characteristics have a documented plan for controlling, improving, and/or handling changes. The control plan is the map that will allow practitioners to make the product and/or service

acceptable to the customer. Although the FMEA identifies the vital signs of the process and/or service, the control plan monitors those vital signs of the process and/or service.

5. *Conduct capability studies*—After the control plan is in place and statistical control has been established, a potential capability or a long capability must be performed.

6. *Work on processes which have a CpK less than or equal to 1.33*—Although the 1.33 generally is accepted as the minimum goal, be aware that some companies require a CpK = 1.67 (Ford Motor Co.) or even a CpK = 2.00 (Motorola). The point is to continually improve the process by eliminating variation. Produce everything around the target.

7. *Work on processes which have CpK greater than or equal to 1.33*—After the minimum standard is reached in step 5, try to go beyond that standard for further improvement. Reduce variation and try to reach or exceed a CpK greater than or equal to 2.00. Remember, all standards are minimum performance. Consequently, continual improvement dictates that one should, at all times, try to exceed all standards, including all CpK targets.

The Four Types of FMEAs

Generally, it is accepted that there are four types of FMEA. In Figure 2.6 the relationships of the four FMEAs are shown with their respective focus and objective. The four types are

1. *System FMEA*—Used to analyze systems and subsystems in the early concept and design stage. A system FMEA focuses on potential failure modes between the functions of the system caused by system deficiencies. *It includes the interactions between systems and elements of the system.*

   The output of the system FMEA is

   - A potential list of failure modes ranked by the RPN
   - A potential list of system functions that could detect potential failure modes

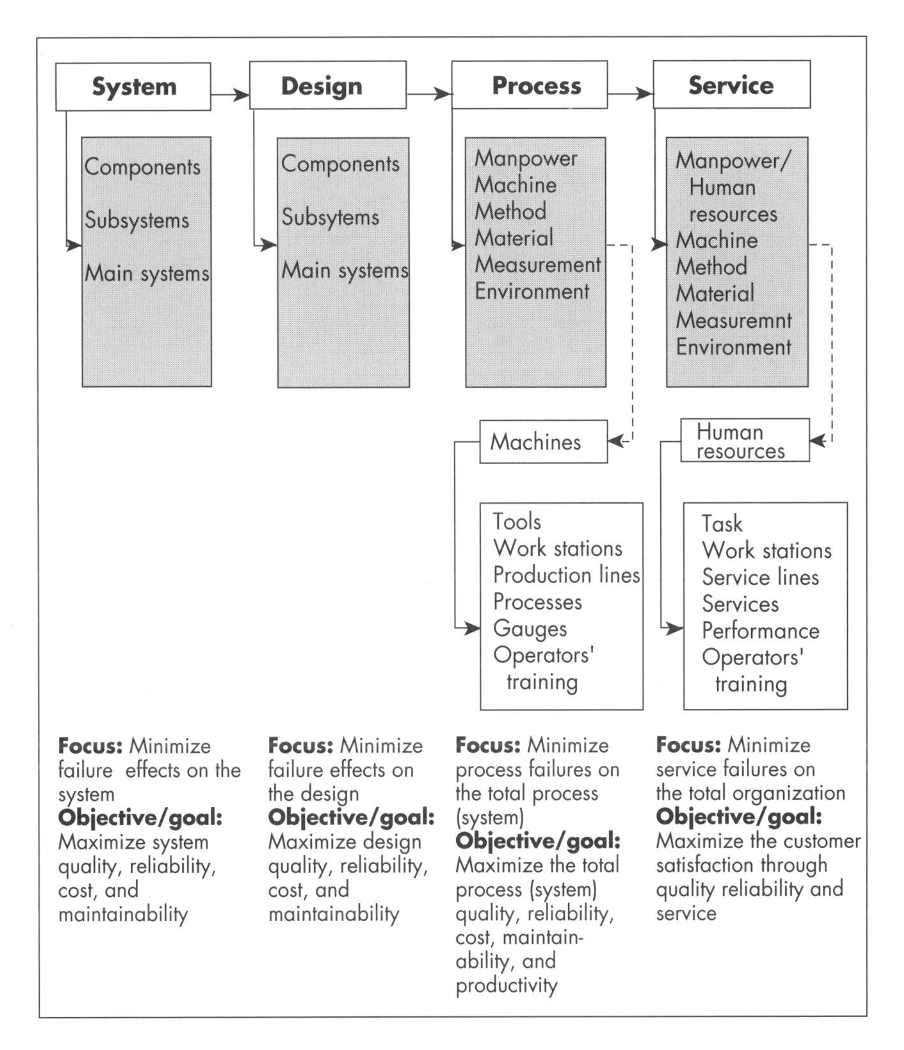

Figure 2.6 Types of FMEA.

- A potential list of design actions to eliminate failure modes, safety issues, and reduce the occurrence

The benefits of the system FMEA are that it

- Helps select the optimum system design alternative
- Helps in determining redundancy
- Helps in defining the basis for system level diagnostic procedures

- Increases the likelihood that potential problems will be considered
- Identifies potential system failures and their interaction with other systems or subsystems

2. *Design FMEA*—Used to analyze products before they are released to manufacturing. A design FMEA focuses on failure modes caused by design deficiencies.

The output of the design FMEA is

- A potential list of failure modes ranked by the RPN
- A potential list of critical and/or significant characteristics
- A potential list of design actions to eliminate failure modes, safety issues, and reduce the occurrence
- A potential list of parameters for appropriate testing, inspection, and/or detection methods
- A potential list of recommended actions for the critical and significant characteristics

The benefits of the design FMEA are that it

- Establishes a priority for design improvement actions
- Documents the rationale for changes
- Provides information to help through product design verification and testing
- Helps identify the critical or significant characteristics
- Assists in the evaluation of design requirements and alternatives
- Helps identify and eliminate potential safety concerns
- Helps identify product failure early in the product development phase

3. *Process FMEA*—Used to analyze manufacturing and assembly processes. A process FMEA focuses on failure modes caused by process or assembly deficiencies.

The output of the process FMEA is

- A potential list of failure modes ranked by the RPN

- A potential list of critical and/or significant characteristics
- A potential list of recommended actions to address the critical and significant characteristics
- A potential list to eliminate the causes of failure modes, reduce their occurrence, and improve defect detection if CpK cannot be improved

The benefits of the process FMEA are that it

- Identifies process deficiencies and offers a corrective action plan
- Identifies the critical and/or significant characteristics and helps in developing control plans
- Establishes a priority of corrective actions
- Assists in the analysis of the manufacturing or assembly process
- Documents the rationale for changes

4. *Service FMEA*—Used to analyze services before they reach the customer. A service FMEA focuses on failure modes (tasks, errors, mistakes) caused by system or process deficiencies.

The output of the service FMEA is

- A potential list of errors ranked by the RPN
- A potential list of critical or significant tasks, or processes
- A potential list of bottleneck processes or tasks
- A potential list to eliminate the errors
- A potential list of monitoring system/process functions

The benefits of the service FMEA are that it

- Assists in the analysis of job flow
- Assists in the analysis of the system and/or process
- Identifies task deficiencies
- Identifies critical or significant tasks and helps in the development of control plans
- Establishes a priority for improvement actions
- Documents the rationale for changes

Guidelines for Process and Service Control

Specifically, with a process and/or service, the flow for control using an FMEA follows.

1. *Select the process and/or service*—The necessary changes and/or improvements must be identified. The goal of the undertaking must also be defined.

2. *Conduct the FMEA*—After the goal and expectations of the process and/or service are established, the FMEA should be pursued.

3. *Conduct a measurement system analysis*—Make sure the measurement system is appropriate and applicable to the process and/or service.

4. *Conduct process potential study*—A short-term (cursory) capability study (sometimes a feasibility study) must be performed to identify whether or not the process and/or service is doable and appropriate.

5. *Develop control plan*—Make sure that a road map exists to identify and prescribe critical processes/services.

6. *Train operators in control methods*—It is imperative that all operators have the appropriate training. Without it, they cannot be expected to know what they have to do. It is management's responsibility to identify and provide the appropriate training.

7. *Implement control plan*—Just because the documentation exists, it does not imply that it is being followed. It is imperative that the control plan be followed at all times if improvement is expected. With an implemented control plan there is a better chance for consistency and reduction of variation than without it.

8. *Determine long-term capability*—Know whether or not the organization can produce and/or service what it says it can produce and/or service. The only way to know for sure is through a capability study.

9. *Review the process and/or service for continual improvement*—Always be cognizant of changes. Because changes occur, one must

be vigilant to make sure that the changes are for a true improvement rather than something different.

10. *Develop an audit system*—The switch from inspection (which is product oriented), to audit system (which is system oriented), must be implemented in the organization if continual improvement is really a concern. Only with audits can one demonstrate true quality orientation. Inspection, by definition, focuses on sorting quality (good versus bad). On the other hand, audits by definition focus on the systems that are in place to produce/service good quality.

11. *Institute improvement actions*—The focus in any organization is to improve. This is done by constantly evaluating current and future activities and implementing those activities that will make the process/services better.

It is this need for improvement that generates the interest for an FMEA. It is the FMEA that will contribute to the improvement by eliminating known and/or potential failures from the process/service. As a consequence, variation is minimized and improvements realized.

Relationships of FMEA and Other Tools

Fault Tree Analysis. FTA is a deductive analytical technique of reliability and safety analysis and generally is used for complex dynamic systems. It provides an objective basis for analysis and justification for changes and additions (Blanchard 1986).

FTA was developed in 1961 by Bell Telephone Company. Later on the Boeing company modified the concept to the point that now the FTA is widely used in many fields and industries.

As it is used today, the FTA is a model that logically and graphically represents the various combinations of possible events, both faulty and normal, occurring in a system that leads to the top undesired event. It uses a tree to show the cause-and-effect relationships between a single, undesired event (failure) and the various contributing causes. The tree shows the logical branches from the single failure at the top of the tree, to the root cause(s) at the bottom of the tree. Standard logic symbols are used.

After the tree has been constructed and the root cause(s) identified, the corrective actions required to prevent or control the causes can be determined. Usually probabilities are associated with the undesired failure.

The FTA always supplements the FMEA and not the other way around. In general, its application may be in a system or subsystem environment with a focus on identifying the root factors that could cause a failure and their interdependent relationships.

The benefits of using FTA are that it

- Helps in visualizing the analysis
- Helps identify the reliability of higher-order (level) assemblies or the system
- Determines the probability of occurrence for each of the root causes
- Provides documented evidence of compliance with safety requirements
- Assesses the impact of design changes and alternatives
- Provides options for qualitative, as well as quantitative, system reliability analysis
- Allows the analyst to concentrate on one particular system failure at a time
- Provides the analyst with insight into system behavior
- Isolates critical safety failures
- Identifies ways that failure of the product can lead to an accident

Figures 2.7 and 2.8 show the elements of the FTA. Figure 2.9 shows how the FTA can be used with the FMEA, and Figure 2.10 shows an example of an FTA diagram.

Task Analysis. After the system has been defined and allocated, the specific tasks that must be performed are analyzed. A task analysis defines

- The stimulus initiating the task
- The equipment used to perform the task
- The task feedback
- The required response of the human
- The characteristics of the task output, including performance requirements

Name of gate	Symbol of gate	Input–output relationship
AND gate	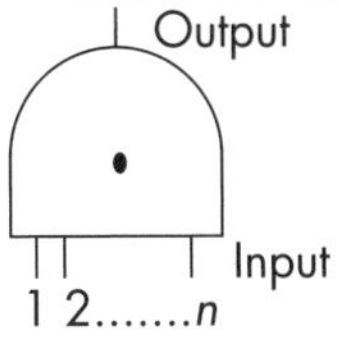 Output • Input 1 2.......*n*	The output event occurs if all of the *n* input events occur.
OR gate	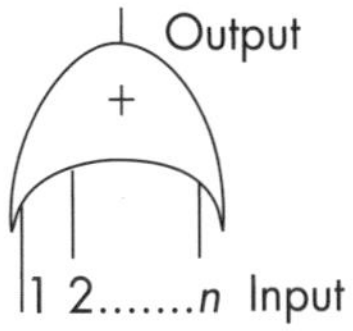 Output + 1 2.......*n* Input	The output event occurs if at least one of the *n* input events occurs.
m-out-of-*n* voting gate	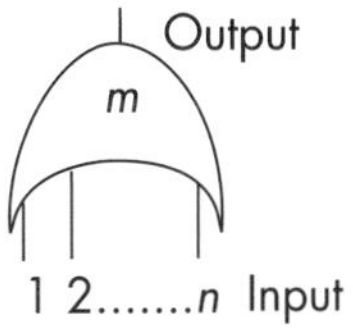 Output *m* 1 2.......*n* Input	The output event occurs if *m* or more out of *n* input events occurs.
Priority AND gate	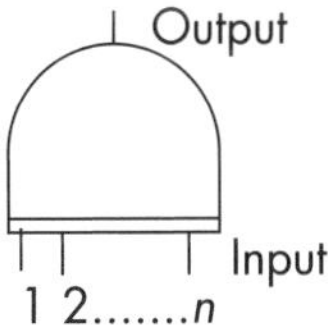 Output Input 1 2.......*n*	The output event occurs if all input events occur in a certain order.
Exclusive OR gate	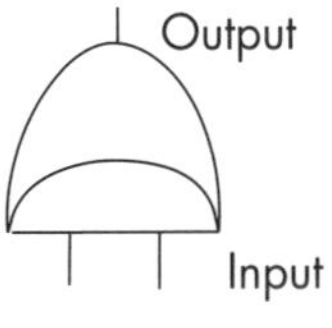 Output Input	The output event occurs if only one of the input events occurs.
Inhibit gate	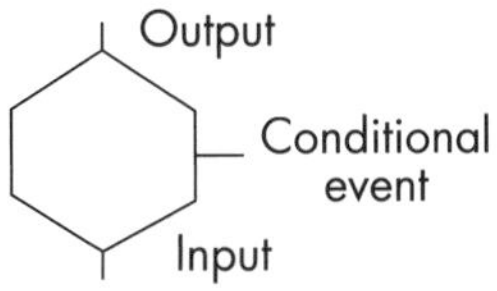 Output Conditional event Input	The input event causes the output event only if the conditional event occurs.

Figure 2.7 Fault tree gate symbols.

Symbol of event	Meaning of symbol
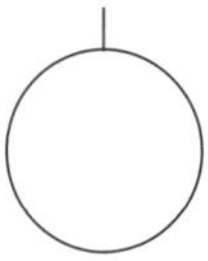 Circle	Basic event
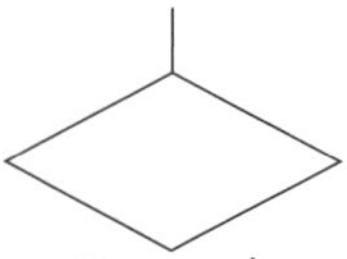 Diamond	Undeveloped event
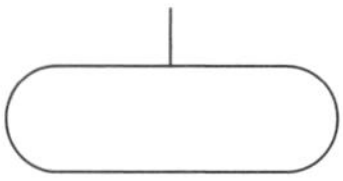 Oval	Conditional event
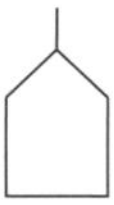 House	Trigger event
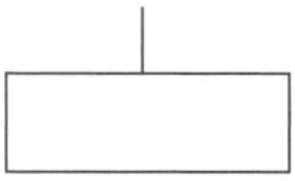 Rectangle	Resultant event
In Triangle Out	Transfer-in and transfer-out events

Figure 2.8 Fault tree event symbols.

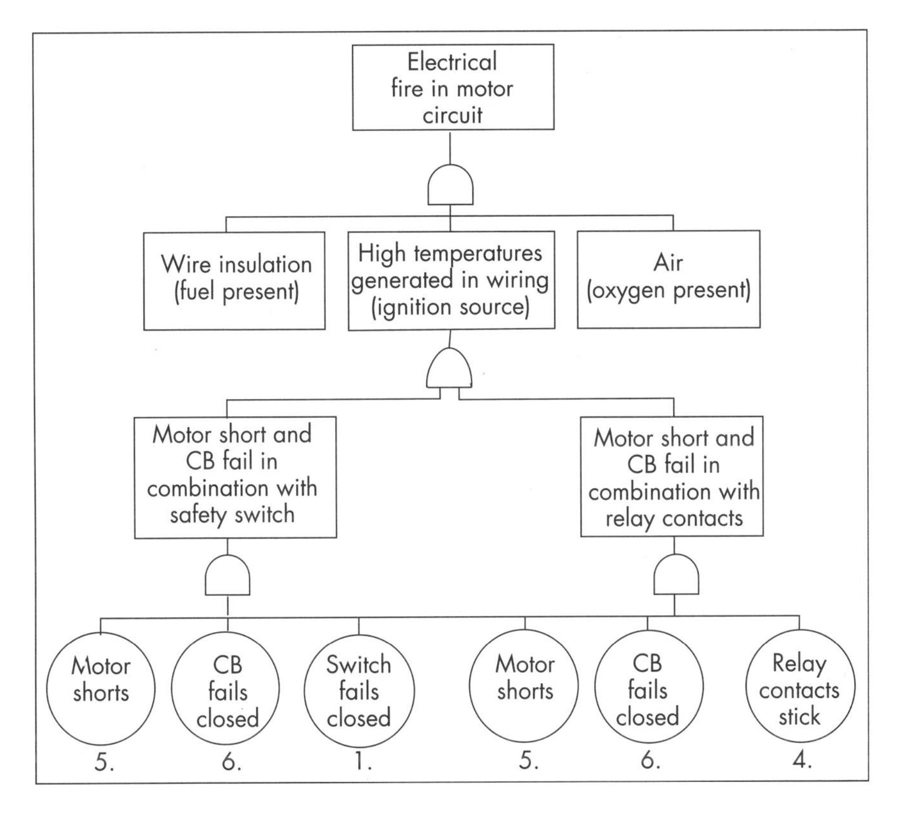

Figure 2.9 FTA and FMEA (possible specific failures).

Process Flowchart. This is the sequence of flow in the operations among processes and personnel using standard symbols for each of the processes. The symbols are

Activity/operations ○

Inspection □

Flow/movement ⟶

Delay D

Inventory storage ▽

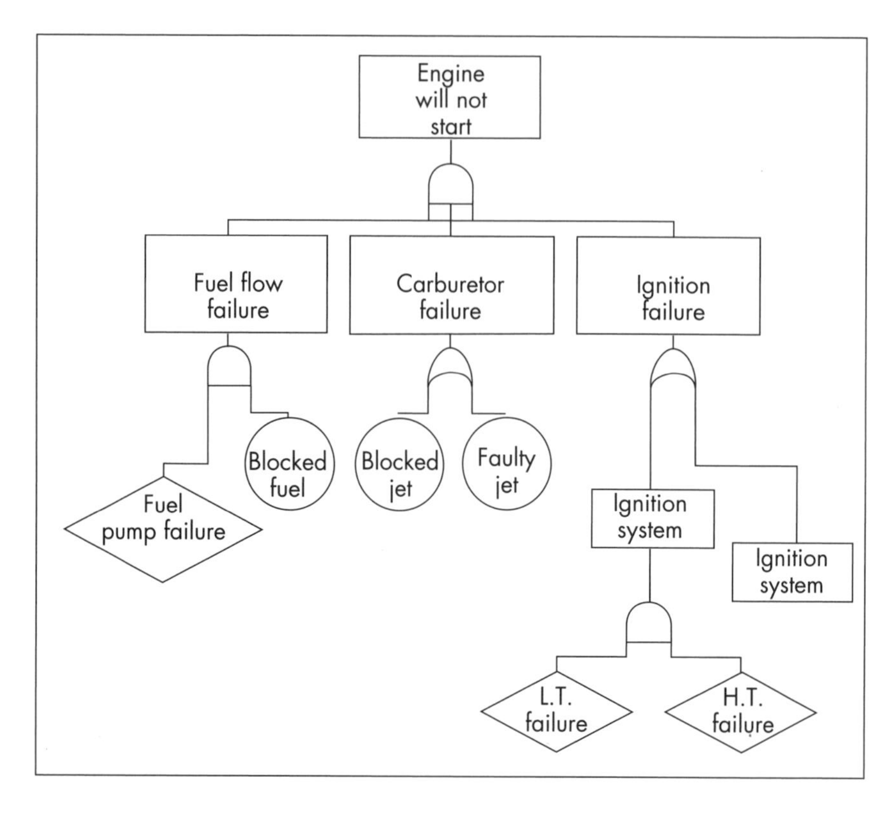

Figure 2.10 FTA for engine (incomplete).

The process flowchart is used primarily in the process FMEA and service FMEA.

Functional Flow Diagrams or Block Diagrams. Block diagrams illustrate the physical or functional relationships as well as interfaces within a system or assembly under analysis. They are used as a mechanism for portraying system design requirements in a pictorial manner, illustrating series–parallel relationships, the hierarchy of system functions, and functional interfaces.

The types of block diagrams used in FMEA are

- System—For identifying the relationships between major components and subsystems

- Detail—For identifying the relationships between each part within an assembly or subsystem
- Reliability—For identifying the series dependence or independence of major components, subsystems, or detail parts in achieving required functions

Block diagrams are not intended to illustrate all the functional relationships which must be considered in the FMEA. They should be made as simple and explicit as possible. An example of a block diagram and logic diagram is shown in Figure 2.11.

System level diagrams are generated for components or large systems which are made up of several assemblies or subsystems. *Detail level diagrams* are generated to define the logical flow and interrelationships of individual components and/or tasks.

Reliability level diagrams generally are used at the system level to illustrate the dependence or independence of the systems, or components contributing to the specific functions (General Motors 1988). They also are used to support predictions of successful functioning for specified operating or usage periods.

Sketches, Layouts, Schematics. These diagrams present a picture of how the product or process is proposed to look (General Motors 1988). The purpose of using these diagrams is to gain a better understanding of the system being studied by the analysis team. Using this information, the team can gain more objective information regarding

- The general size—The relative size of the component and the process operation.
- The overall space involved—How the system fits within the total system. Specifically, information about accessibility and serviceability are of concern.
- The number of items—What is the quantity of bolts, nuts, and so on, or the number of fixtures and/or tools in an operation. Figures 2.12, 2.13, 2.14 show examples of a schematic diagram, functional diagram, and a sketch layout diagram.

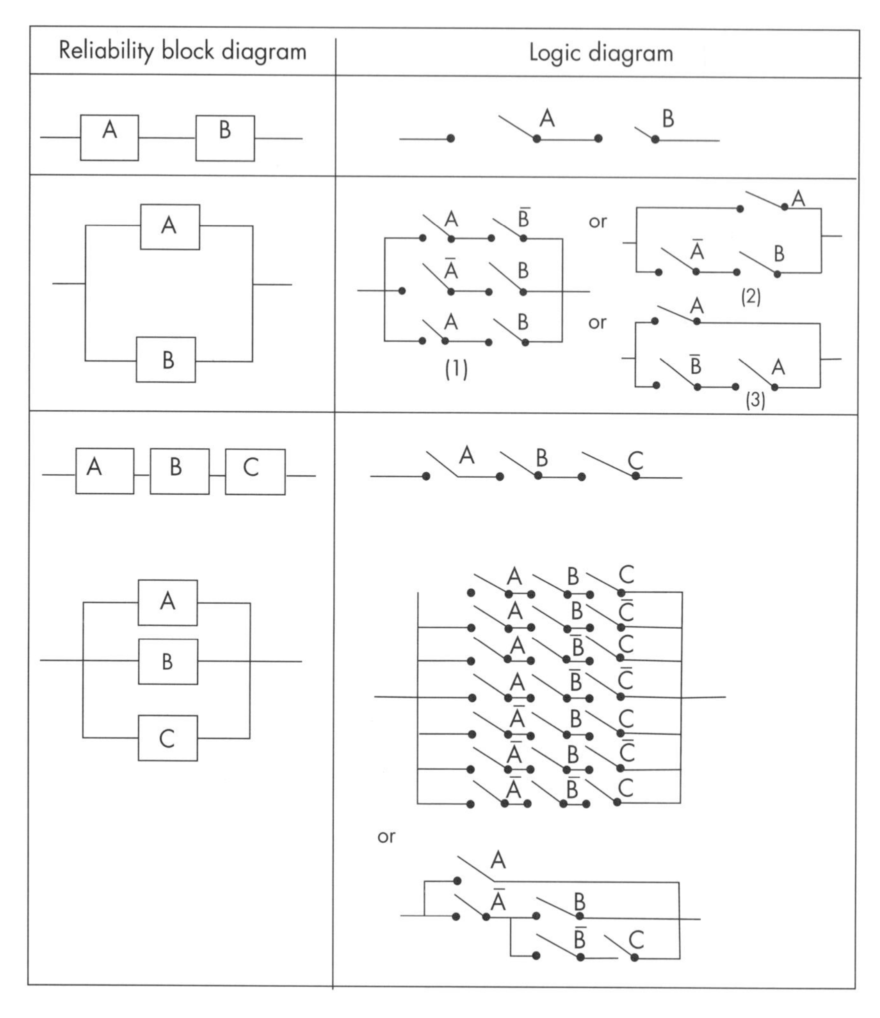

Figure 2.11 Block diagrams and logic diagrams.

Need and Feasibility Analysis. A feasibility analysis often is conducted as part of, or an extension to, a preliminary market analysis to

- Define system operational requirements
- Develop a system maintenance concept
- Identify a system configuration that is feasible within the constraints of available technology and resources

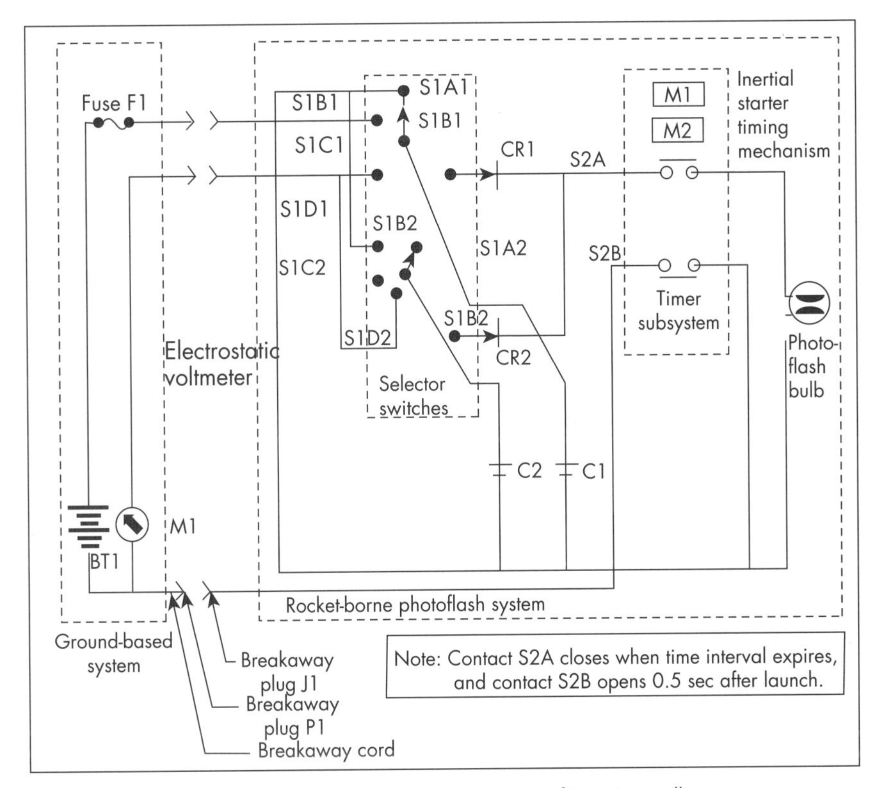

Adapted from Kececioglu 1991. Reprinted by permission of Prentice Hall.

Figure 2.12 Schematic diagram.

The feasibility analysis uses product design and process failure mode effects analysis as its primary tools (Ford 1992).

Failure Mode Analysis. FMA is a systematic approach to quantify the failure modes, failure rate, and root causes of known failures. Usually, the FMA is based on historical information such as warranty, service, field and process data (Omdahl 1988). In a sense, the FMA is a diagnostic tool because it concerns itself with only known and/or occurred failures.

The FMA is used to identify the operation, failure modes, rates, and critical design parameters of existing hardware or processes. Because of the ability to utilize historical data and known failures, the

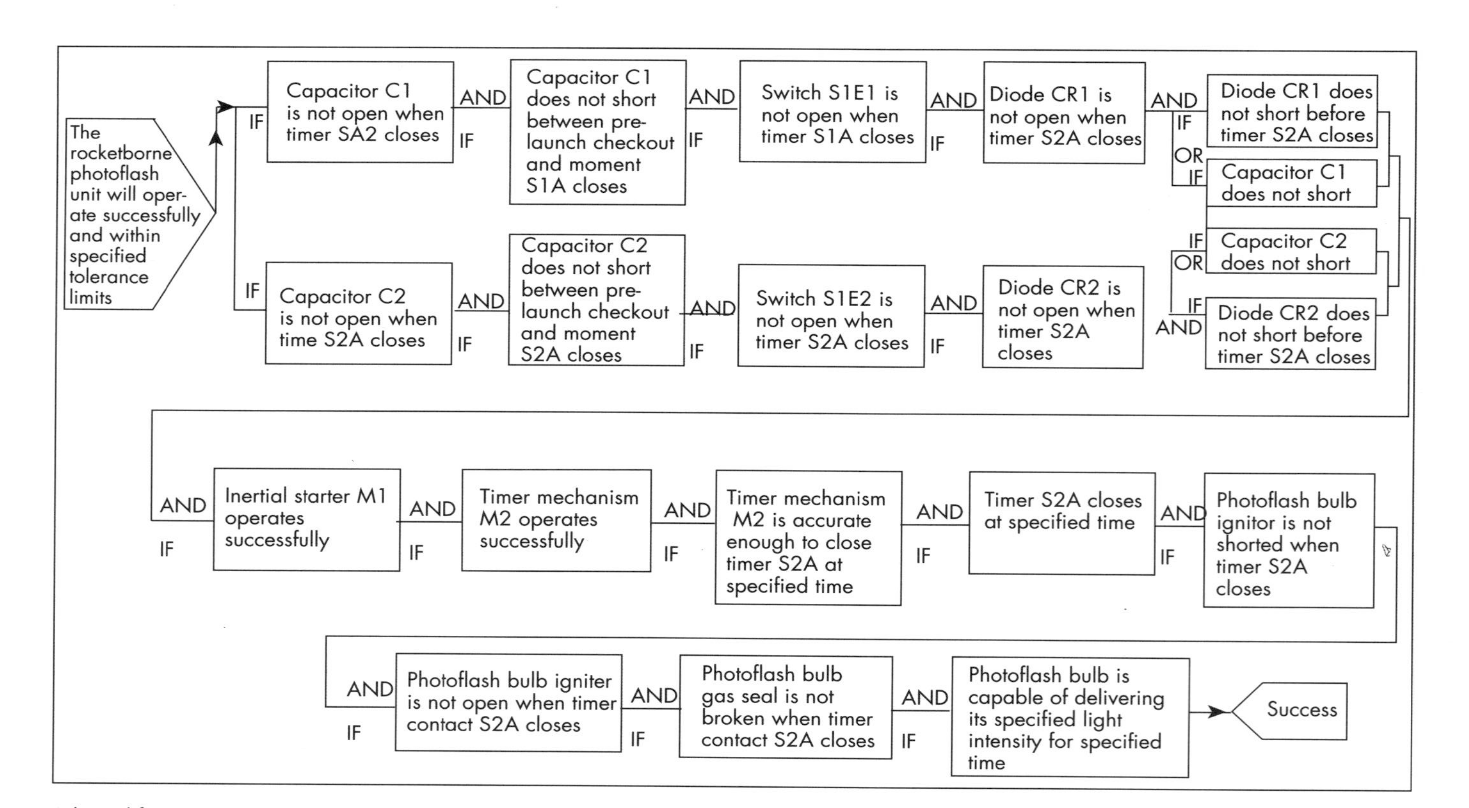

Adapted from Kececioglu 1991. Reprinted by permission of Prentice Hall.

Figure 2.13 Reliability functional diagram.

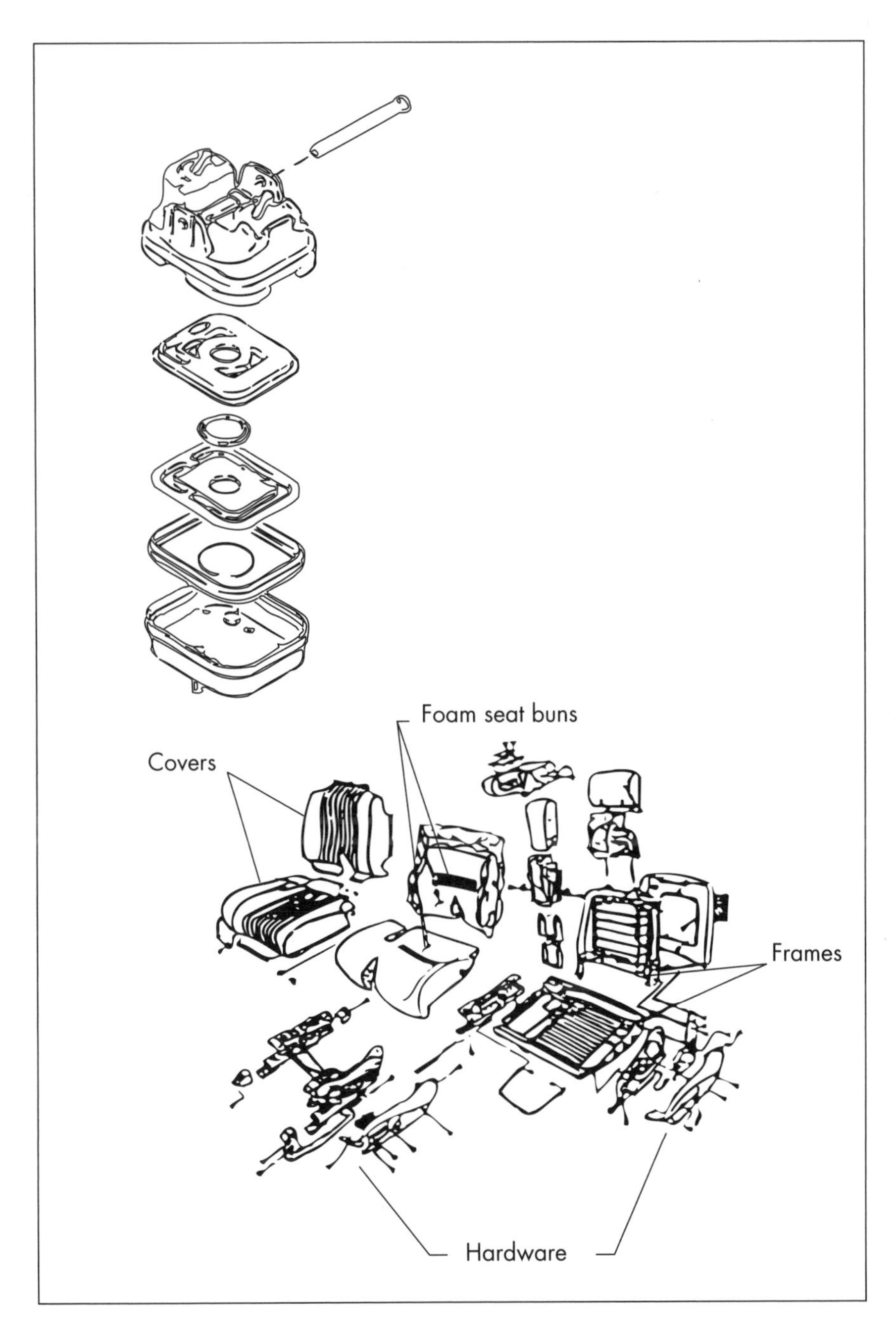

Figure 2.14 A typical sketch layout.

FMA is used primarily on current production as opposed to the FMEA which is used on changed and/or new designs, processes, and/or services.

Both the FMA and the FMEA deal with failure modes and causes. The FMA usually is done first, however, and the information gained is fed into the FMEA.

Control Plan. A control plan is a written summary of the producer's quality planning actions for a specific process, product, and/or service. The control plan lists all process parameters and design characteristics considered important to customer satisfaction and which require specific quality planning actions (Chrysler 1986; Ford 1992; General Motors 1988). The control plan describes the action(s) and reaction(s) required to ensure the process is maintained in a state of statistical control (as agreed upon between customer and supplier).

It is the FMEA that identifies the critical and significant characteristics and therefore the starting point for initiating a control plan. It can never be the other way around.

A typical control plan may include

- A listing of critical and significant characteristics
- Sample sizes and frequency of evaluation
- Method of evaluation
- Reaction and/or corrective action

An example of a control plan is shown in Figure 2.15. Figure 2.16 shows a different format of a control plan.

Process Potential Study. The PPS is the experimental part of new product introduction. It consists of implementing the control plan, which has been developed through the defined process and evaluates the results through statistical capability studies. If the desired capability is not achieved, changes in the control plan are agreed upon and the study repeated. This process may include a design of experiments to determine optimum process parameters.

Failure Mode and Critical Analysis. FMCA is a systematic approach to quantify the failure modes, rates, and root cause(s) from

Control Plan

Original date: ______________________ Prepared by: ______________________
Revised date: ______________________ Page ______ of ______
Authorization: ______________________

Flowchart	Critical characteristic	Sample size	Sample frequency	Inspection procedure	Report document	Additional requirements	Miscellaneous information
Start							
Incoming inspection	Grain size	Gram	1/lot	ASTM No	Lab report		
Storage							
Press	Density	1	Hr	SAE No	*X* chart		
Bake oven	Impact test	1	1/batch	ASTM No	Inspect sheet		
Finish	Cracks, chips, spots, stains, pits	100	Hr	Visual	*U* chart		
Pack	Insulation	1 box	4 Hrs	No	Status sheet		

Figure 2.15 An example of a typical control plan.

Process control plan

Part number: ______________________

Part name/description: ______________________

Drawing revision level: ______________________

Approval: ______________________

Process flow			Controlling parameters		Methods				
Operation number	Process name	Manufacturing equipment/ tooling identification	Control characteristic	Drawing specifications	Measuring device and identification	Last date calibrated	Data monitoring method (chart type)	Data collection frequency	Sampling plan

Prepared by: ______________________ Date: __________ Page_____ of_____

Figure 2.16 A different format of a control plan.

a criticality perspective. It is similar to the FMEA in all other respects (Bass 1986). The FMCA analysis is used primarily with government contracts based on the MIL-STD-1629A where the identification of critical, major, and minor characteristics is important.

One of the most important contributions of the FMCA is the fact that by focusing on criticality one can identify the so-called single point failure modes. A single point failure mode is a single human error or hardware failure that can result in an accident (Motorola 1992).

In Appendix D an example of a design and process FMCA is shown with explanations.

Safety Hazard Analysis; Fault Hazard Analysis; Operating Hazard Analysis; Preliminary Hazard Analysis. These are methods to define hazards during operation, transportation, between products and systems, and to users. All of them supplement the FMEA and cannot take its place (Bass 1986).

Design of Experiments. DOE is a very special way of conducting an experiment or a study. Certain independent variables are changed to a predefined plan, and the effects are determined on the dependent variable (Stamatis 1991c).

DOE is used in reliability testing and can identify the primary factors causing an undesired event. The optimum use of DOE in FMEA application(s) is when there is a concern about several independent variables and/or an interaction effect of the causal factors.

The question of whether or not to use the classical approach as opposed to the Taguchi approach in the experimentation process is always an interesting discussion. It is the opinion of the author that the Taguchi experimentation in the early stages of development and/or manufacturing may produce faster and just-as-correct results as the classical approach. As the experimenter closes in on the design and/or process and more precise evaluation is demanded, the classical approach has the edge. Again, from the FMEA perspective, the difference is minor and as long as the analyst is comfortable with either one, the results should not matter that much.

Quality Function Deployment. QFD is a systematic methodology that brings together the various factions within the corporation (in a planned manner) and causes them to focus on the voice of the customer. The voice of the customer from a QFD perspective is to correctly interpret the needs, wants, and expectations of the customer.

By addressing the planning process with a specific objective, QFD can help identify weaknesses and strengths. It encourages a comprehensive, holistic approach to product development (Clausing and Simpson 1990; Stamatis 1990).

The implementation of QFD can provide the following benefits.

- Strategic benefits
  –Reduced cost
  –Fewer engineering changes
  –Shorter cycle time
  –Larger market share
  –Reduce process variation

- Operational benefits
  –Ties together other quality technologies
  –Enhances communications
  –Identifies conflicting requirements
  –Preserves information for the future

QFD is a tool that translates the customers' requirements, part characteristics, manufacturing operations, and production requirements. Each step is interrelated and tracked through the house of quality until and when all concerns have been resolved.

QFD and FMEA have a lot in common. They both aim at continual improvement; they both focus on elimination of failures; they both look for satisfied customers.

Because of this overlap, one may think that they may be used interchangeably. That is not so. The QFD must be performed first and, based on the results, the system FMEA will follow and so forth.

Figures 2.17, 2.18, and 2.19 show the relationship of the FMEA and QFD. Specifically, in Figure 2.17 the QFD is shown as the impetus for planning. Figure 2.18 illustrates the different phases of QFD. In Figure 2.19 the production planning matrix is shown. Using the total points of the operation evaluation as a guide, the team will identify

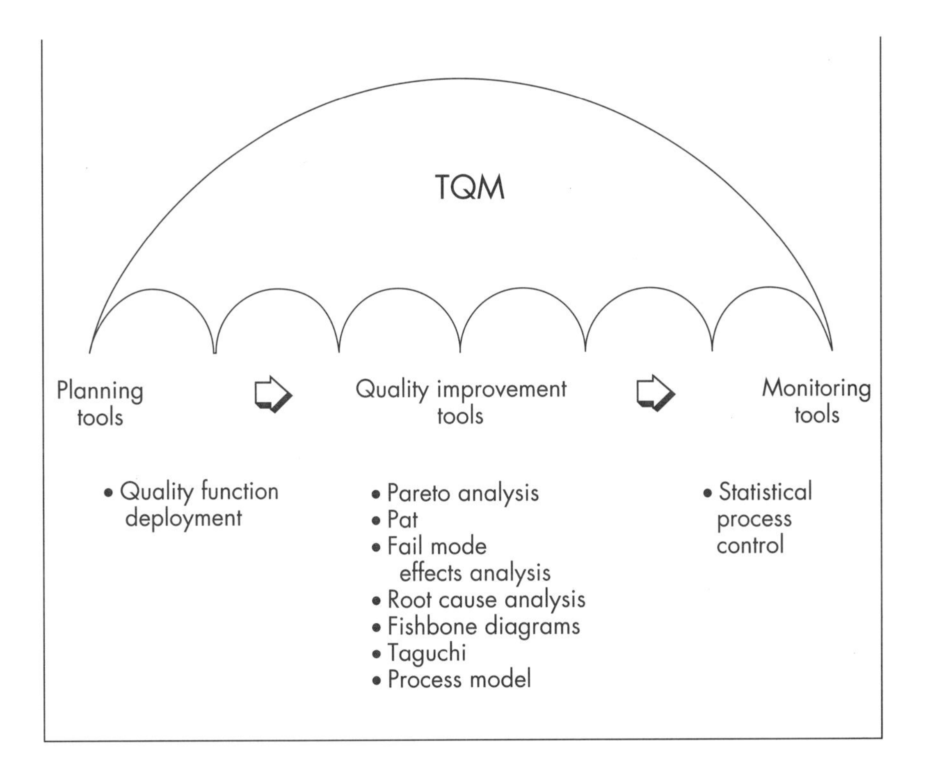

Figure 2.17 QFD—the impetus for planning.

the most appropriate points for an analysis using the FMEA. In this example, a process FMEA should be performed for the part position, die bottoming, and at least the ram cornering pressure. The same principle can be used for a design FMEA.

Brainstorming; Cause-and-Effect Diagram; Kepnor and Tregoe Method. These are techniques that can be used in the FMEA process as a supplement to identify root causes.

Who Is Responsible and Controls the FMEA

The responsibility for the system FMEA is with the system engineer, who makes sure that the FMEA is up to date and properly distributed. The distribution is a control document and should be treated as such.

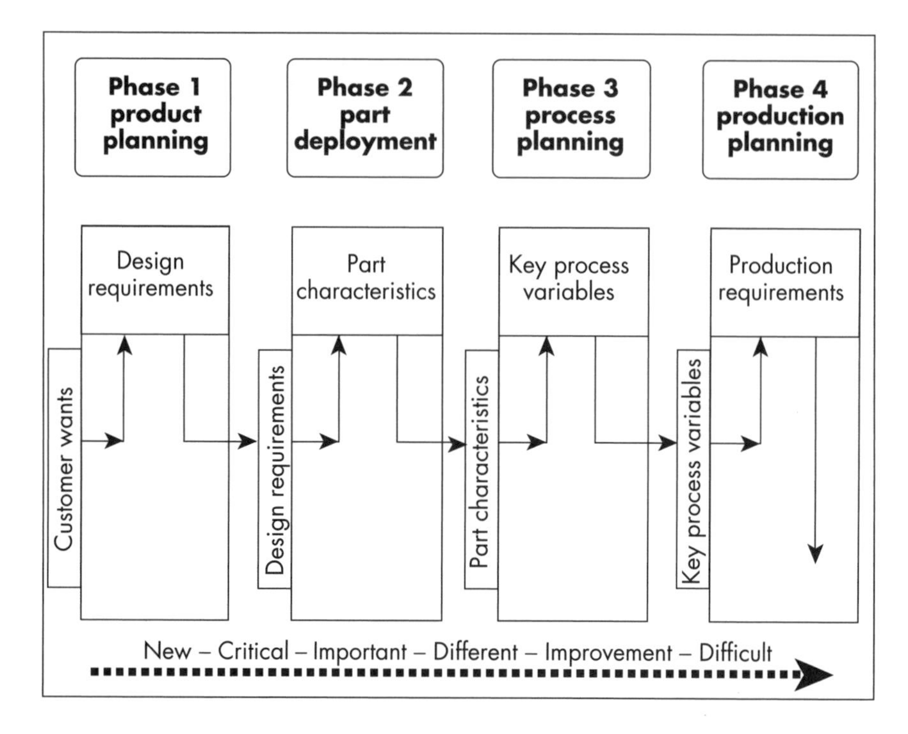

Figure 2.18 The four phases of QFD.

Minimum distribution should be to product engineering, design engineering, and quality assurance.

The responsibility for the design FMEA is with the design engineer, who makes sure that the FMEA is up to date and properly distributed. The distribution is a control document and should be treated as such. Minimum distribution should be to design engineering, manufacturing, product engineering, and quality assurance.

The responsibility for the process FMEA is with the system engineer, who makes sure that the FMEA is up to date and properly distributed. The distribution is a control document and should be treated as such. Minimum distribution should be to manufacturing, design engineering, and quality assurance.

The responsibility for the service FMEA is with the department manager for that service, who makes sure that the FMEA is up to date and properly distributed. The distribution is a control document and

Flow diagram (Material / Subassembly / Main flow)	Panel	Process elements	Critical process parameters	Critical process parameter values	Process capability	Importance	Operation evaluation: Difficulty	Frequency	Severity	Ability to detect	Total points	Planning requirements: Quality control chart	Preventative maintenance standard	Mistake proofing	Education and training required	Operation information: Job instructions	Labor: Direct	Labor: Indirect	Cycle time	Remarks
	Outer panel	Blk																		
		Stmp	Die bottoming	.06 Max. dev.	✓	5	1	1	3	1	15		✓		✓	B1	.02		.012	
			Ram cornering pressure	Setup proc.	✓	4	3	1	3	2	72	✓				C2	.01	.01		
		Trim	Part position	Contact locate	✓	3	2	3	3	3	162			✓	✓	B4	.01			
			Trim steal condition	Std. proc.	✓	3	1	2	2	1	12		✓		✓	A3	.12		.201	
		Spnk	Die bottoming	.06 Max dev.	✓	2	2	3	3	3	108		✓		✓	B1	.02			
	Inner panel	Blk																		
		Stmp	Die bottoming	.06 Max dev.	✓	5	1	1	3	1	15		✓		✓	B1	.02			
			Ram cornering pressure	Setup proc.	✓	4	3	1	3	2	72	✓				C2	.01	.01		
		Trim																		
		Spnk	Die bottoming	.06 Max. dev.	✓	2	2	3	3	3	108		✓		✓	B1	.02			
	Asm	Weld	Current	8000–8500 Amps		1	2	2	2	1	8	✓	✓			D1	.08		.051	
			Inner/outer part location	+\– .02 Inch	✓	3	3	2	3	1	54			✓	✓	D4	.12		.123	

Figure 2.19 The production planning matrix.

should be treated as such. Minimum distribution should be to managers of the affected area, supervisors of the affected area, marketing department, and quality assurance.

Special Considerations

The FMEA can and should be used with any problem in any organization. Its simplicity and its forward methodology lends itself to more than just problems for system, design, manufacturing, and service. It can be used by itself or in conjunction with other tools to help identify and/or remove problems in areas such as safety, repair planning, access, effect on downtime, and others. It is a great disservice for a tool such as the FMEA to be used in a narrow application solely in manufacturing areas. FMEA is widely applicable.

FMEA and Computer Software

FMEA software application will reduce clerical errors in the data input process and will facilitate the correction and updating of the FMEA. There are several available software packages in the market. The two most commonly used are

1. Formuser* By Engineered Work Systems, Inc.
2. FMEAPLUS* By Ford Motor Co.

Another alternative may be to use any spreadsheet software. It is not necessary to have software to do an FMEA, but it makes it easier.

References

American Society for Quality Control Statistics Division. 1983. *Glossary and tables for statistical quality control.* 2d. ed. Milwaukee: ASQC Quality Press.

Bass, L. 1986. *Products liability: Design and manufacturing defects.* Colorado Springs, Colo.: Shepard's/McGraw-Hill.

---

*Formuser and FMEAPLUS are registered trademarks of Engineered Work Systems and Ford Motor Co., respectively.

Blanchard, B. S. 1986. *Logistics engineering and management.* 3d ed. Englewood Cliffs, N.J.: Prentice Hall.

Chrysler Motors. 1986. Design feasibility and reliability assurance. In *FMEA.* Highland Park, Mich.: Chrysler Motors Engineering Office.

Clausing, D., and B. H. Simpson. 1990 Quality by design. *Quality Progress* (January): 41–44.

Ford Motor Company. 1992. *FMEA handbook.* Dearborn, Mich.: Ford Motor Company, Engineering Materials and Standards.

General Motors. 1988. *FMEA reference manual.* Detroit, Mich.: General Motors Corporation, Reliability and Technology Department.

Kececioglu, D. 1991. *Reliability engineering handbook.* Vols. 1 and 2. Englewood Cliffs, N.J.: Prentice Hall.

Motorola. 1992. *Reliability and quality handbook.* Phoenix: Motorola Semiconductor Products Sector.

Omdahl, T. P., ed. 1988. *Reliability, availability, and maintainability dictionary.* Milwaukee: ASQC Quality Press.

Stamatis, D. H. 1990. *QFD—Training manual.* Southgate, Mich.: Contemporary Consultants.

———. 1991a. *FMEA training manual.* Southgate, Mich.: Contemporary Consultants.

———. 1991b. *Effective teams—Training manual.* Southgate, Mich.: Contemporary Consultants.

———. 1991c. *DOE—Training manual.* Southgate, Mich.: Contemporary Consultants.

———. 1993. Failure mode and effect analysis. *Technology* (Engineering Society of Detroit) (December/January): 20–27.

CHAPTER 3

The Language of the FMEA

To further clarify the methodology of a FMEA it seems appropriate to direct attention toward its language and the terms commonly found in conducting the FMEA.

Vocabulary of the FMEA

Every discipline has its own special language. This section addresses the specific words used in FMEA and their special meaning that the methodology of the FMEA employs to communicate. For a more detailed vocabulary list of FMEA and Reliability see Appendix I.

Function. The task that the system, design, process, component, subsystem, service must perform. This function is very important in understanding the entire FMEA process. It has to be communicated in a way that is concise, exact, and easy to understand. It cannot be jargon.

To facilitate this, it is recommended that an active verb be found to describe the function. The active verb defines performance, and performance is what a function is (Stamatis 1989, 1991, 1992). Examples of this may be found in the following words.

Lubricate Position Retain Support

Appendix C provides an extensive (not exhaustive) list of verbs and nouns used in the function identification.

Failure. The problem, concern, error, challenge. The inability of the system, design, process, service, or subsystem to perform based on the design intent. The designed intent usually comes from an analysis and an evaluation of the needs, wants, or expectations of the customer. The tool for such an analysis is quality function development (QFD).

This inability can be defined as both known and potential. As far as the FMEA is concerned, it is especially interesting when potential failures are identified in terms of *functional defectives.* At this point, the FMEA is fulfilling its intent and mission of prevention.

Stamatis (1993) defines functional defectives as failures that do not meet the customer's requirements. The customer, however, receives the product and/or service with some failures (errors) anyway because

- The customer will never detect the failure.
- The customer will find out, but has to use it anyway because
  –There are no other alternatives (short run).
  –It can be used as is.
  –The manufacturer is the single or the sole supplier.
- Based on the application, the product can be used as is with no significant consequences.

Examples of failures are

Broken   Worn   Noise   Rust

Failure Mode. This is the physical description of the manner in which a failure occurs. Examples of failure modes include the following:

Open circuit	Cracked	Warped	Hole missing
Leak	Brittle	Blistered	Rough
Hot surface	Broken	Corroded	Short/long
Wrong invoice	Dirty	Grounded	Misaligned
Bent	Eccentric	Discolored	Omitted
Over/undersize	Melted	Burred	Binding

A failure mode may have more than one level depending on the complexity of the defined function. This level of relationships is shown in Figure 3.1.

	System	Design	Process	Service
Level 1 ***Failure mode***	Failed to work	Cannot generate pulse	Poor material feed	Poor service
Level 2 ***First-level cause***	Material too thin (may be a spec issue)	Open circuit	Operator variability	No availability of said service
Level 3 ***Second-level cause: root cause***	Material broken (may be a stress issue)	On/off switch	Lack of training	Not enough personnel

Note: For a specific application there may be more or fewer levels of failure modes. The idea is to pursue the root cause.

Figure 3.1 Levels of failure modes.

Causes of Failure. What is the root cause of the listed failure. Next to the function, cause of failure is perhaps the most important section of the FMEA. This is where one points the way toward preventive and/or corrective action. The more focused one is on the root cause, the more successful one will be in eliminating failures. When addressing the issue of cause of a failure, be careful not to be too eager for a solution. A quick solution may result in becoming a victim of symptoms and short-term remedies, rather than complete elimination of the real problem(s).

Examples of causes of failure include the following:

- System
  –Item does not work
  –Shorted lead to ground
- Design
  –Vibration
  –Shock loads

- Process
  –Voltage surge
  –Worn bearings
- Service
  –Human error
  –Poor skills

General examples of failures are

Handling damage	Improper _______	Inadequate _____
Inaccurate ___________	Incorrect________	Human error

Of special interest in identifying the failure or error is the situation of human error. A system, design, process, and service may have a failure due to human error. Human error may be due to carelessness (in other words, not following instructions and/or procedures). In some cases, however, human error may occur when the operator follows strict instructions and procedures in the belief that a safe product or service exists (Bass 1986).

The general rule about human error is that organizations must be cognizant of that human error and must build the system, design, process, or service fail proof (Bass 1986; Blanchard 1986; Deming 1986; Kececioglu 1991). In conjunction, with this general rule one also must remember that the majority (92 percent) of all variation is system error as opposed to only 8 percent that is due to operators.

The issue of human error in the FMEA is of profound interest because (1) it offers an expedient answer; (2) it blames someone—and that may or may not be the right person; (3) it focuses on symptoms rather than the root cause; and (4) it is used often.

Before an error can be attributed to human error, management must have placed the workers in a state of self-control by ensuring that

1. They know what is expected of them
   - Have the operators been given proper training?
   - Are there up to date, easy-to-understand written instructions, procedures and so on. Are they available at the work station? Are they appropriate for the expected level of understanding?

- Do the operators receive prompt notice and instructions when there is an official change in the requirements?
- Do the operators have (now) or will they receive the appropriate training for the task?
- Do the operators have ownership of the task?
- Is the empowerment real?
- Is the supervisor available to help, coach, direct, and counsel the operators when there are question and review requirements from time to time?

2. They know whether or not they are accomplishing what is expected of them
   - Are the operators provided with a method to measure their performance level?
   - Do the operators know the criteria for good versus unacceptable work? When to correct the process? Do the operators have the right to adjust the process?
   - Does the supervisor provide the operators with feedback on the quality of their work, good or bad?
3. They have a means of regulating their process
   - Has the process been studied to determine if it is stable and capable, or do chance causes of variation still exist?
   - Do the operators know what action to take to correct the process? Who to notify?
   - Has everything reasonable been done to foolproof the operators?

If management has met all of these criteria, then the means for doing good work with minimum failures clearly is in the hands of the workers. Yet, in cases where these criteria are fully met, errors may occur anyway. Lack of motivation is not the cause. It is a symptom. Specific errors and failures can be identified as a particular root cause and then eliminated.

From an FMEA perspective human errors do occur and they are appropriate and legitimate. More often than not, however, they are only a cover-up to the real cause and as such they should be used sparingly (Stamatis 1991).

Effects of Failure. The outcome of the failure on the system, design, process, or service. In essence the effects of the failure have to do with the questions of: What happens when a failure occurs? What is (are) the consequence(s) of that failure? One must understand, however, that the effects of the failure must be addressed from two points of view. The first viewpoint is local, in which the failure is isolated and does not affect anything else. The second viewpoint is global, in which the failure can and does affect other functions and/or components. It has a domino effect. Generally speaking, the failure with a global effect is more serious than one of a local nature.

The effect of the failure also will define the severity of a particular failure. In fact, the effect of the failure has a direct relationship with severity. So, if the effect is serious, the severity will be high.

Examples of effects of failure follow.

Local: Courtesy lightbulb failure
Global: Power steering failure

General examples include the following:

Noise	Excessive effort required	Loss of life
Unstable	Intermittent operation	Unpleasant odor
Operation impaired	Poor appearance	Unstable
Erratic operation	Does not work	Draft

In the case of the courtesy light failure, one may experience a nuisance, in other words, one cannot read the map. Conversely, the power steering failure may prove catastrophic and life threatening, when loss of control occurs.

Process Validation. Controls that exist now, to prevent the cause(s) of the failure from occurring and to validate repeatability for certain processes, especially with FDA. Examples include

- Validate the process for certain CpK
- Validate the process for certain production

Design Verification. Controls that exist to prevent cause(s) of the failure from occurring in the design phase (Chrysler 1986; Ford 1992; General Motors 1988). Examples include

- Design guidelines
- Design reviews

Current Controls. Controls that exist to prevent the cause(s) of the failure from occurring in the design, process, or service. Some examples are

Capability studies	Operator(s) training
Design guidelines	Durability test
Design review	Simulation testing
Design of experiments	Finite element analysis (FEA)
Foolproof designs	Tolerance build-up study
Function tests	SQA approval
Any SPC tool	
Gauge repeatability and reproducibility (R&R) study	

Data. System installation and checkout procedures, operating and maintenance instructions, inspections, calibration procedures, modifications, drawings, specifications and all performance items related to the system of operation.*

Facilities. All special facilities needed for system, and process operation and the performance of maintenance functions at each level.*

Computer Resources. All computer equipment and accessories, software and its accessories and so on, necessary in the performance of carrying out the objective of FMEA.*

Supply Support. Includes all team members and consumable items used in conducting the FMEA.*

Test and Support Equipment. Includes all tools, monitor, and diagnostic equipment (metrology, calibration, servicing and handling equipment) to support the function of FMEA.*

*Definitions marked with an asterisk are a composite of ASQC; Chrysler; Ford; General Motors; and Omdahl. See references.

There are four types of testing associated with a FMEA.

- Type 1–Testing done with the intent of verifying performance and physical design characteristics.
- Type 2–Prototype testing for the qualification of the system.
- Type 3–Formal tests and demonstrations, conducted after initial qualification and prior to completion of production. Usually these tests are performed at a test site by user personnel.
- Type 4–Formal tests conducted during the operational phase to gain further insight into a specific area. These tests are performed in a realistic environment.

In all testing an outcome is expected. That outcome will drive the decision. The decision will be based on a probability. There are two types of decisions.

1. *Producer's risk (a)*–The probability of rejecting an item when it really should be accepted. This is known as Type I error.
2. *User's or consumer's error (b)*–The probability of accepting an item when it really should be rejected. This is known as Type II error.

The relationship of these risks and testing follows.

True state	Accept H_o Reject H_a	Reject H_o Accept H_a
H_o is true	High P $1 - \alpha$	Low P α
H_o is false H_a is true	Low P error, β	High P $1 - \beta$

Personnel Training. Personnel required for the installation, checkout, operation, handling, and proper conduct of the FMEA.*

Maintenance Planning. Includes all planning and analysis associated with the establishment of requirements for follow-up in the FMEA process.*

Probability. Usually stated as a quantitative expression representing a fraction or a percent signifying the number of times that an event occurs (successes), divided by the total number of trials.*

Reliability. A simple definition is the probability that a system or product will perform in a satisfactory manner for a given period of time when used under specified operating conditions.*

Maintainability. The ability of an item to be maintained.*

Maintenance. A series of actions to be taken to restore or retain an item in an effective operational state.*

Supportability. Relates to the degree to which the system can be supported, both in terms of the inherent characteristics of prime equipment design and the effectiveness of the overall support capability.*

Availability. A function of operating time (reliability) and downtime (maintainability).*

Dependability. A function of operating time (reliability) and downtime (maintainability).*

Failure Rate. The rate at which failures occur in a specified time interval.*

Corrective Maintenance. The unscheduled actions accomplished, as a result of failure, to restore a system to a specified level of performance.*

Preventive Maintenance. The scheduled actions accomplished to retain a system at a specified level of performance by providing systematic inspection, detection, servicing, condition monitoring, and/or replacement to prevent impending failures.*

Mean Time Between Maintenance. The mean time between all maintenance actions (corrective and preventive).*

Achieved Availability. The probability that a system or equipment, when used under stated conditions in an ideal support environment (in other words, readily available tools, spares, personnel, and so on), will operate satisfactorily at any point in time.*

Operational Availability. The probability that a system or equipment, when used under stated conditions in an actual operational environment, will operate satisfactorily when called upon.*

Functional Analysis. A logical and systematic approach to system design and development. It constitutes the process of translating system operational and support requirements into specific qualitative and quantitative design requirements. This is an iterative process and is accomplished through the development of functional flow block diagrams.*

Sensitivity Analysis. Used when the analyst is not confident about the analysis (due to inadequate data, pushing the state of the art, and so on). At this point a typical question may be: How sensitive are the results of analysis variations to these uncertain parameters? Variation is accomplished by applying different multiple factors to the input parameters being used.*

Contingency Analysis. Involves the investigation of decisions in terms of relevant changes in the initial criteria.*

References

Bass, L. 1986. *Products liability: Design and manufacturing defects.* Colorado Springs, Colo.: Shepard's/McGraw-Hill.

Blanchard, B. S. 1986. *Logistics engineering and management.* 3d ed. Englewood Cliffs, N.J.: Prentice Hall.

Chrysler Motors. 1986. Design feasibility and reliability assurance. In *FMEA.* Highland Park, Mich.: Chrysler Motors Engineering Office.

Deming, W. E. 1986. *Out of the crisis.* Cambridge, Mass.: Massachusetts Institute of Technology.

Ford Motor Company. 1992. *FMEA handbook.* Dearborn, Mich.: Ford Motor Company, Engineering Materials and Standards.

General Motors. 1988. *FMEA reference manual.* Detroit, Mich.: General Motors Corporation, Reliability and Technology Department.

Kececioglu, D. 1991. *Reliability engineering handbook.* Vols. 1 and 2. Englewood Cliffs, N.J.: Prentice Hall.

Omdahl, T. P., ed. 1988. *Reliability, availability, and maintainability dictionary.* Milwaukee: ASQC Quality Press.

Stamatis, D. H. 1989, 1991, 1992. *FMEA training manual.* Southgate, Mich.: Contemporary Consultants.

———. 1991. *Effective teams—Training manual.* Southgate, Mich.: Contemporary Consultants.

———. 1993. Failure mode and effect analysis. *Technology* (Engineering Society of Detroit) (December/January): 20–27.

CHAPTER 4

Teams and Team Mechanics of FMEA

To do a complete job with the best results, an FMEA must be written by a team. This is because the FMEA should be a catalyst to stimulate the interchange of ideas between the functions affected (Stamatis 1991). A single engineer or any other single person cannot do it.

The team should be made of five to nine people (preferably five). All team members must have some knowledge of group behavior, the task at hand, the problem to be discussed, and direct or indirect ownership of the problem. Above all, they must be willing to contribute. Team members must be cross-functional and multidisciplined. Furthermore, whenever possible and/or needed, the customer and/or the supplier should participate—not as a regular team member, but as an ad hoc member.

This chapter covers the basic aspects of teams and how the outcome of the team affects the FMEA. The information in this chapter does not represent the exhaustive knowledge of teams, but does include the issues that concern the FMEA.

What Is a Team?

A team is a group of individuals who are committed to achieving common organizational objectives; who meet regularly to identify and solve problems, and improve process; who work and interact openly and effectively together; and who produce desired economic and motivational results for the organization. Figure 4.1 shows this relationship.

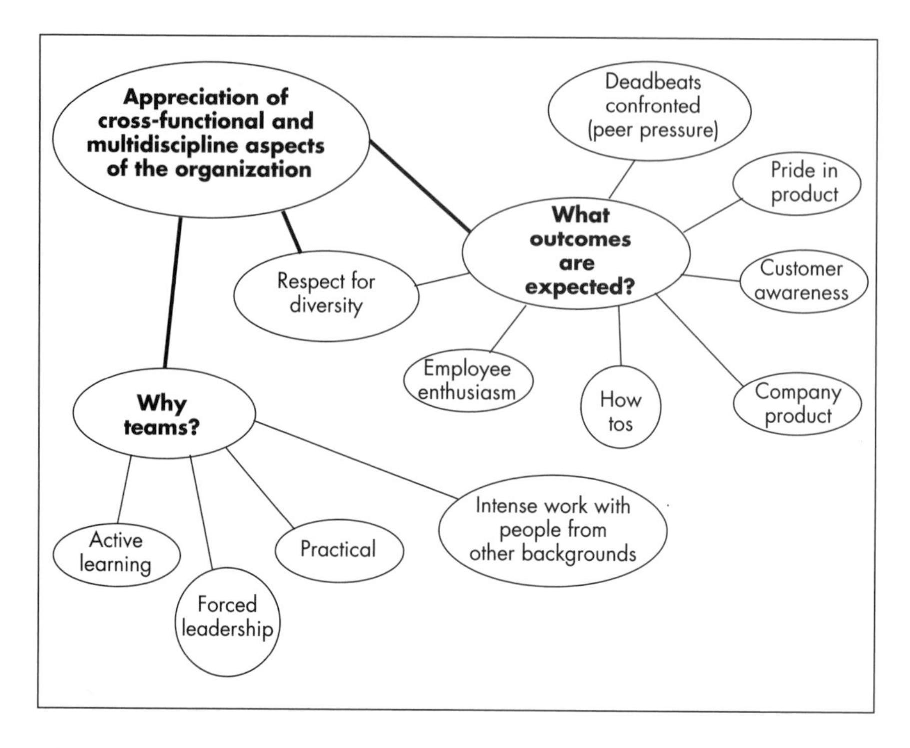

Figure 4.1 Teams and great expectations.

The factors that influence the performance and productivity of the teams are

- The organization as a whole (culture)
  –Philosophy
  –Rewards
  –Expectations
  –Norms
- The team itself
  –Meeting management
  –Roles and responsibility
  –Conflict management

–Operating procedures
–Mission statement

- Individual team members
  –Self-awareness
  –Appreciation of individual differences
  –Empathy
  –Caring

An overview of these factors follows.

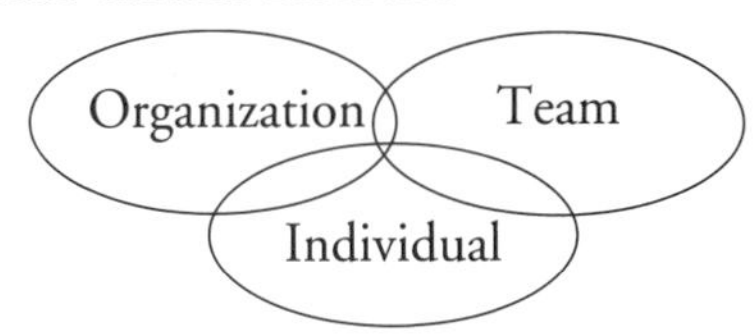

Why Use a Team?

The theory that encourages the team formation as opposed to the individual is *synergy.* Synergy is defined as the sum of the total is greater than the sum of the individuals. Another way of saying the same thing is two heads working together, are better than two heads working individually. From an FMEA perspective the team is the foundation of improvement. The team defines the issue(s) and problem(s) in the specific assigned task environment, identifies and proposes ideas, provides/recommends the appropriate analysis and/or technique, and provides a decision based on consensus. Generally speaking the team is formed to address concerns about

- Work
  –Task complexity
  –Productivity and quality advantages
  –Work system stability
- People
  –Rising expectations
  –Affiliation needs

–Increased cognitive ability
–Specific concerns (time related)
–Direction of the future
–Survival in a global market

All teams regardless of application must be familiar with the problem-solving process, which includes

- Statement of the problem
- Root cause analysis
- Solution based on fact(s)
- Implementation
- Evaluation

and must have a clear charter issued by management to

- Define the task
- Have accountability and responsibility
- Define the boundaries
- Define and communicate the barriers
- Have the authority to request support

To paraphrase Allmendinger (1990): For the team to harness the collective intelligence (synergy) for the benefit of the team, and the organization the following must take place

- *Relevancy*—The information gathered by the team should be of value.
- *Reliability*—The process by which the information is collected should be consistent, isolated as much as possible from changes in organization, personnel, and so on.
- *Accuracy*—The data should be expressed in a manner that most accurately reflects its information content; in other words accuracy should not be confused with precision.
- *Efficiency*—The design and implementation of the tasks should minimize the burden imposed by the data collection process.

About Consensus

Consensus is a collective decision reached through active participation by all members, to which every member is committed (in other words has personal ownership). It requires all members to express a viewpoint, to actively listen, and to differ constructively. Consensus does not mean 100 percent agreement (although it may be), but a decision about which all members of the team can honestly say, "I am not totally sold on it, but...; I am not 100 percent sure, but...; I do not agree with it completely, but...; I can support it, I can live with it."

In a team environment, discussion continues until the team reaches a decision that every member accepts and will implement—even though some may have reservations. Ideally, the team capitalizes on diversity among members to reach a better decision than they could produce independently. Consensus decision making takes time, and like any other skill, requires practice for one to become proficient.

A classic example of true consensus can be seen in the movie *The Twelve Angry Men.* In this movie, one juror (Henry Fonda) holds one opinion which is opposite to the opinions of the other 11. (It is interesting to note that Fonda thought that a guilty verdict was appropriate. His desire to discuss the case from a different perspective, however, made the case quite interesting and appropriate in the discussion of team consensus.) By the end of the movie, all 12 jurors have changed their minds based on probable doubt. There are still unanswered questions about the case, but they all agreed (in the end) that the overwhelming evidence left a doubt—therefore an innocent verdict.

For the team to reach consensus the following four things must take place.

1. Process must be defined as 100 percent participation.
2. Members must actively participate, listen and voice their disagreement in a constructive manner.
3. The requirement is not 100 percent agreement, but 100 percent commitment.
4. Majority does not rule. Minority sometimes has the correct, right decision. Sometimes a single individual may be on the right track, with everyone else being wrong.

To reach consensus, the team members must be willing to

- Be open to influence, ideas
- Contribute, not defend
- Actively listen to other points of view
- Find out the reasons for others' positions
- Avoid averaging the differences
- Confront the differences—politely
- Stand up for one's thoughts and opinions

To recognize consensus, the team and its members must answer yes to the following four questions.

1. Have I honestly listened?
2. Have I been heard and understood?
3. Will I support the decision?
4. Will I say "We decided," as opposed to "My idea went through," or "I decided," or "I told them and they followed my recommendation"?

Team Process Check

For the team to be effective and productive, an occasional process check may be appropriate (Stamatis 1991). This is very important, especially for the most complex problems that the team may face. Some of the items that a process check may review are

- Purpose of meeting not clear
- Meeting was held just to "rubber stamp"
- Repeat of old information
- Too boring; trivial matters discussed
- The leader lectures the team
- Team members not prepared
- Vague assignments

- No summary
- No time or willingness to deal with the unexpected

When the team continues to meet without a process check, errors occur. Some of the most common errors are

- Errors caused by misunderstandings
- Discovery of the need to capture additional information
- Incomplete data because form is too difficult to complete
- Incomplete or biased data caused by fear
- Failure to use existing data

All of these errors may be prevented through testing, training, and auditing.

Handling of Difficult Individuals

The idea of forming a team is to help everyone learn from everyone's experience and knowledge. To do this, all members should participate. In certain areas, however, that does not happen because some individuals either participate at the expense of others or they do not participate at all. These individuals are called problem individuals, and they fall into three general classifications (Jones 1980; Stamatis 1987, 1992).

The Individual Who Talks Too Much. If the discussion turns into a dialogue between the leader and an overtalkative individual, the others will lose interest. Whether or not that individual has something of value to say, the team leader will not want to let the situation be monopolized by the talkative one. Tactful approaches must be used to divert the discussion to others. If the leader knows that someone on the team likes to dominate, the leader should pose questions to the group without looking at that specific individual, or ignore the response that the talkative person gives.

A facilitator and/or the leader of the FMEA team should want to allow everyone to participate. In this participation, however, the leader may find that somebody dominates the discussion because he or she had more experiences to draw from or an educational background that is more extensive. On those occasions, the individual should be used as a resource and a coach for the other team members.

Another situation where a talkative person may interfere is the person who wants to make an impression. This is the individual who is looking to satisfy his or her own ego. The only way to handle such an individual is to let him or her know in advance that the group disapproves of such behavior and/or through team pressure at the time of the incident.

Yet another situation where a talkative person may interfere is the person who takes a long time to express his or her ideas. This is perhaps one of the most sensitive areas of interference because the person participates as expected but simultaneously annoys the rest of the team. The leader must handle this situation in a delicate manner because if he or she says or does the wrong thing, the participant will lose self-confidence and ultimately will withdraw. Usually it is better to tolerate a certain amount of this difficult behavior, rather than discourage the individual too much.

Finally, a situation where a talkative person may interfere is when that person starts a private conversation with the neighbor(s). One can eliminate this problem by asking a direct question to those who are involved or make the team large enough to allow generation of a variety of ideas and small enough to sustain small cliques. Such a team usually consists of five to nine persons with five being the most common.

Members Who Talk Too Little. Members may not want to be there, feel out of place, or do not understand the problem at hand. For this type of person, it is the responsibility of the leader and/or the team facilitator to actively draw this individual into the discussion. This can be done through direct questions about the subject at hand and/or motivational statements outside the team environment such as: "We need your input," "We value your contribution," "You were hand picked because of your experience and knowledge," and so forth.

Members Who Say the Wrong Things. This problem is common in a team environment (especially in the early stages of team development) where individuals have their own agenda. They talk about all things except what is on the agenda. In this situation, it is the responsibility of the leader to point out the official agenda and/or outline. On rare occasions the leader may want to bring in the whole team by asking, "Do we agree that this point should be taken up right now?"

Problem Solving

This text will not discuss the methods and tools available in the problem-solving phase of the team. The focus is to help to understand the mechanics and rationale for pursuing problem-solving methods to eliminate and/or reduce problems, concerns, and so on. Some examples of specific tools and their application are found in Appendix H. Detailed descriptions of tools may be found in basic SPC books, statistical literature, and/organizational development sources.

For most people, the mere presence or prediction of a problem indicates a need for a change in behavior. When an individual or group is actually or potentially in trouble, a unique set of strategies is required. Such strategies usually involve at least a temporary change in behavior—a new course of action. In the absence of a deliberate strategy for deciding on a new course of action, one's revised behaviors may make the situation worse.

Usually problems are not clear to the individuals who have them. It is difficult to isolate the problem and its related components. Even if this is possible, the selection and implementation of a solution involves degrees of physical or psychological risk. Familiar patterns of behavior are safe. In a problem situation, a person is torn between the need to change and the desire to maintain the old patterns. This conflict results in strong emotions and anxieties, which impose on the cognitive processes that are required to make workable decisions. If the problem is sufficiently severe, cognitive paralysis may result (Pfeiffer 1991).

People and groups who are in trouble need useful tools for understanding the nature of their problem situations, for making decisions about their courses of action, and for managing the new directions once they are chosen. The contents of a generic model of problem identification and problem solving are

Stage 1. Identify

- Identify the problem

Stage 2. Scope
- Gather the facts
- Organize the data

Stage 3. Define
- Define the problem

Stage 4. Analyze
- Analyze the problem
- List the alternative solutions
- Select a feasible solution

Stage 5. Implement
- Implement the solution

Stage 6. Evaluate
- Evaluate the solution

Stage 7. Follow-up
- Monitor the solution

Stage 8. Improve
- Continually improve

These steps in problem solving represent a category of techniques presented over the years under different names by many people. Some of the specific tools for each stage may be found in Appendix H. Many of the tools ignore the drives, emotions, needs, preferences, values, and conflicts that are attendant to most human problems. Furthermore, they are of little use in attacking the type of problem that people frequently refer to as intangible. The techniques may be useful for evaluating alternative business plans or buying a new washing machine, but they offer little help in interpersonal problems. Therefore, this book has presented items in this section that incorporate some human issues into the problem-solving process.

Planning the Meeting

Before the team activates itself for the project, some preliminary steps must take place. The first order of business is to plan the meeting. Bradford (1976), Nicoll (1981), Schindler-Rainman, Lippit, and Cole

(1988), and Stamatis (1991) have identified the following items of concern.

1. *People*—All meetings involve people. Meeting participants may differ in values, attitude, experience, sex, age, and education. All these differences, however, must be accounted for in the planning of the meeting.
2. *Purpose*—All meetings have reasons for existing. The purpose, objective, and the goal of the meeting must be understood by all, both management and participants.
3. *Atmosphere or climate*—The atmosphere contributes to the effectiveness of the meeting. It is imperative that whoever plans the meeting takes into consideration the climate and atmosphere.
4. *Place and space*—All meetings are held in a space and a place. Therefore, planners must consider the following:
   - Access to the space, available parking
   - Size of the space
   - Acoustics, lighting, temperature control
   - Cost
   - Equipment needed
5. *Costs*—Cost of FMEA is of paramount importance since it has been established that the preparation time of the FMEA is lengthy. In addition, consideration should be given to the fact that often the system, design, process, or service personnel assigned to do the FMEA may be in different places, miles apart.
6. *Time dimensions*—How long will this take? Is an alternate schedule available? Can the participants be spared for this task? Without evaluating time constraints and recognizing that the meeting may be prolonged for unexpected reason, the agenda items and objectives may suffer.
7. *Prework and after the official meeting work*—All the work that the meeting produces is directly related to the amount of planning that goes into the meeting. For the lengthy and complex tasks, it occasionally is required that major portions

of the work be done outside of the meeting and only reviewed by the participants in the meeting.

8. *Plans, program, and agenda*—All meetings have an agenda. Without an agenda there cannot be a meeting. A detailed, planned program or agenda, which can be shared (no surprises) by all participants, is a valuable addition to a meeting. When planning the agenda, make sure all the objectives of the meeting are covered.
9. *Beginning, middle, and end*—All meetings, regardless of duration and significance, have a beginning, middle, and an end. Proper planning is essential. Without it, failure to focus on the agenda will cause an unproductive gathering and failure to meet the objectives.
10. *Follow-up*—After the meeting has ended, there is a need for some follow-up in the areas of
    - Implementing action items
    - Communicating information to all appropriate personnel
    - Publishing minutes
    - Writing report

In-Process Meeting Management

In addition to more detailed meeting planning, managers are finding it necessary to pay more attention to the management of meeting participants. Every organization has a hierarchy; part is overt (job titles, designation of managers and subordinates, and so on), and part is unspoken. Within each group of people there tends to be a pecking order, even if the people technically are colleagues on the same rung of the hierarchical ladder. Some members act domineering: they are talkative, they tend to interrupt others, and so on. Less-aggressive members may not feel comfortable challenging the dominant member(s) and may remain silent for the duration of the meeting. This results in uneven participation, which often produces side effects such as boredom and stilted lines of communication.

Mosvick and Nelson (1987) identify 11 steps for ensuring effective decision making in meetings. These items also are good tips for effective meeting management.

1. Spend enough time stating and restating the initial question until everyone agrees on the problem or issue to be discussed.
2. Solicit participants' honest opinions at the outset of the meeting.
3. Think of opinion as hypotheses; test them instead of arguing over them.
4. Plan a method of testing opinions against reality, considering the issue and the goal.
5. Establish a rule that additional information given during the meeting must be relevant to the agreed-upon topic.
6. Encourage disagreement and differences of opinions.
7. Do not judge others' opinions hastily. Learn to appreciate the diversity of others' point of view.
8. Encourage meeting members' commitment to resolving the issue whenever possible.
9. Compromise as needed.
10. Ask whether a decision is necessary. Remember that choosing to do nothing is a legitimate choice.
11. Construct a process for feedback to determine whether the decision was successful.

Avoiding Common Meeting Pitfalls

The following are some dysfunctional patterns and behaviors that commonly are found in meetings (Bradford 1976).

- Vying for power, often by challenging the leader or by wooing a group of supporters, thus dividing the group
- Joking and clowning excessively, which not only is a distraction but also may disguise hostility

- Failing to agree on the issue or problem
- Arguing about others' opinions or suggestions, which stifles the brainstorming process and can cause embarrassment or discomfort
- Wandering off the topic at hand
- Forcing meeting members to answer to the chairperson (usually someone who is higher on the organizational ladder than they are)

Awareness of these traps can help the meeting facilitator avoid them. Constructive, rather than punitive, confrontation is an effective technique for dealing with many disruptive and dysfunctional meeting behaviors. A meeting leader who chooses to confront must be sure to discuss the behaviors, not the person. More desirable behaviors should be suggested in a direct but caring way.

Jones (1980) suggests two approaches to dealing with disruptive meeting participants. The first approach requires the meeting leader to communicate directly with the disruptive person. Some examples follow.

- Turn a dominating person's question into statements, thus forcing the person to take responsibility for his or her opinion.
- Refuse to engage in a debate. Point out that debates have winners and losers; therefore, the desired win-win outcome is impossible.
- Suggest that the meeting leader and the disruptive person swap roles. This gives the person a sense of what he or she is doing to the group.
- Use active-listening techniques to mirror the person's feelings. For examples, "You seem particularly upset today, especially when I disagree with you."
- Agree with the person's need to be heard and supported.

The second approach that Jones suggests to deal with disruptive meeting members uses the other meeting participants as allies against the disruptive person. Some examples follow.

- Ask the participants to establish norms that will discourage "You're wrong, I'm right" thinking.

- Post all participants' input anonymously on flip charts. This makes information available to all and lessens repetition.
- Break the participants into small groups. This immediately limits a dominating person's sphere of influence. Give the groups a task that requires them to reach consensus.

Utilizing the Meeting-Management Guidelines

Meeting leaders may find that the use of small groups can help prevent the participants from falling into the common meeting traps. When people break into small groups to discuss an issue, less-assertive persons often become more willing to participate. A small group is not as likely to wander off the subject as a large group. Because fewer people are competing for attention in a small group, members feel a stronger sense of commitment. Finally, small groups can diffuse aggressive members' tendency to dominate the conversation.

Meeting leaders will find that their meetings will become more interesting, lively, and balanced as they follow the guidelines that have been presented in this section. The core points to remember are that all meeting participants must be treated equally; honesty must be the norm; and all opinions must be respected (Stamatis 1992).

References

Allmendinger, G. 1990. Performance measurement: Impact on competitive performance. *Technology* (Engineering Society of Detroit) (December): 10–13.

Bradford, L. P. 1976. *Making meetings work: A guide for leaders and group members.* San Diego: University Associates.

Jones, J. E. 1980. Dealing with disruptive individuals in meetings. In *The 1980 annual handbook for group facilitators,* edited by J. W. Pfeiffer, and J. E. Jones. San Diego: University Associates.

Mosvic, R. K., and R. B. Nelson. 1987. *We've got to start meeting like this! A guide to successful business meeting management.* Glenview, Ill.: Scott, Foresman and San Diego: University Associates.

Nicoll, D. R. 1981. Meeting management. In *The 1981 annual handbook for group facilitators,* edited by J. W. Pfeiffer, and J. E. Jones. San Diego: University Associates.

Pfeiffer, J. W., ed. 1991. *Theories and models in applied behavioral science: Management leadership.* Vols. 2 and 3. San Diego: Pfeiffer.

Schindler-Rainman, E., R. Lippit, and J. Cole. 1988. *Taking your meetings out of the doldrums.* Rev. ed. San Diego: University Associates.

Stamatis, D. H. 1987. Conflict: You've got to accentuate the positive. *Personnel* (December): 47–50.

———. 1991. *Team building training manual.* Southgate, Mich.: Contemporary Consultants.

———. 1992. *Leadership training manual.* Southgate, Mich.: Contemporary Consultants.

CHAPTER 5

System FMEA

This chapter discusses, in detail, the concept and method of constructing an FMEA for the system.

A system FMEA usually is accomplished through a series of steps to include conceptual design, detail design and development, and test and evaluation. A typical flow of this development is shown in Figure 2.3. The design in this phase is an evolutionary process involving the application of various technologies and methods to produce an effective system output. This result will be used as an input for the design FMEA which in turn becomes an input for the process/assembly, part, and/or the service FMEA. This is illustrated in Figures 5.1, 5.2, and 5.3.

The selection of appropriate technologies may include the utilization of existing system(s), standardized approaches currently known or proposed, results of directed research, or a combination of all of these.

Effective system FMEA is basically realized through the system engineering process, product development, research and development (R&D), or a combination of all these entities (Blanchard 1986). The focus in this stage is to

1. Transform an operational need into a description of system performance parameters and as perfect as possible system configuration through the use of an interactive process of functional analysis, synthesis, optimization, definition, design, test, and evaluation.
2. Integrate related technical parameters and assure compatibility of all physical, functional, and program interfaces in a manner that optimizes the total system definition and design.

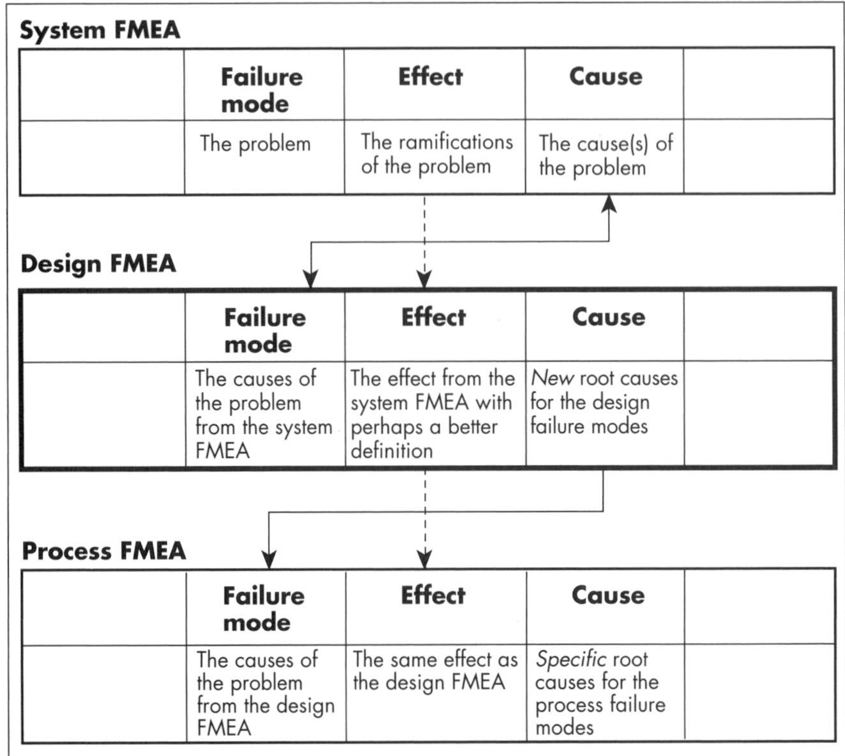
System FMEA
Failure mode
Effect
Cause
The problem
The ramifications of the problem
The cause(s) of the problem
Design FMEA
Failure mode
Effect
Cause
The causes of the problem from the system FMEA
The effect from the system FMEA with perhaps a better definition
New root causes for the design failure modes
Process FMEA
Failure mode
Effect
Cause
The causes of the problem from the design FMEA
The same effect as the design FMEA
Specific root causes for the process failure modes
Note: The failure modes of the system FMEA generate all the essential information for the design and process FMEA. Although the effect stays the same, the causes in the system FMEA become the failure modes in the design, which in turn generate their own causes, which ultimately become the failure modes in the process FMEA. It is imperative that the failures modes in the manufacturing (process) should not be listed in the design FMEA.

Figure 5.1 Relationship of system, design, and process FMEA.

3. Integrate reliability, maintainability, engineering support, human factors, safety, security, structural integrity, producibility, and other related specialties into the total engineering effort.

The goal of the system FMEA is to define and demonstrate a proper balance among operational (in other words, effectiveness and performance) and economic factors. To accomplish the objective, the system FMEA must base its requirements on solid needs, wants, and expectations of the customer. As a general rule that information may be

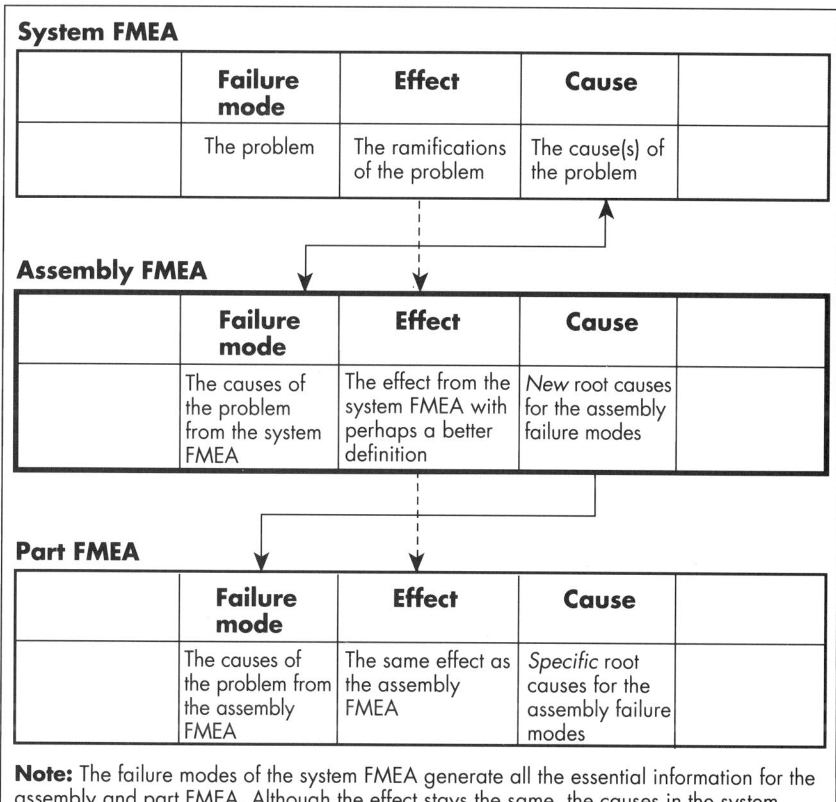

Figure 5.2 Relationship of system, assembly, and part FMEA.

the result of a quality function deployment (QFD) (preferred) or an internal need for improvement. In either case, one of the first steps in conducting the FMEA should be to include a feasibility study directed toward defining a set of useful solutions to the problem being addressed. The objective of this early (not a definitive) stage is to identify, establish, and evaluate alternative technical approaches and a functional baseline.

The outcome of the system FMEA is a preliminary design (often called advance development stage) with a baseline configuration and

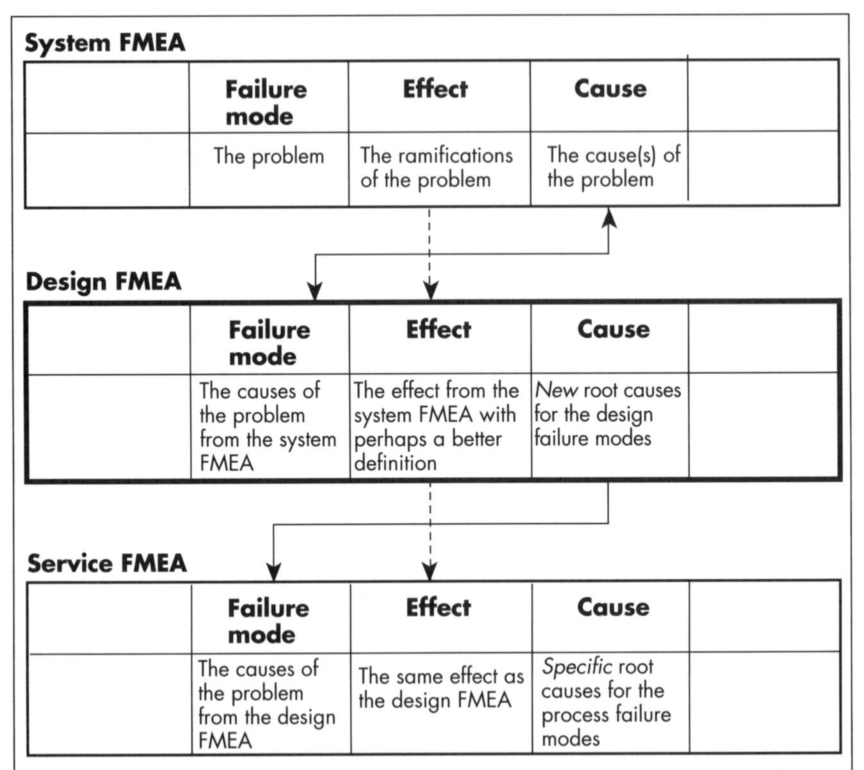
System FMEA
Failure mode
Effect
Cause
The problem
The ramifications of the problem
The cause(s) of the problem
Design FMEA
Failure mode
Effect
Cause
The causes of the problem from the system FMEA
The effect from the system FMEA with perhaps a better definition
New root causes for the design failure modes
Service FMEA
Failure mode
Effect
Cause
The causes of the problem from the design FMEA
The same effect as the design FMEA
Specific root causes for the process failure modes
Note: The failure modes of the system FMEA generate all the essential information for the design and service FMEA. Although the effect stays the same, the causes in the system FMEA become the failure modes in the design, which in turn generate their own causes, which ultimately become the failure modes in the service FMEA. Quite often in a service FMEA one goes directly from the system FMEA to the service bypassing the design all together. The methodology and results are the same.

Figure 5.3 Relationship of system, design, and service FMEA.

functional specifications toward translating the established requirements into detailed qualitative and quantitative design and process characteristics. Some of the generic concerns in a system FMEA may be the following:

General concerns

- System operational requirements defined
- Effectiveness factors established
- System maintenance concept defined

Support elements

In this area one must do a thorough investigation as to whether or not the requirements are known and/or can be optimized for

- Test and support equipment
- Personnel and training
- Repair and spare parts

Design features

- Standardization
- Accessibility
- Technical data
- Transportability
- Reliability
- Test provisions
- Controls
- Procedures
- Producibility
- Software
- Interchangeability
- Functional analysis
- Connectors
- Safety

Step-by-Step System FMEA Analysis

There are two requirements to complete a system FMEA. The first requirement is identification of the appropriate form; the second is identification of the rating guidelines.

The form for the system FMEA is not universal. It is not standardized. Each company has its own form that reflects the needs of the organization and concerns of the customer. In the automotive industry, however, efforts have been successful and as of July 1, 1993 there is a standardized form and approach published by the Automotive Industry Action Group (AIAG). (See Appendix E, Figure E.10.)

This section addresses a form to show the generally accepted items that should be addressed as part of a system FMEA. Appendix E includes additional system FMEAs which show the diversity that exists between industries. Remember, there is no such thing as *the* system FMEA form.

Rating guidelines also are not universal or standardized. Each company has its own guidelines that reflect the needs of the organization, the product, and the concerns of the customer.

Generally, there are two ways that the rating guidelines can be formulated—qualitative and quantitative. In either case, the numerical values can be from 1 to 5 or 1 to 10, with the 1 to 10 range being the most common. Again, there is no such thing as *the* rating guideline for the system FMEA.

Figure 5.4 shows the most common system FMEA form. The form is divided into three parts. The first part, items 1 through 9 reflect the introduction of the form. None of the items are mandatory; however, they do add information to the system FMEA and provide essential information that may be needed in the course of writing the FMEA.

The second part of the form consists of items 10 through 23. They reflect the mandatory items for any system FMEA. The order of the columns may be changed, more columns may be added but none of the columns presented may be removed. Items 10 through 23 may be viewed as the body of the system FMEA.

The third part of the form includes items 24 and 25. Although they are not mandatory, they do reflect the authority and responsibility of the team to undertake the project of writing the system FMEA. The signatures may be viewed as the closure of the FMEA. All numbers in parentheses are coded numbers for the discussion of the form.

System Identification (1). Identify the system name or the identification title of the FMEA.

System Responsibility (2). Name the responsible organization, division, or department that has responsibility for the system design.

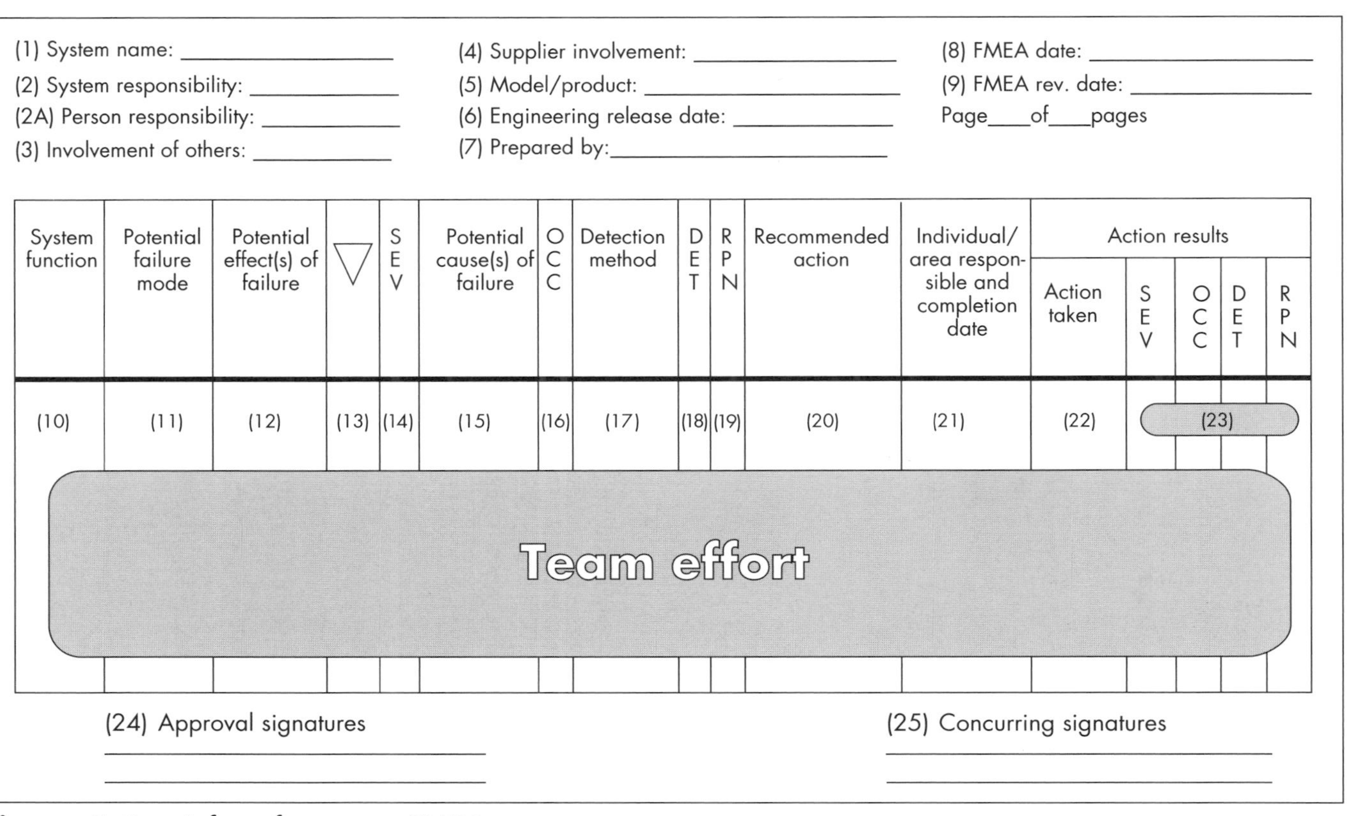

(1) System name: ______
(2) System responsibility: ______
(2A) Person responsibility: ______
(3) Involvement of others: ______
(4) Supplier involvement: ______
(5) Model/product: ______
(6) Engineering release date: ______
(7) Prepared by: ______
(8) FMEA date: ______
(9) FMEA rev. date: ______
Page____of____pages

System function	Potential failure mode	Potential effect(s) of failure	▽	SEV	Potential cause(s) of failure	OCC	Detection method	DET	RPN	Recommended action	Individual/area responsible and completion date	Action results				
												Action taken	SEV	OCC	DET	RPN
(10)	(11)	(12)	(13)	(14)	(15)	(16)	(17)	(18)	(19)	(20)	(21)	(22)	(23)			

(24) Approval signatures

(25) Concurring signatures

Figure 5.4 A form for system FMEA.

Person Responsibility (2A). Sometimes it is necessary to name the person who is responsible for the system design.

Involvement of Other Areas (3). Name other people or activities (within the organization) that affect the design of the system.

Involvement of Suppliers or Others (4). Name other people, suppliers, and/or plants (outside the organization) that affect the design of the system, and are involved either in the design, manufacturing or assembly, or service of the system.

Model or Product (5). Name the model and/or the product using the system.

Engineering Release Date (6). Identify the date (Mo–Day–Yr) that the system design specification is scheduled to be released.

Prepared by (7). Generally, the name of the system design engineer responsible for the FMEA is identified. Sometimes, additional information also is recorded, such as

- Telephone number of the system design engineer
- Address of the system design engineer
- Organizational activity (in other words, division, department, and so on)
- Team members (name, telephone, address, and so on)

FMEA Date—Original (8). Record the date (Mo–Day–Yr) of the initiation of the system FMEA.

FMEA Date—Revision (9). Record the date (Mo–Day–Yr) of the latest revision.

System Function (10). The engineer writes the design intent, purpose, goal, or objective of the system. The system function must be derived from customer needs, wants, and expectations. Typically these include, safety requirements, government regulations, and other constraints identified as either internal or external to the organization.

Generally, these needs, wants, and expectations are defined through a QFD and include several other considerations. Some of these considerations are the result of courts through product liability issues, warranty concerns, industrial standards, and/or very specific customer requisitions.

For the system function to be effective it must be identified in detail with a statement that is (1) concise, (2) exact, and (3) easy to understand (no jargon). It may also be identified through a functional block diagram which will show the system elements (components) as functional blocks into which the system may be decomposed. (Figure 2.13 is such an example.) It is important to note that the objective of the functional block diagram is to show the major elements of the system and to understand how the interaction of those elements affects the system itself or the other system(s) outside itself.

If a statement is used to describe the function, that function should be described in very specific terms. To facilitate this, the writer of the FMEA should try to think of active verbs and appropriate nouns. The active verbs define performance and performance defines function. The combination of the active verb with the noun defines the relationship; consequently, the identification process becomes much easier. Examples include

- Incorrect logic code
- Corrupted data
- Inappropriate algorithm
- Control speed

Potential Failure Mode (11). The problem. The concern. The opportunity to improve. The failure. When one thinks of the potential failure mode one must think of the loss of a system function—a specific failure. The more specific the team is, the better opportunity it will have to identify the effects and causes of the failure.

For each system function identified in column 10 of the form, one must list the corresponding failure of the function. There can be more than one failure from one function. To help in the identification of the potential failure mode one may think of the negative or loss of the function. Examples include

- Fails to open
- Coil fails to produce EMF
- Fails to provide adequate power
- Fails to operate
- Fails to close
- Cannot control speed

Potential Effect(s) of Failure (12). A potential effect of the failure is the consequence of a system failure mode. The question usually asked is: "What happens or what is (are) the ramification(s) of this problem or failure?" The consequences may be to the system itself, the product, the customer, and/or government regulations. Often the failure effect is evaluated from a customer's perspective or experiences.

To identify the potential effects, some of the documents one may review are

- Warranty documents
- Customer complaints
- Field service data
- Reliability data
- Feasibility studies

No matter how the potential effect(s) is (are) identified the ramifications of the loss to the system function must be determined. Consideration must be given to the system itself, other systems, the product, and the customer. If safety considerations may be an issue, this is the column where the appropriate notation should be made. Examples of potential effect of failure may be

- Next higher system: fails to operate circuit relay
- Next lower system: none
- Other system(s): none

- Product: motor overheats
- Customer: complete dissatisfaction; system fails to operate
- Government: may not comply with STD-XXX

Critical Characteristics (13). Critical characteristics usually are not associated with system FMEAs because that hardware has not yet been defined in this early stage. Until hardware is defined, critical and/or significant characteristics cannot be identified (Slone 1986). The place where the identification of critical characteristics is made is in the design FMEA where the characteristics are used only to designate special controls for the process, assembly, and/or service FMEA. From here they are transferred to the control plan.

Severity of Effect (14). Severity is a rating indicating the seriousness of the effect of the potential system failure mode. The severity always applies to the effect of a failure mode. In fact, there is a direct correlation between effect and severity. For example, if the effect is critical, the severity is high. On the other hand, if the effect is not critical, the severity is very low.

The severity is reviewed from the perspective of the system itself, other systems, the product, the customer, and/or the government regulations. For evaluation purposes there usually is a rating table that reflects the issues of the organization in conjunction with the customer and/or the government regulations. An example of such rating may be seen in Table 5.1.

In the system FMEA the severity rating should be based on the worst effect of the failure mode. After this is done, rank the failure modes on the basis of the severity of their effects. At this point the FMEA is identical to the FMCA.

Potential Cause(s) of Failure (15). The cause of a system failure mode is the system design deficiency that results in the failure mode. There are two ways failures may be examined.

1. As they relate to specific failures
2. As they relate to the reliability bathtub curve, in terms of early, chance, and wear-out failure causes

Effect	Rank	Criteria	Resolution
No	1	No effect	If the numerical value falls between two numbers *always* select the higher number. If the team has a disagreement in the ranking value the following may help. 1. If the disagreement is an adjacent category, average out the difference. For example, if one member says 5 and someone else says 6, the ranking in this case should be 6 (5 and 6 are adjacent categories. Therefore 5 + 6 = 11, 11/2 = 5.5) 2. If the disagreement jumps one category, then consensus must be reached. Even with one person holding out total consensus must be reached. No average, no majority. Everyone in that team must have ownership of the ranking. They may not agree 100 percent, but they can live with it.
Very slight	2	Customer not annoyed. Very slight effect on product or system performance	
Slight	3	Customer slightly annoyed. Slight effect on product or system performance	
Minor	4	Customer experiences minor nuisance. Minor effect on product or system performance	
Moderate	5	Customer experiences some dissatisfaction. Moderate effect on product or system performance	
Significant	6	Customer experiences discomfort. Product performance degraded, but operable and safe. Partial failure, but operable	
Major	7	Customer dissatisfied. Product performance severely affected but functionable and safe. System impaired.	
Extreme	8	Customer very dissatisfied. Product inoperable but safe. System inoperable.	
Serious	9	Potential hazardous effect. Able to stop product without mishap—time dependent failure. Compliance with government regulation is in jeopardy.	
Hazardous	10	Hazardous effect. Safety related—sudden failure. Noncompliance with government regulation.	

Table 5.1 Severity guideline for system FMEA* (1–10 qualitative scale).

*All the above guidelines and rankings may be changed to reflect specific situations.

Examples of these two conditions are

- Early failure causes: Insufficient burning in; insufficient debugging; substandard parts, human error; improper installation, and so on.
- Chance failures: Misapplication; abuse; act of God; insufficient design, and so on.
- Wear-out failures: Corrosion; aging; wear; fatigue; short life design; creep, and so on.

Illustrations of these failure modes are in Figures 5.5, 5.6, 5.7.

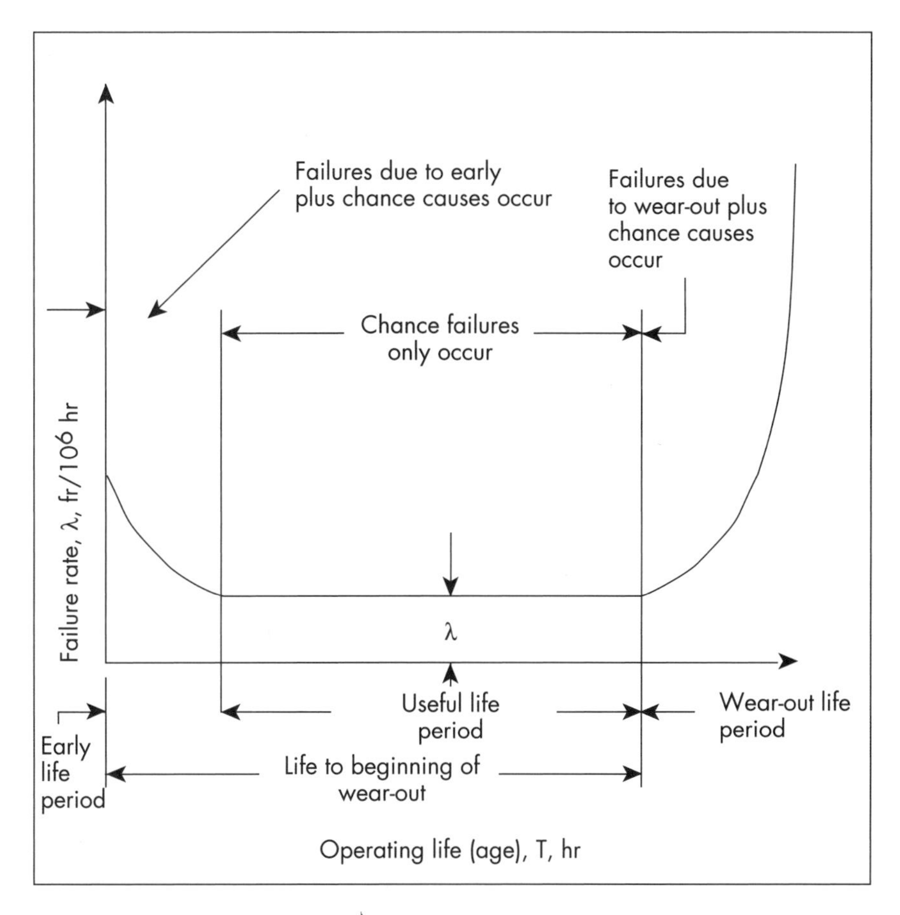

Figure 5.5 Reliability bathtub curve.

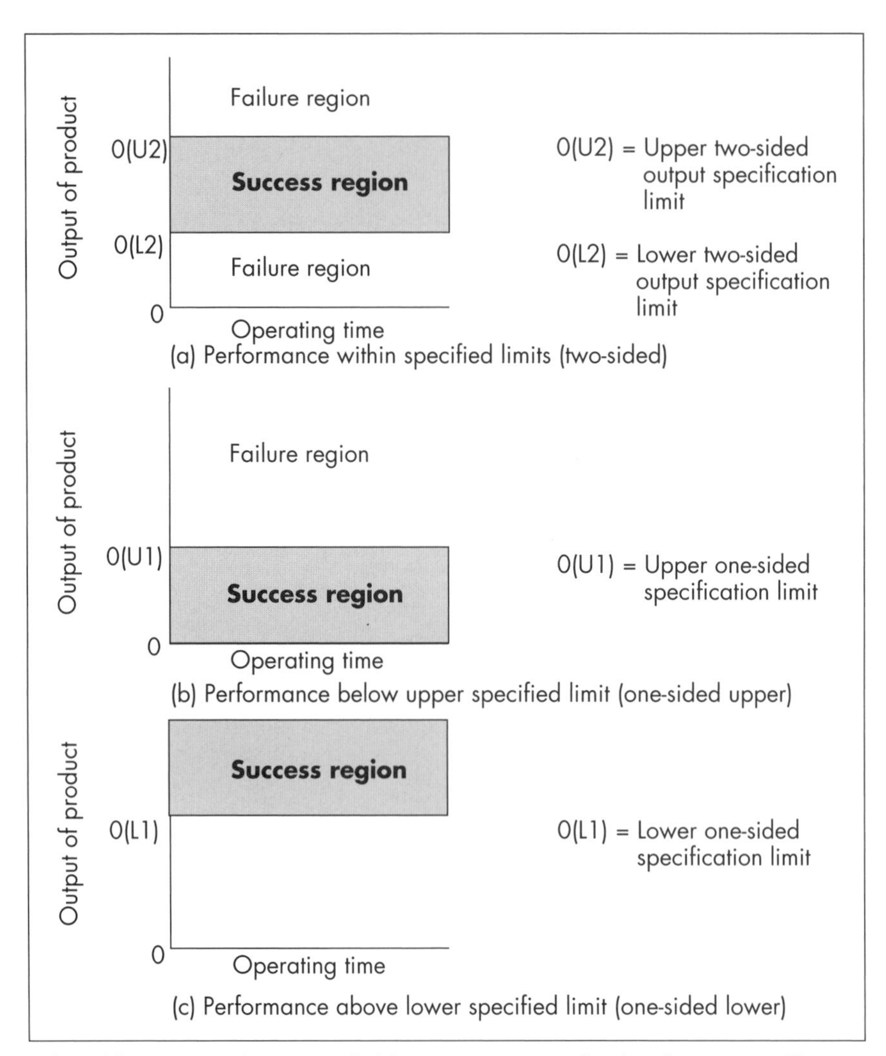

Adopted from Kececioglu 1991. *Reliability Engineering Handbook.* Vol. 1. Reprinted by permission of Prentice Hall, Englewood Cliffs, N.J.

Figure 5.6 Cases of no-failure performance.

It must be emphasized repeatedly that when one focuses on the cause(s) one must look at the *root cause,* not the symptom of the failure.

To do a good job of proper potential cause(s) of failure identification, one must understand the system and ask the appropriate

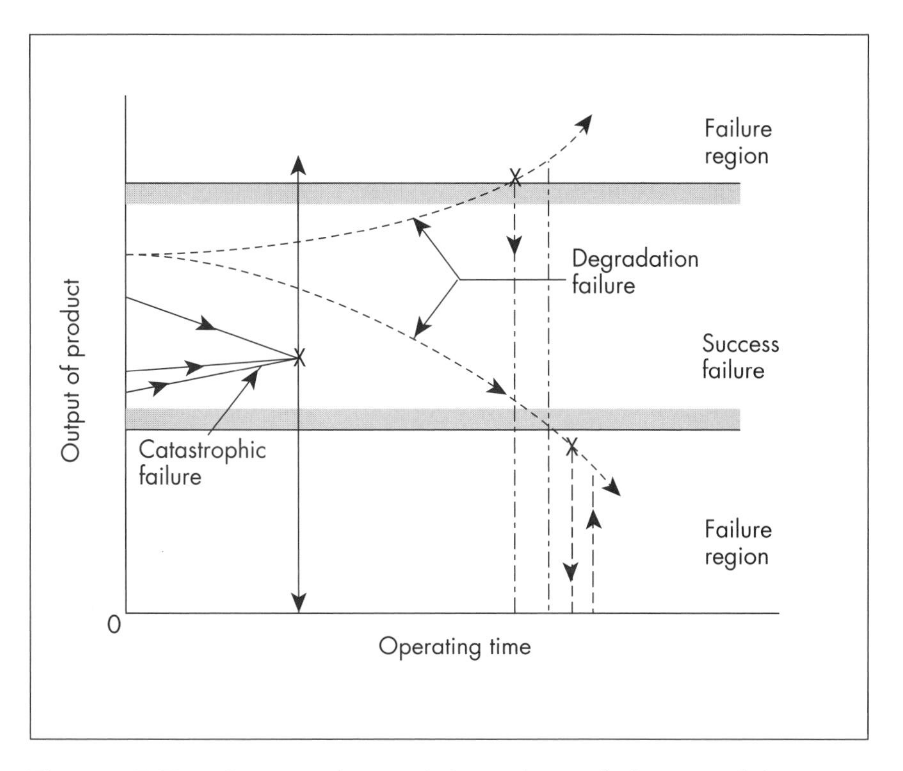

Figure 5.7 Catastrophic and degradation failures and their effects on output.

questions. Some of the techniques that may be used are brainstorming, cause-and-effect analysis, analysis of the block diagram, and affinity charts.

The basic question to ask is "In what way can this system fail to perform its intended function?" Another method is to ask five *whys* in a row. The rationale for this is that it becomes a progressively more difficult and thought-provoking assignment to identify the whys. The first questions are superficial, but the later ones are more substantive.

A failure mode can be caused by one or more individual components or by

- Interaction with other components
- Interaction with components of other systems

- Interaction with the government
- Interaction with the customer

At this point, it must be emphasized that a major benefit of the system FMEA is identification of potential system failure modes caused by system and/or component interactions. These interactions also may involve human factors and as such they must be reviewed thoroughly.

The relationship between the failure mode and the cause(s) is not linear or one-to-one. Do not be surprised if there are several if not many causes for one failure mode. (Sometimes a one-to-one relationship exists.) List as many causes as possible—all of them. These causes will be transferred to the design FMEA as potential failure modes (see Figure 5.1). The more causes identified in the system FMEA, the easier the design FMEA becomes.

Examples of causes of failures are

- Intermittent operation
- Software errors
- Failure to stop
- Degradation of output
- Failure to start

In the system FMEA the failure causes sometimes are not that obvious. In fact, there are at least three conditions that one should examine.

1. The specific cause is unknown, but it does exist. In this case, there are two outcomes.
   a. The failure mode is detected, in which case the detection mechanism is adequate. What is necessary, however, is that a design action is required to remove the cause, or further analysis is needed to precisely identify the cause.
   b. The failure mode is not detected, in which case the detection mechanism is not working. As part of the system FMEA, recommendations should be to increase sample quantity or develop a new test/technique for detection.
2. A specific cause exists, but cannot be detected. In this case there are two outcomes.

a. The verification/detection technique is capable, in which case the sample may be too low and it should be increased.
b. The verification/detection technique is not capable, in which case development of a new or a modification of the verification/detection test or technique is needed. The new or modified test/technique should be more sensitive to the existing technique for detecting the specific cause.

3. A specific cause exists and can be detected. In this case there are two outcomes.
   a. Cause is detected, in which case further analysis and/or testing is required to determine the appropriate action to remove the root cause failure.
   b. Cause is not detected, in which case a design problem may exist or insufficient tests are performed. In this case, DOE and/or a review of existing testing is highly recommended.

Occurrence (16). Occurrence is the rating value corresponding to the estimated number (sometimes cumulative number) of failures that could occur for a given cause over the design life of the system. To identify the frequency for each of the causes, one may use reliability mathematics that are beyond the scope of this book, use expected frequencies, or more simply use a cumulative number of component failures (CNF) per 100 or 1000 components (CNF/100 or CNF/1000, respectively) over the design life of the component under study. Design life in the system FMEA is the durability target of the component (Bass 1991). The specific attribute of the target will be component dependent.

Another way to define the design life for the system FMEA is the target (goal) period or useful life after which the component is discarded because (1) it ceases to function as designed (normal wear), and (2) it is too expensive to repair.

If the expected frequency and/or cumulative number of failures cannot be estimated, it is acceptable for the system FMEA to look at similar or surrogate systems and/or components for similar information.

Generally, the system FMEA operates under the assumption of a single-point failure (in other words, if the component fails, the system fails). A single-point failure is defined as a component failure that would cause the system failure and which is not compensated by either redundancy or an alternative method. For example, single pieces of hardware and heavily loaded cable runs, place a high degree of dependence on single components, which usually can be avoided through the use of redundancy. In this case, the installation of duplicate cables into a heavily loaded area, with terminals intermingled on one of the two cables, can minimize service disruption in the event of a cable cut.

It is imperative when the occurrence/frequency is calculated, it must be for every single cause of the failure. It also must be a consensus agreement of the entire team. A typical occurrence guideline is shown in Table 5.2.

Detection Method (17). A method (procedure), test, design review, or an engineering analysis. These are some of the first-level methods to detect a failure in the system. They can be very simple (in other words, brainstorming) or very technical and advanced (in other words, finite element analysis, computer simulation, and laboratory tests).

The objective is to detect a design deficiency as early as possible. That deficiency may be viewed as a weakness in the system to reveal, detect, or eliminate the problem from the system (Chien 1985). The idea of early detection in the system FMEA is to provide efficient design controls.

Because the system FMEA is performed very early, it sometimes is difficult to assess the detection rating. In these cases one may use historical information, or similar types of information from similar components and/or systems. In some cases, it is possible to have no method, test, or technique to identify the failure. In that case, the entry in this column should state something like "None identified at this time."

Another way of focusing on the detection is to use the brainstorming technique to identify new methods, and tests as they apply to the task at hand. Two of the leading questions in the brainstorming process should be

- How can this failure be discovered?
- In what way can this failure be recognized?

Detection	Rank	Criteria	CNF/1000	Resolution
Almost never	1	Failure unlikely. History shows no failures.	<.00058	If the numerical value falls between two numbers *always* select the higher number.
Remote	2	Rare number of failures likely.	.0068	If the team has a disagreement in the ranking value the following may help.
Very slight	3	Very few failures likely.	.0063	
Slight	4	Few failures likely.	.46	1. If the disagreement is an adjacent category, average out the difference. For example, if one member says 5 and someone else says 6, the ranking in this case should be 6 (5 and 6 are adjacent categories. Therefore 5 + 6 = 11, 11/2 = 5.5)
Low	5	Occasional number of failures likely.	2.7	
Medium	6	Medium number of failures likely.	12.4	
Moderately high	7	Moderately high number of failures likely.	46	
High	8	High number of failures likely.	134	2. If the disagreement jumps one category, then consensus must be reached. Even with one person holding out, total consensus must be reached. No average, no majority. Everyone in that team must have ownership of the ranking. They may not agree 100 percent, but they can live with it.
Very high	9	Very high number of failures likely.	316	
Almost certain	10	Failure almost certain. History of failures exists from previous or similar designs.	>316	

Table 5.2 Occurrence guideline for system FMEA* (1–10 qualitative scale).

*All the above guidelines and rankings may be changed to reflect specific situations.

To answer such questions a checklist may be of help. An extensive checklist is provided in Appendix B. A typical system design review checklist should cover the following (partial list):

- General
  –System operational requirements defined
  –Effectiveness factors established
  –System maintenance defined
- Support elements
  –Test and support equipment
  –Personnel training
- Spare and repair parts
- Design features
  –Standardization
  –Interchangeability
  –Safety
  –Producibility
  –Test provisions
  –Handling
  –Storage
  –Reliability

Detection (18). Detection is a rating corresponding to the likelihood that the proposed system controls will detect a specific root cause of a failure mode (first-level causes) before the part is released for design. To identify a detection rating one must estimate the ability for each of the controls identified in item 17 to detect the failure before it reaches the customer. In other words, are the controls identified in item 17 effective for the system design?

If the ability of the controls to detect the failure is unknown or the detection cannot be estimated, then the detection rating should be 10. A typical detection guideline is shown in Table 5.3.

Risk Priority Number (RPN) (19). This number is the product of severity, occurrence, and detection. The RPN defines the priority of the failure. By themselves the RPNs have no value or meaning. They are used only to rank (define) the potential system deficiencies.

Detection	Rank	Criteria	Resolution
Almost certain	1	Proven detection methods available in concept stage	If the numerical value falls between two numbers *always* select the higher number. If the team has a disagreement in the ranking value the following may help. 1. If the disagreement is an adjacent category, average out the difference. For example, if one member says 5 and someone else says 6, the ranking in this case should be 6 (5 and 6 are adjacent categories. Therefore 5 + 6 = 11, 11/2 = 5.5) 2. If the disagreement jumps one category, then consensus must be reached. Even with one person holding out total consensus must be reached. No average, no majority. Everyone in that team must have ownership of the ranking. They may not agree 100 percent, but they can live with it.
Very high	2	Proven computer analysis available in early design stage	
High	3	Simulation and/or modeling in early stage	
Moderately high	4	Tests on early prototype system elements	
Medium	5	Tests on preproduction system components	
Low	6	Tests on similar system components	
Slight	7	Tests on product with prototypes with system components installed	
Very slight	8	Proving durability tests on products with system components installed	
Remote	9	Only unproven or unreliable technique(s) available	
Almost impossible	10	No known techniques available	

Table 5.3 Detection guideline for system FMEA* (1–10 qualitative scale).

*All the above guidelines and rankings may be changed to reflect specific situations.

Recommended Action (20). No FMEA should be done without a recommended action. The recommended action may be specific action(s) or it may be further studying. The idea of the recommended action in the system FMEA is to reduce the severity, occurrence, detection, or all of them. In essence, the system FMEA is done to eliminate system deficiencies and therefore to eliminate failures.

To facilitate this goal the FMEA team must prioritize those failure modes with

- The highest RPN
- The highest severity
- The highest occurrence

Typical recommendations may be

- No action at this time
- Add built-in detection devices
- Provide alternatives to the system
- Add a redundant subsystem

Responsible Area or Person and Completion Date (21). This section looks for the responsible person/area and the target completion date for the recommended action.

Action Taken (22). This is the follow-up. Just because something was recommended, that does not mean that something was done. It is imperative that someone (usually the system design engineer) will follow up on the recommendations to determine if they have been addressed adequately, properly, and/or if they are in need of updating.

Note that all FMEAs are living documents and as such someone must be responsible to update them. Often the person who is responsible for updating is the system design engineer. She or he has the responsibility to make sure that the system FMEA is indeed a living document and that it reflects the latest relevant information and actions.

After the action has been taken, the effective date or completion date with a brief description of the action should be entered.

Revised RPN (23). After the actions are incorporated in the system, the FMEA team should reevaluate the consequences of severity, occurrence, and detection. The results should be reviewed by the FMEA team and a new RPN is calculated and the failures are ranked. This process is repeated as needed until such time the FMEA team decides that all relevant information has been covered. If no actions are taken, then these columns will remain blank.

Approval Signatures (24). These signatures define the authority to carry out the FMEA. The names and titles will depend on the organization. Typical names may be those of the system design manager, R&D director, and engineering manager.

Concurrence Signatures (25). They define the responsibility of carrying out the completion and implementation of the FMEA. The names and titles will depend on the organization. Typical names may be those of the engineering manager, manufacturing manager, and quality assurance manager.

Recommended Team

A team is necessary to conduct a system FMEA. The team makeup should be five to nine individuals with a multidisciplined and multifunctional background. In addition, all members should have ownership of the problem (Stamatis 1992). A typical team may include the following:

- System engineer (mandatory)
- Reliability engineer
- Test engineer
- Marketing representative
- Design engineer (mandatory)

Other recommended participants may include

- Quality engineer
- Material engineer

- R&D representative
- Process engineer
- Field service engineer
- Product engineer

Note that there is no such thing as *the* team. The team composition should reflect the needs and requirements of the problem and the culture of the organization.

References

Bass, L. 1991. Cumulative supplement to *Products liability: Design and manufacturing defects.* Colorado Springs, Colo.: Shepard's/McGraw-Hill.

Blanchard, B. S. 1986. *Logistics engineering and management.* 3d ed. Englewood Cliffs, N.J.: Prentice Hall.

Chien, J. 1985. Detailed tests show how well industrial local network performs. *Data Communications* 14 (August): 119–131.

Slone, J. P. 1986. Broadband LANs. *Journal of Information Systems Management* (summer): 49.

Stamatis, D. H. 1992. *FMEA handbook.* Southgate, Mich.: Contemporary Consultants.

CHAPTER 6

Design FMEA

A design FMEA is a disciplined analysis/method of identifying potential or known failure modes and providing follow-up and corrective actions before the first production run occurs. A first production run is viewed as the run that generates a product or service for a specific customer with the intent of getting paid. This definition of the first run is very important because it excludes initial sample runs (ISR), trial runs, occasional prototype run(s), and so on. The threshold of the first production run is important, because up to that point modifying and/or changing the design is not a major problem. After that point, however, the customer gets involved through the letter of deviation, waiver of change, or some other kind of formal notification.

A design or product FMEA usually is accomplished through a series of steps to include component, subsystems/subassemblies, and/or systems/assemblies. The design FMEA is an evolutionary process (dynamic as opposed to static) involving the application of various technologies and methods to produce an effective design output. This result will be used as an input for the process or assembly, and/or the service FMEA (see Figures 5.1, 5.2, and 5.3).

Selection of appropriate technologies may include the utilization of existing system(s), standardized approaches currently known or proposed, results of directed research, results of the system FMEA, or a combination of all these factors.

Effective design FMEA is basically realized through the system engineering process, product development, research and development (R&D), marketing, manufacturing, or a combination of all these entities (Blanchard 1986). The focus in this stage is to *minimize failure effects on the system, regardless of what level FMEA is being performed.*

This can be realized through a definition of design specifications which may include the following:

- I. Scope of design
- II. Applicable documents
  - A. Standards
  - B. Safety and warranty documents
  - C. Documents on prior or similar products
- III. General information
  - A. Product functions
  - B. Understanding who the customer is
  - C. Customer's needs, wants, and expectations
  - D. Understanding of customer's uses and misuses
- IV. Requirements
  - A. Design requirements
    1. Electrical
    2. Mechanical
    3. Reliability
    4. Service life
    5. Safety
    6. Material
    7. Environmental
    8. Controls
    9. Parts standardization
  - B. Maintenance considerations
  - C. Cost objective
  - D. Design alternatives
  - E. Critical systems
- V. Product assurance
  - A. Documentation requirements
  - B. Testing and inspection requirements
  - C. Packaging and handling requirements

The goal, purpose, and/or objective of the design FMEA is to define and demonstrate engineering solutions in response to functional requirements as defined by the system FMEA and the customer.

To accomplish this objective the design FMEA must base its requirements on solid needs, wants, and expectations of the customer. As a general rule that information may be the result of a quality function deployment QFD (preferred), or an internal need for improvement, or the results of a system FMEA. In either case, one of the first steps in conducting the FMEA should be to include a feasibility study and/or a risk-benefit analysis directed toward defining a set of useful solutions to the problem(s) being addressed. The objective of this early (not definitive) stage is to maximize the system quality, reliability, cost, and maintainability, regardless of what level the FMEA is being performed. This can be accomplished by at least the following considerations.

- Transform an operational need into a description of system performance parameters and as perfect as possible system configuration through the use of an interactive process of functional analysis, synthesis, optimization, definition, design, design reviews, test, and evaluation.
- Integrate related technical parameters and assure compatibility of all physical, functional, and program interfaces in a manner that optimizes the total system definition and design.
- Integrate reliability, maintainability, engineering support, human factors, safety, security, structural integrity, producibility, and other related specialties into the total engineering effort.

The outcome of the design FMEA is a preliminary design (it may change with new or modified information) with a baseline configuration and functional specifications toward translating the established requirements into detailed qualitative and quantitative process and assembly or service characteristics. Some of the generic concerns in a design FMEA may be the following:

General concerns

- Design operational requirements defined
- Effectiveness factors established
- Design maintenance concept defined

Support elements

In this area one must do a thorough investigation as to whether or not the requirements are known and/or can be optimized for

- Test and support equipment
- Personnel and training
- Repair and spare parts

Design features

- Standardization
- Accessibility
- Connectors
- Safety
- Test provisions
- Controls
- Transportability
- Reliability
- Interchangeability
- Technical data
- Producibility
- Software

Specific questions in the course of performing a design FMEA may be

1. What does the product do and what are its intended uses?
2. How does the product perform its function?
3. What raw materials and components are used to build the product?
4. How, and under what conditions does the product interface with other products?
5. What by-products are created by the product or by the use of the product?
6. How is the product used, maintained, repaired, and disposed of at the end of its useful life?

7. What are the manufacturing steps in the production of the product?
8. What energy sources are involved and how?
9. Who will use or be in the vicinity of the product, and what are the capabilities and limitations of these individuals?

Finally, when conducting a design FMEA, it is assumed that the system is the best it can be. If this assumption is not made, the FMEA team will end up doing the system and design FMEAs at the same time and will move in a circular pattern not accomplishing its task. The only way to address the system FMEA in the process of conducting the design FMEA is when the root causes of the failure modes in the design are caused by the system specifications.

Step-by-Step Design FMEA Analysis

Traditionally, there have been two methods of designing products: design-to-cost and design-to-customer requirements. In the design-to-cost approach, the designer's aim is to develop the design within certain cost limits (Stamatis 1993). This approach is called *value engineering analysis* and is beyond the scope of this book. In the design-to-customer requirements approach, the designer gives the customer what the customer wants with added requirements to satisfy regulatory obligations, safety concerns, and any other criteria that seem to be appropriate for the design. This second method will be pursued in this section.

To perform a design FMEA there are two requirements. The first requirement is the identification of the appropriate form. The second requirement is identification of the rating guidelines.

The form for the design FMEA is not universal. It is not standardized. Each company has its own form that reflects the needs of the organization and the concerns of the customer. In the automotive industry, however, efforts have been successful and on July 1, 1993 a standardized form and procedure was published by AIAG. (See Appendix E, Figure E.10.)

This section addresses a form displaying generally accepted items that should be addressed as part of a system FMEA. In Appendix E there are additional design FMEAs that show the diversity that exists between industries. Remember, there is no such thing as *the* design FMEA form.

The rating guidelines are not universal. They are not standardized. Each company has its own guidelines to reflect the needs of the organization, the product, and the concerns of the customer.

Generally, there are two ways that the rating guidelines can be formulated. The first method is qualitative; the second method quantitative. In either case the numerical values can be from 1 to 5 or 1 to 10, with the 1 to 10 range being the most common. Examples of both guidelines will be shown.

Figure 6.1 shows the most common design FMEA form. The form is divided into three parts. The first part, items 1 through 10 reflect the introduction of the form. None of the items are mandatory; however, they do add information to the design FMEA and provide essential information that may be needed in the course of writing the FMEA.

The second part of the form includes items 11 through 24. They reflect the mandatory items for any design FMEA. The order of the columns may be changed; more columns may be added but none of the columns presented may be removed. Items 11 through 24 may be viewed as the body of the system FMEA.

The third part of the form consists items 25 and 26. Although they are not mandatory, they do reflect the authority and responsibility of the team to undertake the project of writing the system FMEA. The signatures may be viewed as the closure of the FMEA. All numbers in parentheses are coded numbers for the discussion of the form.

Subsystem Identification (1). Identifies the subsystem name or the identification title of the FMEA.

Design Responsibility (2). Name the responsible organization, division, or department that has responsibility for the system design.

Person Responsibility (2A). Sometimes it is necessary to name the person who is responsible for the system design.

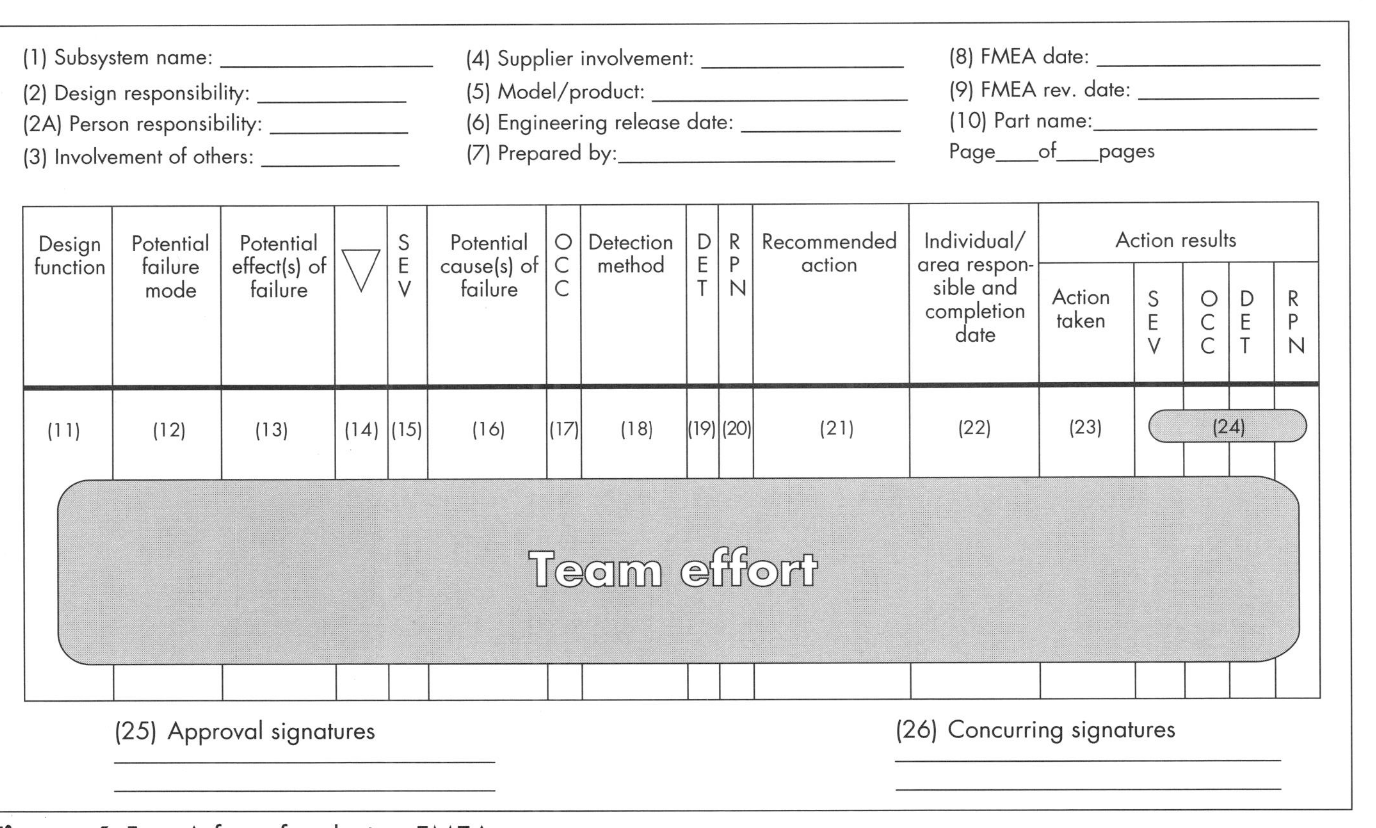

(1) Subsystem name: ____________
(2) Design responsibility: ____________
(2A) Person responsibility: ____________
(3) Involvement of others: ____________

(4) Supplier involvement: ____________
(5) Model/product: ____________
(6) Engineering release date: ____________
(7) Prepared by: ____________

(8) FMEA date: ____________
(9) FMEA rev. date: ____________
(10) Part name: ____________
Page____of____pages

Design function	Potential failure mode	Potential effect(s) of failure	▽	SEV	Potential cause(s) of failure	OCC	Detection method	DET	RPN	Recommended action	Individual/ area responsible and completion date	Action results				
												Action taken	SEV	OCC	DET	RPN
(11)	(12)	(13)	(14)	(15)	(16)	(17)	(18)	(19)	(20)	(21)	(22)	(23)	(24)			

(25) Approval signatures
____
____

(26) Concurring signatures
____
____

Figure 6.1 A form for design FMEA.

Involvement of Other Areas (3). Name other people or activities (within the organization) that affect the design of the system.

Involvement of Suppliers or Others (4). Identify other people, suppliers, and/or plants (outside the organization) that affect the design and are involved in the design, manufacturing or assembly, or service of the system.

Model or Product (5). Name the model and/or the product using the system.

Engineering Release Date (6). Identify the date (Mo–Day–Yr) that the product is scheduled to be released.

Prepared by (7). Generally, the name of the design engineer responsible for the FMEA is identified. Sometimes, additional information also is recorded, such as

- Telephone number of the system design engineer
- Address of the system design engineer
- Organizational activity (in other words, division, department)
- Team members (name, telephone, address, and so on)

FMEA Date–Original (8). Record the date (Mo–Day–Yr) of the initiation of the design FMEA.

FMEA Date–Revision (9). Record the date (Mo–Day–Yr) of the latest revision.

Part Name (10). Identify the part name or number. Often the latest engineering drawing number is identified.

Design Function (11). The engineer writes the design intent, purpose, goal, or objective of the design. The design function must be derived from customer needs, wants, and expectations. Typically they include safety requirements, government regulations, and other internal or external constraints to the organization.

Generally, these needs, wants, and expectations are defined through a QFD and include several other considerations. Some of these considerations are a result of courts through product liability issues, warranty concerns, industrial standards, and/or specific customer requisitions.

For the design function to be effective, it must be identified in detail through a statement that is concise, exact, and easy to understand (no jargon). It also can be identified through a functional block diagram, which will show the system elements as functional blocks into which the system may be decomposed. It is important to note that the objective of the functional block diagram is to show the major elements of the system and to understand how the interaction of those elements affects the system itself or the other external system(s).

If a statement is used to describe the function, that function should be described in specific terms. To facilitate this the writer of the FMEA should try to think of active verbs and appropriate nouns. The active verbs define performance and performance defines function. The combination of the active verb with the noun defines the relationship; consequently, the identification process becomes much easier. This can be facilitated through a part function worksheet (Figure 6.2).

Examples of functions include

- Provide bonded unit
- Provide cured subassembly
- Facilitate manufacturing
- Provide vibration damping

Potential Failure Mode (12). The problem. The concern. The opportunity to improve. The failure. The defect. When considering the potential failure mode one must think of the loss of a design function—a specific failure. The more specific one is the better opportunity there will be to identify the effects and causes of the failure. Design failures occur when a product does not adequately protect against risks of injury, fails to perform intended functions safely, or fails to minimize avoidable consequences in the event of an accident.

For each design function identified in item 11 the corresponding failure of the function must be listed. There can be more than one failure from one function. To help identify of the potential failure mode one may think of the negative or loss of the function.

Project name: ______________________________
Scope key element(s): ______________________________
Project restrictions: ______________________________
Drawing number ______________ Team number: __________ Date: ______

List of functions			Basic	Second	Specifications / Product requirements
No.	Verb	Noun			How much? When?
1					
2					
3					
4					
5					
6					
7					
8					

Figure 6.2 Function evaluation worksheet.

Examples of corresponding failure include

- Fails to open
- Component shorts
- No pressure
- Broken
- Coil fails to produce EMF
- Subassembly leaks
- Corroded
- Cannot control speed

Another way to identify the failure mode anticipated is to ask the question "How could this system, design, component, subsystem, or process fail?" "Can it break, wear, bind, and so on?" The emphasis is on the engineer who must try to anticipate how the design being considered could possibly fail, not whether or not it will fail.

Still another way of identifying failure mode is through a fault tree analysis (FTA). In the FTA structure the top level is the loss of the part function and then progressively on the lower levels the failure modes are identified. An example of an FTA may be viewed in Appendix D, Example 11.

Potential Effect(s) of Failure (13). A potential effect of the failure is the consequence of its failure on the next higher design, system, product, customer, and/or government regulations. The questions usually asked are: "What does the customer experience as a result of the failure mode described?" or "What happens or what is (are) the ramification(s) of this problem or failure?" The consequences may be to the design itself, the product, the customer, and/or government regulations. Often, the failure effect is evaluated from a customer's perspective or experiences.

To identify the potential effects, some of the documents one may review are

- Historical data
- Warranty documents
- Field service data
- Feasibility studies
- Customer complaints
- Similar current or past FMEAs
- Reliability data

No matter how the potential effect(s) is (are) identified, the ramifications of the loss to the design function must be determined. Consideration must be given to the design itself, other systems, the product, and the customer. If safety considerations may be an issue, this is the column where the appropriate notation should be made. Examples of potential effect of failure may be

- Next higher system: fails to operate
- Next lower system: none
- Other system(s): none
- Product: performance degradation
- Customer: complete dissatisfaction; system fails to operate
- Government: may not comply with STD-XXX

Critical Characteristics (14). Critical characteristics usually are associated with design FMEAs because the hardware begins to be formalized in the design stage. Until and when hardware is defined, critical and/or significant characteristics cannot be identified (Slone 1986). This is the place where the identification of critical characteristics is made. The identification of the criticality or significance in the design FMEA is only to designate special controls for the process, assembly, and/or service FMEA. From here they are transferred to the control plan.

Examples of possible critical items may be dimensions, specifications, tests, processes, tooling, usage. Critical characteristics are identified when

- Process requirements can affect safety.
- Process requirements can affect compliance with government regulations.
- Process requirements are necessary for special actions/controls.

The entry to this column is a "Y" for yes, "N" for no, or a notation symbol (in other words, inverted delta). Its purpose is to flag a potential critical characteristic that may or may not exist. A good indication of criticality is when severity is rated 9 or 10 with occurrence and detection higher than 3.

Severity of Effect (15). Severity is a rating indicating the seriousness of the effect of the potential design failure mode. The severity always applies to the effect of a failure mode. In fact, there is a direct correlation between effect and severity. For example, if the effect is critical, the severity is high. Conversely, if the effect is a nuisance, the severity is very low.

Severity is reviewed from the perspective of the system, design itself, other systems, the product, the customer and/or the government regulations. For evaluation purposes there usually is a rating table that reflects the issues of the organization in conjunction with the customer and/or the government regulations. An example of such rating may be seen in Table 6.1.

In the design FMEA the severity rating should be based on the worst effect of the failure mode. When complete, rank the failure modes on the basis of the severity of their effects. At this point the FMEA is identical to the FMCA.

Potential Cause(s) of Failure (16). The cause of a design failure mode is the design deficiency that results in the failure mode. It must be emphasized repeatedly that when one focuses on the cause(s) one must look at the *root cause,* not the symptom of the failure.

To do a good job of proper potential cause(s) of failure identification, one must understand both the system and design, and ask appropriate questions. Specificity is of paramount importance. The more one zooms in on the root cause, the better one understands the failure. For example, "Would poor wire insulation cause the short?" Some of the techniques that may be used are brainstorming, cause-and-effect analysis, analysis of the block diagram, and affinity charts.

The basic question to ask is "In what way can this system fail to perform its intended function?" Another way is to ask five "whys" in a row. The rationale for this is that it progressively becomes a more difficult and thought-provoking assignment to identify the whys. The early ones are superficial where the later ones are more substantive. Other questions that may be asked are: "What circumstances could cause the failure?" "How or why can the part fail to meet its engineering specifications?"

A failure mode can be caused by one or more of the individual components or by (partial list)

- Hardware failure due to inadequate product design
- Improper selection of component parts
- Improper use of processes

Effect	Rank	Criteria	Resolution
None	1	No effect	If the numerical value falls between two numbers *always* select the higher number. If the team has a disagreement in the ranking value the following may help. 1. If the disagreement is an adjacent category, average out the difference. For example, if one member says 5 and someone else says 6, the ranking in this case should be 6 (5 and 6 are adjacent categories. Therefore 5 + 6 = 11, 11/2 = 5.5) 2. If the disagreement jumps one category, then consensus must be reached. Even with one person holding out, total consensus must be reached. No average, no majority. Everyone in that team must have ownership of the ranking. They may not agree 100 percent, but they can live with it.
Very slight	2	Customer not annoyed. Very slight effect on product performance. Nonvital fault noticed sometimes.	
Slight	3	Customer slightly annoyed. Slight effect on product performance. Nonvital fault noticed most of the time.	
Minor	4	Customer experiences minor nuisance. Minor effect on product performance. Fault does not require repair. Nonvital fault always noticed.	
Moderate	5	Customer experiences some dissatisfaction. Moderate effect on product performance. Fault on nonvital part requires repair.	
Significant	6	Customer experiences discomfort. Product performance degraded, but operable and safe. Nonvital part inoperable.	
Major	7	Customer dissatisfied. Product performance severely affected but functionable and safe. Subsystem inoperable.	
Extreme	8	Customer very dissatisfied. Product inoperable but safe. System inoperable.	
Serious	9	Potential hazardous effect. Able to stop product without mishap—time-dependent failure. Compliance with government regulation is in jeopardy.	
Hazardous	10	Hazardous effect. Safety related—sudden failure. Noncompliance with government regulation.	

Table 6.1 Severity guideline for design FMEA* (1–10 qualitative scale).

*All the above guidelines and rankings may be changed to reflect specific situations.

- Inadequate control procedures
- Failure to enforce process and quality controls
- Improper installation, maintenance
- Lack of safety devices, environmental factors
- Misuse, abuse
- Alteration of the product
- Improper operating instructions
- Human error
- Improper choice of materials
- Stress concentrations
- Fatigue, uniform attack
- Corrosion, galvanic corrosion, crevice corrosion
- Hydrogen damage, pitting, blistering
- Decarbonization, abrasion and wear, shock and vibration
- Interaction with other components
- Interaction with components of other systems
- Interaction with the government
- Interaction with the customer

This area in the FMEA is important because 76 percent of all engineering changes are due to corrections of bad design and only 24 percent of engineering changes are due to improvements (Curley and Ryder 1992). It is imperative that the focus in performing the FMEA should be to identify *all* potential failures.

At this point, it must be emphasized that a major benefit of the design FMEA is identification and removal of potential failure modes caused by system and/or component interactions. These interactions also may involve human factors and must be reviewed thoroughly.

The relationship between the failure mode and the cause(s) is not linear or one-to-one. Do not be surprised if there are several if not many causes for one failure mode. (Sometimes a one-to-one relationship exists.) List as many causes as possible—all of them. These causes will be transferred to the process FMEA as potential failure modes.

Therefore, the more causes identified in the design FMEA, the easier the process FMEA becomes.

Examples of failure causes include

- Torque too high or low
- Wrong usage of fastener
- Hardness
- Viscosity too high or low
- Porosity

Note: If the effect of the failure is rated 8 through 10, special effort should be made to identify as many root causes as possible.

Occurrence (17). Occurrence (frequency) is the rating value corresponding to the estimated number of frequencies and/or cumulative number of failures that could occur for a given cause over the life of the design. To identify the frequency for each of the causes one may use reliability mathematics (which is beyond the scope of this book), expected frequencies, or a cumulative number of component failures (CNF) per 100 or 1000 components (CNF/100 or CNF/1000, respectively) over the design life of the component under study. Design life in the design FMEA is the component's durability target. The specific attribute of the target will be component dependent.

Another way to define the design life is the target (goal) period or useful life after which the component is discarded because it ceases to function as designed (normal wear). Thus, it is too expensive to repair.

If expected frequencies and/or cumulative number of failures cannot be estimated, it is acceptable for the design FMEA to examine similar or surrogate systems and/or components for similar information.

Generally, the design FMEA operates under the assumption of a single-point failure (in other words, if the component fails, the system fails). A single-point failure is defined as a component failure, which would cause the system failure and is not compensated by redundancy or an alternative method. For example, single pieces of hardware and heavily loaded cable runs that place a high degree of dependence on single components, usually can be avoided through the use of redundancy. In this case, the installation of duplicate cables into a heavily loaded area with terminals intermingled on one of the two cables could minimize service disruption in the event of a cable cut.

When occurrence/frequency is calculated it must be for every single cause of the failure. If it cannot be estimated, then the occurrence should be entered as 10. It must also be a consensus agreement of the entire team. A typical occurrence guideline is shown in Table 6.2.

Detection Method; Design Verification; Existing Control (18). A method (procedure), test, design review, or an engineering analysis. These are some of the first-level methods to detect a failure in the design or part (Blanchard and Lowery 1969). They can be very simple (in other words, brainstorming) or very technical and advanced (in other words, finite element analysis, design reviews, computer simulation, and laboratory tests). In either case, the focus is on the effectiveness of the control method/technique to catch the problem before it reaches the customer.

The objective is to detect a design deficiency as early as possible. That deficiency may be viewed as a weakness in the design to reveal, detect, or eliminate the problem from the design (Chien 1985). The idea of early detection in the design FMEA is to provide efficient design controls.

Because the design FMEA is done very early, it sometimes is difficult to assess the detection rating. In these cases one may use historical information, or similar types of information from similar components and/or systems. In some cases, it is possible to have no method, test, or technique to identify the failure. In that case, the entry in this column should state something like "None identified at this time."

Another way to focus on the detection is to use the brainstorming technique to identify new methods and tests as they apply to the task at hand. Two of the leading questions in the brainstorming process should be

- How can this failure be discovered?
- In what way can this failure be recognized?

Occurrence	Rank	Criteria	CNF/1000	Resolution
Almost impossible	1	Failure unlikely. History shows no failures.	<.00058	If the numerical value falls between two numbers *always* select the higher number. If the team has a disagreement in the ranking value the following may help. 1. If the disagreement is an adjacent category, average out the difference. For example, if one member says 5 and someone else says 6, the ranking in this case should be 6 (5 and 6 are adjacent categories. Therefore 5 + 6 = 11, 11/2 = 5.5 ≅ 6). 2. If the disagreement jumps one category, then consensus must be reached. Even with one person holding out, total consensus must be reached. No average, no majority. Everyone in that team must have ownership of the ranking. They may not agree 100 percent, but they can live with it.
Remote	2	Rare number of failures likely	.0068	
Very slight	3	Very few failures likely	.0063	
Slight	4	Few failures likely	.46	
Low	5	Occasional number of failures likely	2.7	
Medium	6	Medium number of failures likely	12.4	
Moderately high	7	Moderately high number of failures likely	46	
High	8	High number of failures likely	134	
Very high	9	Very high number of failures likely	316	
Almost certain	10	Failure almost certain. History of failures exists from previous or similar designs	>316	

Table 6.2 Occurrence guideline for design FMEA* (1–10 qualitative scale).

*All the above guidelines and rankings may be changed to reflect specific situations.

To answer such questions, a checklist may be helpful; however, some of the most effective ways to detect a failure in the design stage are

- Proven simulation techniques
- Mathematical modeling
- Prototype testing
- Design of experiments
- Design verification testing
- Specific product testing
- Tolerance stack-up studies
- Design review
- Material review

The majority of the items in detecting failures are quantifiable. The design review, however, is also an important tool that is used to review the appropriateness of the system and/or design. It can be quantifiable, but it can also be a qualitative and systematic methodology of questioning the design. A typical design review may include

- *Preliminary design review*—The purpose for the preliminary design review is to define and select a design approach to meet the functional requirements of the product. The result is a description of product features, production cost estimates, estimates of life use, and the description of the foreseeable environment of use. In this stage, probabilistic, reliability, and statistical modeling and testing may be required.
- *Intermediate design review*—The purpose of the intermediate design review is to determine whether the product will achieve its functional requirements at an acceptable level of safety, producibility, and profitability. In this stage, design trade-offs can be assessed, test results reviewed, safety margins examined, material selections evaluated, and tooling and manufacturing processes reviewed.
- *Final design review*—The purpose of the final design review is to review and approve the detailed design information necessary to manufacture the product.

In this stage, the completeness of the documentation is assessed. It provides a last check of the functions, features, producibility, compliance to the appropriate standards, operator misuse, profitability, and safety of the design before manufacturing the product.

Design review checklist—A typical checklist may consider the following (Bass 1991; Blanchard 1986; Ford 1989; Stamatis 1992):

Define product in its use environment

- What are the product's uses?
- What are the foreseeable environments of use?
- Describe the skill and capability of foreseeable users?

Identify safety and assess risk

- What are the hazards?
- Estimate the probability of occurrence and seriousness of resulting harm for each hazard

Evaluate alternatives

- What alternative design features or production techniques are available, including warnings and instructions, that can be expected to reduce or eliminate safety issues?
- Evaluate alternative designs by considering:
  –Characteristics and comparisons of different products
  –Other safety issues introduced by the alternative design
  –Their effect on the usefulness of the product
  –Their effect on the ultimate cost of the product

Appendix B includes an extensive checklist. It should be modified to reflect one's organization and requirements before it is used.

In the case of human errors a detection method may be developed with the following criteria based on MIL-STD-1472c and Woodson's (1981) (partial) list.

- Control and display integration
  –Controls and displays should be together.
  –Controls and displays with similar functions should be grouped.
  –Displays should reflect the proper direction for control movement.

- Visual displays
  - –Visual displays should provide only the information necessary for the operation of a system.
  - –Critical displays should be located in the operator's optimum viewing area.
  - –Indicator lights must follow certain standard color codes.

Figure size must be based on operator viewing distance.

- Audio displays
  - –Audio signals must be of a frequency and amplitude that can be heard in the operating environment.
  - –The frequency response and range must be appropriate for the working environment.
- Controls
  - –Control movement must relate to standard norms and to the direction of movement of the equipment which they control.
  - –Controls should be arranged in the sequence in which they are used.
  - –Control color coding standards should be followed.
  - –Controls should be coded by shape, color, size, and location.
- Labels/warnings
  - –Labels/warnings should be readable and understandable under foreseeable operating conditions by expected users.
  - –Labels and warning must (where appropriate)
    - –Identify the fact that there is a safety problem
    - –Indicate the level of safety problem
    - –Indicate the likelihood of the safety issue resulting in harm
    - –Explain how to avoid the safety issue
    - –Describe the consequences of the safety issue if the warning is not heeded
- Anthropometry
  - –Equipment should be designed to accommodate the full range of potential users.
- Operating area criteria
  - –Controls must be placed within the reach of the operator.

–Design criteria must exist for standing/seating operator.
–Design criteria must exist for operator's seat and control console.

- Environmental design criteria
  –Heating, ventilating, air conditioning, and humidity standards for safe and efficient job performance
  –Proper illumination
  –Proper noise levels
  –Proper vibration and acceleration limits
- Maintainability design criteria
  –Accessibility criteria
  –Weight limitations
- Checklists
  –Specific checklists for specific functions

Detection (19). Detection is a rating corresponding to the likelihood that the proposed design controls will detect a specific root cause of a failure mode before the part is released for production. To identify a detection rating one must estimate the ability for each of the controls identified in item 18 to detect the failure before it reaches the customer. In other words, are the controls identified in item 18 effective for the design?

If the ability of the controls to detect the failure is unknown or the detection cannot be estimated, then the detection rating should be 10. A typical detection guideline is shown in Table 6.3.

Risk Priority Number (RPN) (20). This number is the product of severity, occurrence, and detection. The RPN defines the priority of the failure. By themselves the RPNs have no value or meaning. They are used only to rank (define) the potential design deficiencies.

In the design FMEA one must always remember that the goal is to reduce the RPN, but in a specific way. The specific way is through a reduction in severity, occurrence, and detection.

The severity can be reduced only through a change in design. If that is attainable, then the failure is eliminated.

The occurrence can be reduced by improving engineering specifications and/or requirements with the intent of preventing causes or reducing their frequency.

Detection	Rank	Criteria	Resolution
Almost certain	1	Has the highest effectiveness in each applicable category	If the numerical value falls between two numbers *always* select the higher number. If the team has a disagreement in the ranking value the following may help. 1. If the disagreement is an adjacent category, average out the difference. For example, if one member says 5 and someone else says 6, the ranking in this case should be 6 (5 and 6 are adjacent categories. Therefore 5 + 6 = 11, 11/2 = 5.5 ≅ 6). 2. If the disagreement jumps one category, then consensus must be reached. Even with one person holding out total consensus must be reached. No average, no majority. Everyone in that team must have ownership of the ranking. They may not agree 100 percent, but they can live with it.
Very high	2	Has very high effectiveness	
High	3	Has high effectiveness	
Moderately high	4	Has moderately high effectiveness	
Medium	5	Has medium effectiveness	
Low	6	Has low effectiveness	
Slight	7	Has very low effectiveness	
Very slight	8	Has lowest effectiveness in each applicable category	
Remote	9	Is unproven, or unreliable, or effectiveness is unknown	
Almost impossible	10	No design technique available or known, and/or none is planned	

Table 6.3 Detection guideline for design FMEA* (1–10 qualitative scale).

*All the above guidelines and rankings may be changed to reflect specific situations.

The detection can be reduced by adding or improving the design evaluation technique or increasing sample size, and/or adding detection equipment. The result will be improvement in the ability to detect the failure before it reaches the customer.

Recommended Action (21). No FMEA should be done without a recommended action. The recommended action may be specific action(s) or it may be further studying. The idea of the recommended action in the design FMEA is to reduce the severity, occurrence, detection, or all of these elements. In essence the design FMEA is done to eliminate design deficiencies and therefore eliminate failures.

To facilitate this goal, the FMEA team must prioritize those failure modes with the highest RPN, the highest severity, the highest occurrence. Typical recommendations may be

- No action at this time
- Add build-in detection devices
- Provide alternatives to the design
- Add redundant subsystem

Responsible Area or Person and Completion Date (22). Identify the responsible person/area and the target completion date for the recommended action.

Action Taken (23). This is the follow-up. Just because something was recommended, does not mean that something was done. It is imperative that someone (usually the design engineer) will follow up on the recommendations to determine if indeed they have been addressed adequately, properly, and/or if they are in need of updating.

Note that all FMEAs are a living document and as such someone must be responsible to update them. Often the person who is responsible is the design engineer. She or he has the responsibility to make sure that the design FMEA is a living document and that it reflects the latest relevant information and actions.

After the action has been taken, the effective date or completion date with a brief description of the action should be entered.

Revised RPN (24). After the actions are incorporated in the design, the FMEA team should reevaluate the consequences of severity, occurrence, and detection. The results should be reviewed by the FMEA team, a new RPN must be calculated and the failures ranked. This process is repeated as needed until such time the FMEA team decides that all relevant information has been covered. If no actions are taken, these columns will remain blank.

Approval Signatures (25). Define the authority to carry out the FMEA. The names and titles will depend on the organization. Typical names may be those of the design manager, reliability manager, and engineering manager.

Concurrence Signatures (26). Define the responsibility of carrying out the completion and implementation of the FMEA. The names and titles will depend on the organization. Typical names may be those of the engineering, manufacturing, or quality assurance manager.

Sometimes a design FMEA is associated with a product FMEA. The method for the development and the rationale for the product FMEA is the same as that for the design. A pictorial overview of the product development and flow from the system to design to product is shown in Figures 6.3 and 6.4, respectively.

Recommended Team

A team is necessary to perform a design FMEA. The team makeup should be five to nine individuals with a multidisciplined and multifunctional background. In addition, all members should have ownership of the problem (Stamatis 1992). A typical team may include the following:

- System engineer (mandatory)
- Reliability engineer
- Test engineer
- Material engineer
- Process engineer (mandatory)
- Marketing representative
- Design engineer (mandatory)

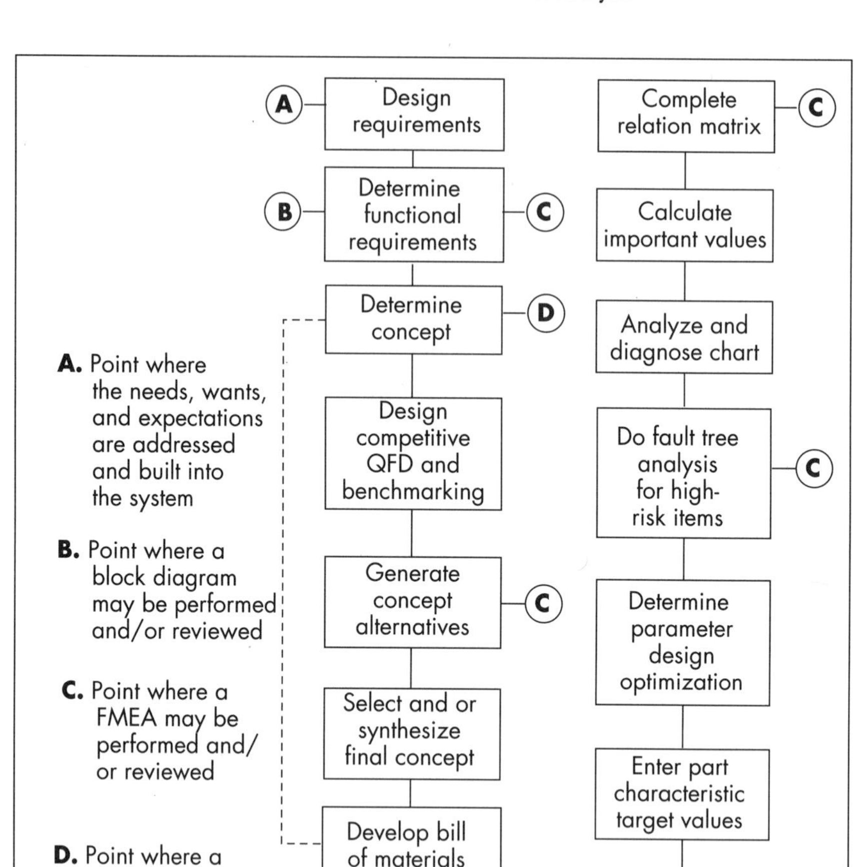

Figure 6.3 Part deployment.

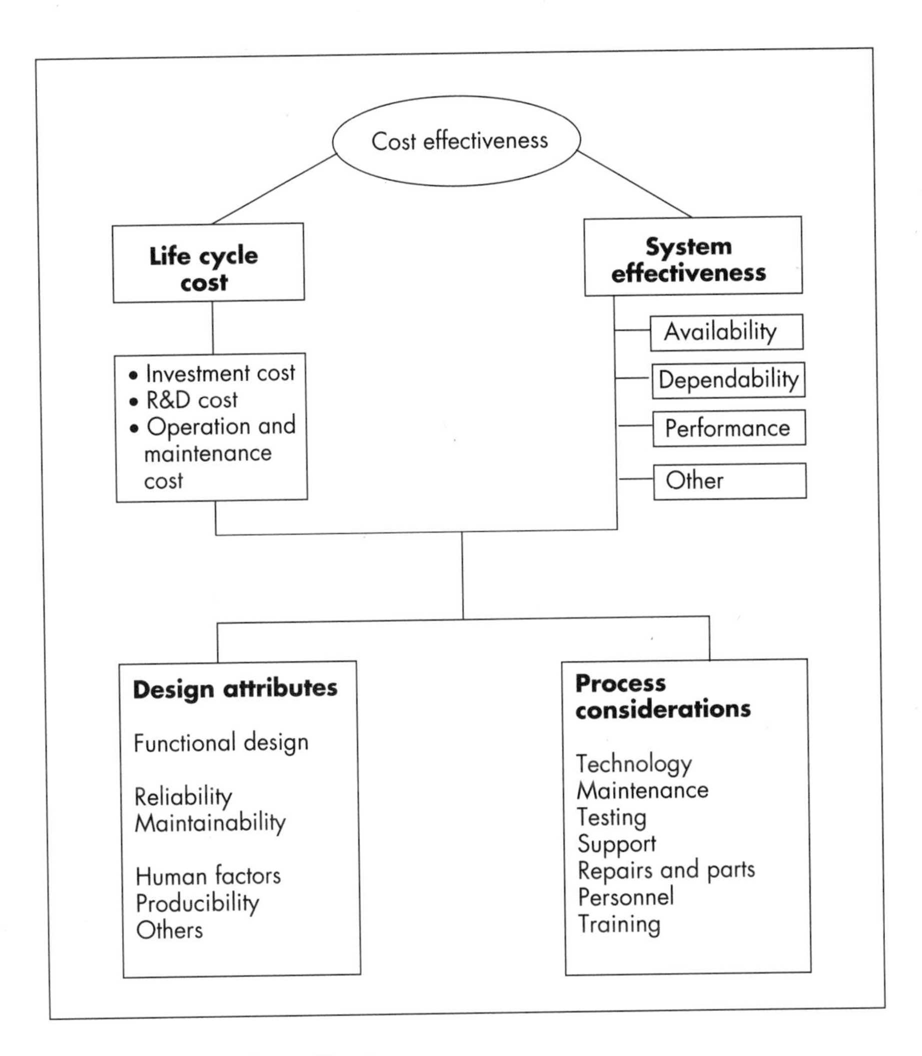

Figure 6.4 Cost effectiveness.

Other recommended participants may include

- Quality engineer
- Process engineer
- Material engineer
- Field service engineer
- R&D representative
- Tooling engineer
- Product engineer

Note that there is no such thing as *the* team. A team is made to reflect the needs and requirements that the problem and culture of the organization requires.

References

Bass, L. 1991. Cumulative supplement to *Products liability: Design and manufacturing defects.* Colorado Springs, Colo.: Shepard's/McGraw-Hill.

Blanchard, B. S. 1986. *Logistics engineering and management.* 3d ed. Englewood Cliffs, N.J.: Prentice Hall.

Blanchard, B. S., and E. E. Lowery. 1969. *Maintainability—Principles and practices.* New York: McGraw-Hill.

Chien, J. 1985. Detailed tests show how well industrial local network performs. *Data Communications* 14 (August): 119–131.

Curley, J. J., and R. E. Ryder. 1992. Project management: Improving product development process. *Technology* (Engineering Society of Detroit) (October): 23–27.

Ford Motor Company. 1988. *Potential failure mode and effect analysis.* Dearborn, Mich.: Ford Motor Company.

———. 1989. *Potential failure mode and effect analysis.* Dearborn, Mich.: Ford Motor Company.

MIL-STD-1472C. May 2, 1981. Washington, D.C.: Department of Defense.

Slone, J. P. 1986. Broadband LANs. *Journal of Information Systems Management* (summer): 49.

Stamatis, D. H. 1992. *FMEA handbook.* Southgate, Mich.: Contemporary Consultants.

———. 1993. Value engineering: Maximizing value in specific areas. *Technology* (Engineering Society of Detroit) (April): 10–15.

Woodson, W. 1981. *Human factors design handbook.* New York: McGraw-Hill.

CHAPTER 7

Process FMEA

A process FMEA is a disciplined analysis/method of identifying potential or known failure modes and providing follow-up and corrective actions before the first production run occurs. A first production run is viewed as the run that produces a product or service for a specific customer with the intent of getting paid. This definition of the first run is very important because it excludes initial sample runs (ISR), trial runs, an occasional prototype run(s), and so on. The threshold of the first production run is important because up to that point modifying and/or changing the design is usually not a major event. At the point of the true first production, process, product, and procedure validation is defined. The customer has the important role of defining the process, product, procedure, and so forth. After that point, however, the customer becomes involved through the letter of deviation, waiver of change, or some other formal notification.

A process FMEA usually is accomplished through a series of steps to include labor, machine, method, material, measurement, and environment considerations. Of course, each of these components has its own components, which may react individually, in tandem, or as an interaction to create a failure. Because of this convolution, completing a process FMEA is more complicated and time-consuming than the system and/or design FMEAs.

The process FMEA is an evolutionary process (dynamic as opposed to static). It involves the application of various technologies and methods to produce an effective process output. The result is a defect-free product or it may be used as an input for the product, assembly, and/or the service FMEA.

The selection of appropriate technologies may include the customer's request, the utilization of existing system(s), standardized approaches and/or procedures currently known or proposed, results of directed research, results of the design FMEA, or a combination of all the above.

Effective process FMEA is realized basically through the design engineering process, product development, R&D, quality assurance, marketing, manufacturing, or a combination of all these entities (Blanchard 1986). Thus, the focus of the process FMEA is to *minimize production process failure effects on the process (system), regardless of what level FMEA is being performed.*

This can be realized through a specific definition of design specifications and a good understanding of what the process can do. For the understanding of design specifications see chapter 6. To understand the process, however, the following may be helpful.

Production (manufacturing) involves utilization of six components: labor, machine, method, material, measurement, and environment. The goal of these components is the production of an end item that meets or exceeds the safety and quality characteristics of the design documentation. An integral element of the process documentation should be the design FMEA. It is extremely difficult (if not impossible) to do a thorough process FMEA without completion (or at least some information) of a design FMEA (Stamatis 1992, 1993).

It is true, however, that it is difficult to evaluate the entire production process in the early stages—the initiation of production. In most cases, the reality is that the process evaluation develops over time. As such, the process FMEA becomes a living document (dynamic as opposed to static) to reflect the process' changes.

Generally, there are two basic types of process evaluation techniques that are utilized in the early stages.

1. Process capability studies. Such studies are used to determine the inherent capability of specific elements of the production processing. Examples include machine acceptance capability, process potential study (short-term capability), and long-term capability.

2. Mandatory process evaluation. As mentioned, it is difficult to evaluate all process parameters. Thus, each company establishes mandatory evaluation points for specific variables that are critical to the operation and/or the customer. They may be helped in this identification by

- Customer requirements
- Government regulations
- Internal engineering guidelines
- Design FMEA
- Industrial standards/guidelines
- Generally accepted practices
- Courts through product liability

Some of the evaluation points may be

- Certification of operators. Certification may be necessary for critical skills (in other words, boiler operators, welders).
- Tool proofing. Tools, jigs, and fixtures may be required to be validated.
- Critical process. Most critical processes as defined by safety, customers, or government regulations require evaluation and prior approval (in other words, practically all drug and medical device processes, heat treating).
- Test operation. Most complex testing operations require review and approval to ensure accuracy.

The goal, purpose, and/or objective of the process FMEA is to define, demonstrate, and maximize engineering solutions in response to quality, reliability, maintainability, cost, and productivity as defined by the design FMEA and the customer. The key in this definition is that one cannot emphasize one of the elements (quality, reliability, maintainability, cost, productivity) at the expense of the others. All of them must be satisfied at optimum so the process can be at maximum. The optimum for each of the elements is an operational definition and may be defined in any way that the organization views itself in the market. This optimum really defines niches in the market for differentiation of product and/or service.

To accomplish this objective the process FMEA must base its requirements on solid needs, wants, and expectations of the customer. As a general rule that information may be the result of a QFD (preferred), or an internal need for improvement, or the results of a design FMEA. In either case, one of the first steps in conducting the FMEA should be to include a feasibility study and/or a risk-benefit analysis directed toward defining a set of useful solutions to the problem(s) being addressed. The objective of this early (not definitive) stage is to maximize the system quality, reliability, cost, productivity, and maintainability, regardless of what level the FMEA is being performed. This can be accomplished through the following considerations.

1. Transform an operational need into a description of process performance parameters and as perfect as possible process configuration through the use of an interactive process of functional analysis, synthesis, optimization, definition, design, design reviews, test, and evaluation.
2. Integrate related technical parameters and ensure compatibility of all physical, functional, and program interfaces in a manner that optimizes the total process definition and manufacturing.
3. Integrate reliability, maintainability, engineering support, human factors, safety, security, structural integrity, producibility, and other related specialties into the total engineering effort.

The outcome of the process FMEA is a process (it may change with new or modified information) with a baseline configuration and functional specifications toward translating the established requirements into detailed qualitative and quantitative product and assembly or service characteristics. This change may cause a process FMEA to iterate the causes of failures. The flow of this iteration is shown in Figure 7.1.

Some of the generic concerns in a process FMEA follow.

General concerns

- Process operational requirements defined
- Effectiveness factors established
- Process maintenance concept defined

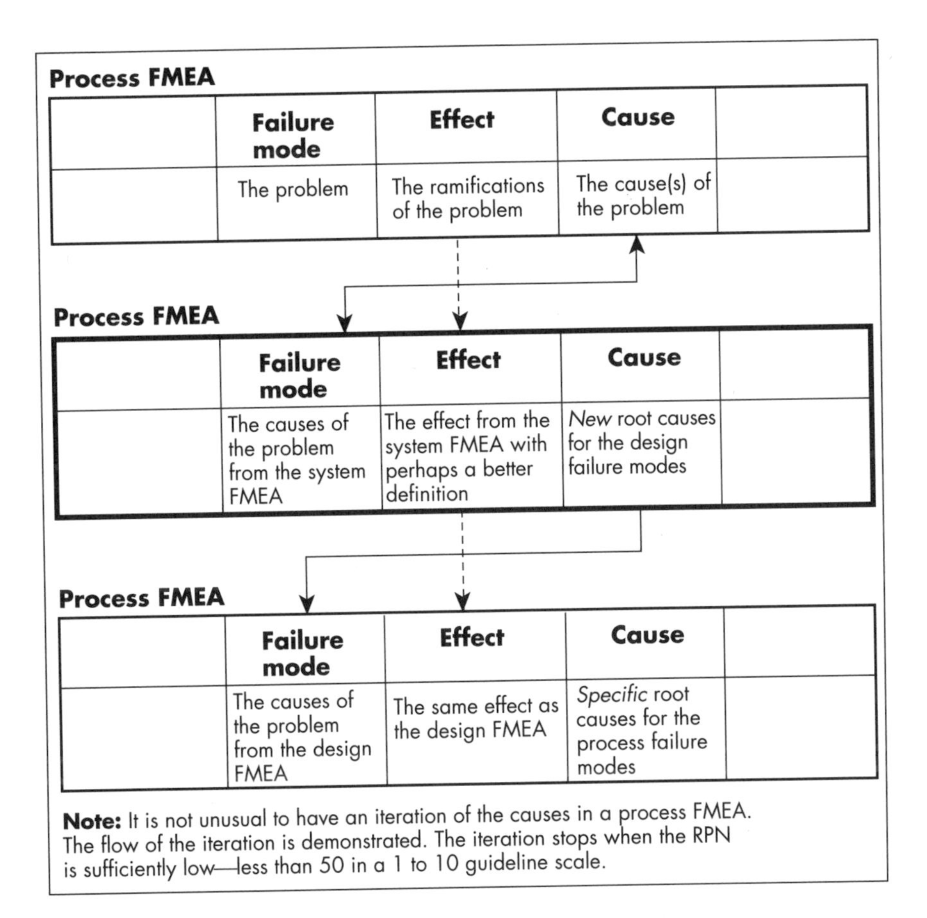

Process FMEA
Failure mode
Effect
Cause
The problem
The ramifications of the problem
The cause(s) of the problem
Process FMEA
Failure mode
Effect
Cause
The causes of the problem from the system FMEA
The effect from the system FMEA with perhaps a better definition
New root causes for the design failure modes
Process FMEA
Failure mode
Effect
Cause
The causes of the problem from the design FMEA
The same effect as the design FMEA
Specific root causes for the process failure modes
Note: It is not unusual to have an iteration of the causes in a process FMEA. The flow of the iteration is demonstrated. The iteration stops when the RPN is sufficiently low—less than 50 in a 1 to 10 guideline scale.

Figure 7.1 Relationship of a process FMEA in an iteration mode of failure identification.

Support elements

One must do a thorough investigation of support elements as to whether or not the requirements are known and/or can be optimized for

- Test and support equipment
- Personnel and training
- Repair and spare parts

Process features

- Standardization
- Test provisions
- Interchangeability
- Accessibility
- Controls
- Technical data, procedures
- Transportability
- Producibility
- Safety
- Reliability
- Software

Specific questions in the course of performing a process FMEA may be

1. What is the true performance and effectiveness of the process?
2. What does the product do and what are its intended uses?
3. What is the true effectiveness of the support capability?
4. Are the initially specified requirements appropriate for the process? Are they being met?
5. How does the process perform its function?
6. What raw materials and components are used in the process?
7. How, and under what conditions, does the process interface with other processes?
8. What by-products are created by the process or by the use of this process?
9. How is the process used, maintained, repaired, and disposed of at the end of its useful life?
10. What are the manufacturing steps in the production of the product?
11. What energy sources are involved and how?

12. Who will use or be in the vicinity of the process, and what are the capabilities and limitations of these individuals?
13. Is the process cost-effective?

Finally, when conducting a process FMEA, it is assumed that the design is the best it can be. If this assumption is not made, the FMEA team will perform the design and process FMEAs simultaneously and will move in a circular pattern not accomplishing its task. The only way to address the design FMEA in the process of conducting the process FMEA is when the root causes of the failure modes in the process are caused by the design specifications.

Step-by-Step Process FMEA Analysis

There are two requirements to perform a process FMEA. The first requirement is identification of the appropriate form. The second requirement is identification of the rating guidelines.

The form for the process FMEA is not universal. It is not standardized. Each company has its own form to reflect the needs of the organization and the concerns of the customer. In the automotive industry, however, efforts have been successful and as of July 1, 1993 there is a standardized form and procedure published by AIAG. (See Appendix E, Figure 62.)

This section introduces a form to illustrate the generally accepted items that should be addressed as part of a process FMEA. Appendix E includes additional process FMEAs that show the diversity that exists between industries. Remember, there is no such thing as *the* process FMEA form.

The rating guidelines also are not universal. They are not standardized. Each company's rating system reflects the needs of the organization, the product, and the concerns of the customer.

Generally, there are two ways that the rating guidelines can be formulated: qualitative and quantitative. In either case the numerical values can be from 1 to 5 or 1 to 10, with the 1 to 10 range being the most common. Remember, there is no such thing as *the* rating guideline for the process FMEA. Both kinds of guidelines will be shown.

Figure 7.2 shows the most common process FMEA form. The form is divided into three parts. The first part, items 1 through 9 reflect the introduction of the form. None of the items are mandatory; however, they do add information to the process FMEA and provide essential information that may be needed in the course of writing the FMEA.

The second part of the form contains items 10 through 23. These items are the mandatory items for any process FMEA. The order of the columns may be changed, and more columns may be added but none of the columns presented may be removed. Items 10 through 23 may be viewed as the body of the process FMEA.

The third part of the form, items 24 and 25 are the signatures. Although they are not mandatory, they do reflect the authority and responsibility of the team to undertake the project of writing the system FMEA. The signatures may be viewed as the closure of the FMEA. All numbers in parentheses are coded numbers for the discussion of the form.

Process Identification (1). Identify the process or assembly name or reference numbers or process codes as appropriate.

Part Name (1A). On special occasions the part name or number is identified. Often the latest engineering drawing number is identified.

Manufacturing and/or Design Responsibility (2). Name the primary responsibility for the process (machine, material, and so on). Enter the name of the activity responsible for the design of the system, assembly, and even the component, if appropriate. This is used strictly for a cross-reference point to the design and/or assembly.

Person responsibility (2A). Sometimes it is necessary to name the person who is responsible for the process FMEA.

Involvement of Other Areas (3). Name other persons or activities (within the organization) that are affected or are involved in the manufacturing or assembly of the part.

Involvement of Suppliers or Others (4). Identify other people, suppliers, and/or plants (outside the organization) that affect the design and are involved in the part's design, manufacturing, or assembly.

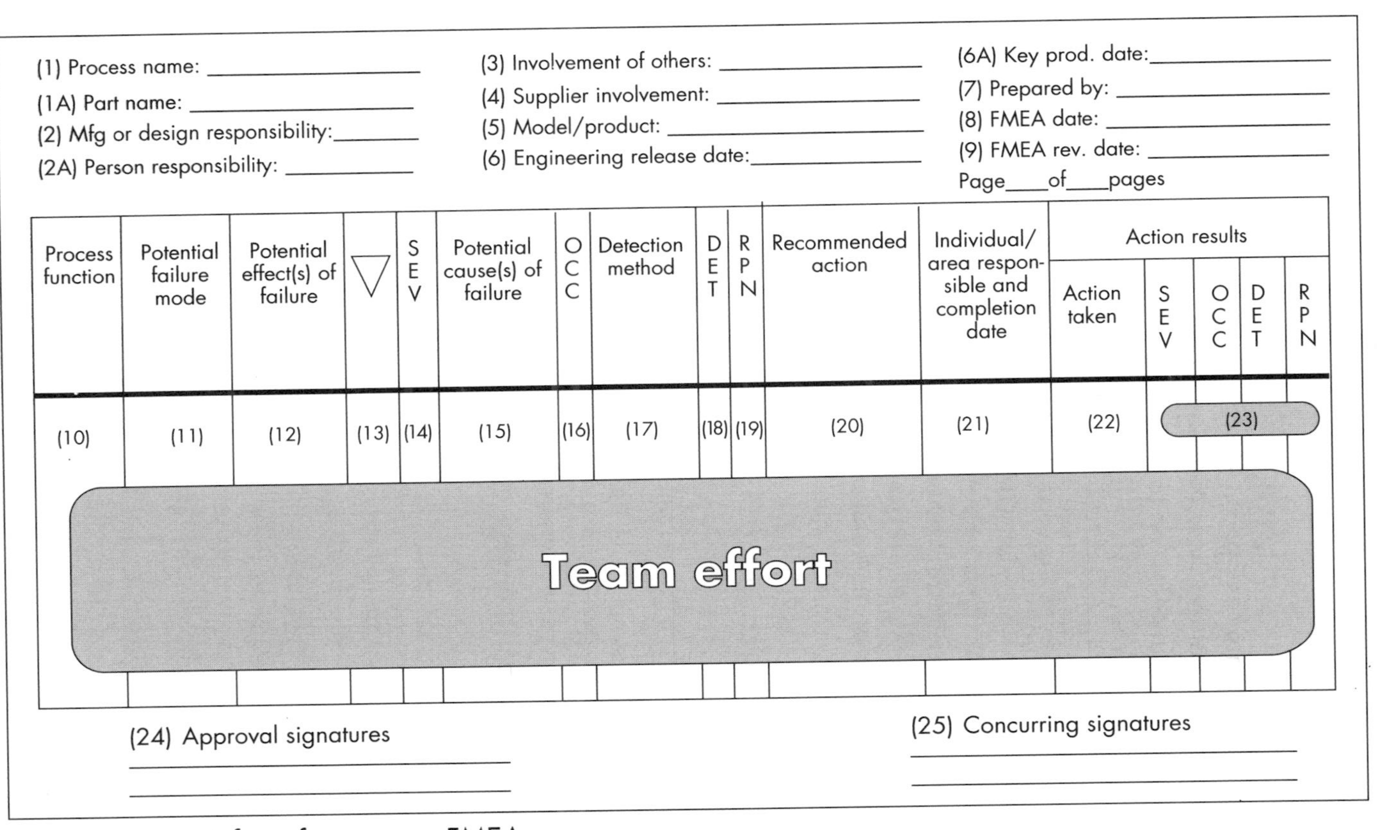

(1) Process name: ______
(1A) Part name: ______
(2) Mfg or design responsibility: ______
(2A) Person responsibility: ______

(3) Involvement of others: ______
(4) Supplier involvement: ______
(5) Model/product: ______
(6) Engineering release date: ______

(6A) Key prod. date: ______
(7) Prepared by: ______
(8) FMEA date: ______
(9) FMEA rev. date: ______
Page ____ of ____ pages

Process function	Potential failure mode	Potential effect(s) of failure	▽	SEV	Potential cause(s) of failure	OCC	Detection method	DET	RPN	Recommended action	Individual/ area respon- sible and completion date	Action results				
												Action taken	SEV	OCC	DET	RPN
(10)	(11)	(12)	(13)	(14)	(15)	(16)	(17)	(18)	(19)	(20)	(21)	(22)	(23)			

(24) Approval signatures

(25) Concurring signatures

Figure 7.2 A form for process FMEA.

Model or Product (5). Name the model and/or the product using the process (manufacturing and/or assembly).

Engineering Release Date (6). Identify the date (Mo–Day–Yr) that the product is scheduled to be released.

Key Production Date (6A). Identify milestone dates (Mo–Day–Yr), such as those for specific reviews, date for initial sample report (ISR), and so on.

Prepared by (7). Generally, the name of the process engineer responsible for the FMEA is recorded. Sometimes, additional information, with an attachment, also is recorded such as

- Telephone number of the system design engineer
- Address of the system design engineer
- Organizational activity (in other words, division, department, and so on)
- Team members (name, telephone, address, and so forth)

FMEA Date—Original (8). Record the date (Mo–Day–Yr) of the initiation of the process FMEA.

FMEA Date—Revision (9). Record the date (Mo–Day–Yr) of the latest revision.

Process Function (10). The engineer writes the process intent, purpose, goal, or objective of the process. The process function must be derived from the design specifications and the *what is* the process now. Not *what should* the process be.

Generally, the process function is identified with a process flow diagram followed by a task analysis. The process flow diagram will identify sequentially the flow of operations among personnel and the interaction among personnel and major equipment components.

Conversely, the task analysis will serve as the basis of workload analysis by defining the specific sequence of tasks that each person in the process must perform. This step is important because inefficient distribution of workload can result in increased human error and subsequent safety or critical problems (Bass 1991).

Task analysis and task identification are not the same nor can they be used interchangeably. A task analysis defines

- What initiates the task
- Equipment used to perform the task
- Human response
- Task feedback
- Characteristics of the task output, including performance requirements

Task identification defines the work through one or more of the following techniques.

- System analysis
  –Functional flow block diagrams
  –Decision/action diagrams
  –Functional allocation
- Time lines
- Time and motion analysis
- Human reliability analysis
- Operational sequence diagram

For the process function to be effective it must be identified in detail through a statement that is concise, exact, and easy to understand (no jargon). In the statement that is used to describe the function, that function should be described in specific terms. To facilitate this, the FMEA writer should try to think of active verbs and appropriate nouns. The active verbs define performance and performance defines function. The combination of the active verb with the noun defines the relationship; consequently, the identification process becomes easier. Examples of functions include

- Provide bonded unit
- Provide cured subassembly
- Facilitate manufacturing
- Provide vibration damping

Another way to facilitate the formation of the function is to ask questions such as "What is the purpose, objective, function, goal of the process?" "What is the process supposed to do?" If there is more than one purpose or function it is imperative that they should all be identified separately because they probably will have different potential failure modes.

Potential Failure Mode (11). The problem. The concern. The opportunity to improve. The failure. The reject. The defect. When one thinks of the potential failure mode one must think of the loss of a process function—a specific failure. The more specific one is, the better opportunity there will be to identify the effects and causes of the failure. Process failures occur when a product does not adequately protect against risks of injury, fails to perform intended functions safely (as defined by engineering specifications), or fails to minimize avoidable consequences in the event of an accident.

Generally, there are four categories of process failure modes.

- Testing and/or inspection
  –Accept or reject bad or good parts, respectively
- Assembly
  –Relational concerns, misoriented parts and/or missing parts
- Receiving inspection
  –Why is the received part rejected?
- Manufacturing
  –Visual characteristics
  –Dimensional characteristics
  –Design characteristics

For each process function identified in item 10 one must list the corresponding failure of the function. There can be more than one failure from one function. To help identify the potential failure mode one may think of the negative or loss of the function.

Examples include

- Fails to open
- Part leaking
- Broken

- No pressure
- Cannot control speed
- Hole is not round (eccentric)
- Part undersized, oversized, porous, damaged

Another way to identify the failure mode anticipated is by asking the following questions (partial list).

- How could this process fail to complete its intended function?
- Why could this part be rejected at this operation?
- What does the customer find unacceptable?
- How would the part not conform to specifications at this operation?

The emphasis is on the engineer who must try to anticipate how the part being considered could possibly fail, not whether or not it will fail. Another way of identifying failure modes is through a review of warranty records, historical documentation, customer complaints, design FMEA, and any other applicable documentation.

Potential Effect(s) of Failure (12). A potential effect of the failure is the consequence of its failure on the next process, operation, product, customer, and/or government regulations. The questions usually asked are: "What does the customer experience as a result of the failure mode described?" or "What happens or what is (are) the ramification(s) of this problem or failure?" The consequences may be to the design itself, the product, the customer, and/or government regulations. Quite often, the failure effect is evaluated from a customer's perspective or experiences.

To identify the potential effects, some of the documents one may review are

- Historical data
- Warranty documents
- Customer complaints
- Field service data
- Reliability data

- Feasibility studies
- Similar current or past FMEAs (both process and design)

No matter how the potential effect(s) is (are) identified, the ramifications of the loss to the process function must be determined. Consideration must be given to the process itself, other processes, the product, safety, government regulations, machines and equipment, and the customer (both the next and the ultimate). If safety considerations may be an issue, this is the column where the appropriate notation should be made. Examples of potential effect of failure may be

- Next process: fails to open
- Subsequent operation: cannot position part correctly
- Other operation(s): none
- Part: part function incomplete
- Product: poor performance
- Customer: complete dissatisfaction; product incomplete
- Government: may not comply with STD-XXX

Note: A special consideration for the effects of the failure is that the process engineer *must* interface with the design engineer to correctly describe the effect(s) of a potential process failure on the component, process, or assembly (Bass 1991; Blanchard 1986).

Critical Characteristics (13). Critical characteristics usually are associated with design FMEAs because the hardware begins to be formalized in the design stage. In the process FMEA, however, the critical characteristics become of paramount importance because they define the process requirements, sequences, tooling, and anything that can affect the customer or government regulations (Chrysler 1986; Ford 1988, 1989, 1992; General Motors 1988).

The critical characteristic column applies only when compliance with the government regulations, safety, and engineering specifications for the product and/or process is of concern.

The identification of the criticality or significance in the process FMEA is only to designate special controls for the process, assembly, and/or service FMEA. From here they are transferred to the control plan.

Examples of possible critical items may be

- Dimensions
- Specifications
- Tests
- Processes
- Tooling
- Usage

Critical characteristics are identified when

- Process requirements can affect safety
- Process requirements can affect compliance with government regulations
- Process requirements are necessary for special actions/controls

The entry to this column is a "Y" for yes, or "N" for no, or a notation symbol (in other words, inverted delta). Its purpose is to flag a potential critical characteristic which may or may not exist. A good indication of criticality is when severity is rated 9 or 10 with occurrence and detection higher than 3.

Severity of Effect (14). Severity is a rating indicating the seriousness of the effect of the potential process failure mode. The severity always applies to the effect of a failure mode. In fact, there is a direct correlation between effect and severity. For example, if the effect is critical, the severity is high. On the other hand, if the effect is not critical, the severity is very low.

The severity is reviewed from the perspective of the system, design itself, other systems, the product, the customer, and/or the government regulations. For evaluation purposes there usually is a rating table that reflects the issues of the organization in conjunction with the customer and/or the government regulations. An example of such rating may be seen in Table 7.1.

Rank			Resolution
1	Minor: Unreasonable to expect that the minor nature of this failure would cause any real effect on the product and/or service. Customer will probably not even notice the failure.	Unreasonable to expect that the minor nature of the failure would cause any noticeable effect on the product and/or the service. Customer most likely will not be able to detect the failure.	If the numerical value falls between two numbers *always* select the higher number. If the team has a disagreement in the ranking value the following may help. 1. If the disagreement is an adjacent category, average out the difference. For example, if one member says 2 and someone else says 6, the ranking in this case should be 4 (2 and 6 are adjacent categories. Therefore 2 + 6 = 8, 8/2 = 4). 2. If the disagreement jumps one category, then consensus must be reached. Even with one person holding out, total consensus must be reached. No average, no majority. Everyone in that team must have ownership of the ranking. They may not agree 100 percent, but they can live with it.
2–3	Low: Low severity ranking due to nature of failure causing only a slight customer annoyance. Customer probably will notice a slight deterioration of the product and/or service, a slight inconvenience in the next process, or minor rework action.	Low severity ranking due to a slight annoyance of the failure. Customer probably will notice a very minor deterioration of the product and/or service.	
4–6	Moderate: Moderate ranking because failure causes some dissatisfaction. Customer is made uncomfortable or is annoyed by the failure. May cause the use of unscheduled repairs and/or damage to equipment.	Moderate failure causes customer dissatisfaction. Customer is made uncomfortable and/or is annoyed by the failure. Some degradation of performance is noticeable.	

Table 7.1 Severity process and/or service guidelines.*

*All the above guidelines and rankings may be changed to reflect specific situations.

Rank		Resolution
7–8 High: High degree of customer dissatisfaction due to the nature of the failure such as an inoperable product or inoperative convenience. Does not involve safety issues or government regulations. May cause disruptions to subsequent processes and/or services.	High degree of customer dissatisfaction due to the nature of the failure. No safety or government regulations issues.	If the numerical value falls between two numbers *always* select the higher number. If the team has a disagreement in the ranking value the following may help. 1. If the disagreement is an adjacent category, average out the difference. For example, if one member says 2 and someone else says 6, the ranking in this case should be 4 (2 and 6 are adjacent categories. Therefore 2 + 6 = 8, 8/2 = 4). 2. If the disagreement jumps one category, then consensus must be reached. Even with one person holding out total consensus must be reached. No average, no majority. Everyone in that team must have ownership of the ranking. They may not agree 100 percent, but they can live with it.
9–10 Very high: Very high severity is when the failure affects safety and involves non-compliance with government regulations. In this scale 9–10 is reserved only for safety and government compliance requirements. All other rankings may be used as they seem applicable.	Very high severity ranking when safety issues are involved or compliance to government regulations is ignored.	

Table 7.1 (continued)

*All the above guidelines and rankings may be changed to reflect specific situations.

In the process FMEA the severity rating should be based on the worst effect of the failure mode. When complete, rank the failure modes on the basis of the severity of their effects. At this point the FMEA is identical to the FMCA.

Potential Cause(s) of Failure (15). The cause of a process failure mode is the process *deficiency* that results in the failure mode. It must be emphasized repeatedly that when one focuses on the cause(s) one must look at the *root cause,* not the symptom of the failure.

To do a good job of proper potential cause(s) of failure identification, one must understand both the design and process and ask the appropriate questions. Specificity is essential. The more one focuses on the root cause, the better one understands the failure. For example, "Would inadequate venting and gauging cause misruns, porosity, and leakers?" "Would inefficient die cooling cause die hot spots?" Some of the techniques that may be used are brainstorming, FTA, cause-and-effect analysis, analysis of the block diagram, and affinity charts.

The basic question is "In what way can this system fail to perform its intended function?" Another method is to ask five "whys" in a row. The rationale for this is that it progressively becomes a more difficult and thought-provoking assignment to identify the whys. The early questions are superficial, but the later ones are more substantive. Two other questions that may be asked are "What circumstances could cause the failure?" "How or why can the part fail to meet its engineering specifications?"

A failure mode can be caused by one or more individual components or by (partial list)

- Hardware failure due to inadequate product design
- Improper selection of component parts
- Improper use of processes
- Inadequate control procedures
- Failure to enforce process and quality controls
- Improper installation, maintenance
- Lack of safety devices, environmental factors
- Misuse, abuse

- Alteration of the product
- Improper operating instructions
- Human error
- Improper choice of materials
- Stress concentrations
- Fatigue
- Corrosion, galvanic corrosion, uniform attack, crevice corrosion
- Hydrogen damage, pitting, blistering
- Decarbonization, abrasion and wear, shock and vibration
- Interaction with other components
- Interaction with components of other systems
- Interaction with the government
- Interaction with the customer

At this point, it must be emphasized that a major benefit of the process FMEA is the identification of potential failure modes caused by process and/or component interactions. These interactions also may involve human factors and as such they must be reviewed thoroughly.

The relationship between the failure mode and the cause(s) is not linear or one-to-one. Do not be surprised if there are several if not many causes for one failure mode. (Sometimes a one-to-one relationship exists.) List as many causes as possible—all of them. These causes may be transferred to the product or assembly FMEA as potential failure modes. Therefore, the more causes identified in the process FMEA, the easier the product and/or assembly FMEA becomes.

Examples of failure causes include

- Torque too high or low
- Air pressure too high or low
- Cure time too short or long
- Tool worn
- Speed not constant
- Human error

Note: If the effect of the failure is rated 8 through 10, special effort should be made to identify as many root causes as possible.

Occurrence (16). Occurence is the rating value corresponding to the estimated number of frequencies and/or cumulative number of failures that could occur for a given cause over a given quantity of parts produced with the existing controls. (Usually, this is given to the process from the life of the design.) To identify the frequency for each of the causes one may use reliability mathematics (beyond the scope of this book), use the expected frequencies, or use a cumulative number of component failures (CNF) per 100 or 1000 components (CNF/100 or CNF/1000, respectively) over the design life of the component under study. Design life was explained in chapter 6.

Another way to help identify occurrences is the target (goal) period or useful life after which the component is discarded because it (1) ceases to function as designed (normal wear) and/or (2) is too expensive to repair.

If expected occurrences and/or cumulative number of failures cannot be estimated, it is acceptable for the process FMEA to study similar or surrogate processes and/or components for similar information.

Generally, the process FMEA operates under the assumption of single-point failure (in other words, if the component fails the system fails). A single-point failure is defined as a component failure that would cause the system failure and which is not compensated by either redundancy or an alternative method. For example, single pieces of hardware and heavily loaded cable runs that place a high degree of dependence on single components usually can be avoided through the use of redundancy. In this case, the installation of duplicate cables into a heavily loaded area (with terminals intermingled on one of the two cables), can minimize service disruption in the event of a cable cut.

When the occurrence/frequency is calculated, it is imperative that it must be for every single cause of the failure. If it cannot be estimated then the occurrence should be entered as 10. It also must be a consensus agreement of the entire team. There are a variety of ways to generate occurrence guidelines. A typical occurrence guideline is shown in Table 7.2.

Rank		Rank		Resolution
1	Remote probability of occurrence. Capability shows at least X-bar ± 3σ within specifications (1/10,000).	1	Failure is unlikely. CpK greater or equal to 1.67 (<1 in 10^6 or ~ ± 5σ)	If the numerical value falls between two numbers *always* select the higher number.
2–5	Low probability of occurrence. Process in statistical control. Capability shows at least X-bar ± 3σ within specifications (1/5000–1/500).	2	Very low: Process is in statistical control. Isolated failures exist. CpK is greater or equal to 1.33 (1 in 20,000 or ~ ± 4σ).	If the team has a disagreement in the ranking value the following may help.
6–7	Moderate probability of occurrence. Process in statistical control with occasional failures, but not in major proportions. Capability shows more than X-bar ± 2.5σ within specifications (1/20–1/200).	3	Low: Process in statistical control. Isolated failures occur sometimes. CpK is greater or equal to 1.00 (1 in 4,000 or ~ ± 3.5σ)	1. If the disagreement is an adjacent category, average out the difference. For example, if one member says 2 and someone else says 6, the ranking in this case should be 4 (2 and 6 are adjacent categories. Therefore 2 + 6 = 8, 8/2 = 4).
8–9	High probability of occurrence. Process in statistical control with failures often occurring. Capability shows X-bar ± 1.5σ (1/100–1/20).	4–6	Moderate: Process in statistical control with occasional failures but not in major proportions. CpK is less or equal to 1.00 (1 in 1,000 to 1 in 80 or ~ ± 3σ).	2. If the disagreement jumps one category, then consensus must be reached. Even with one person holding out total consensus must be reached. No average, no majority. Everyone in that team must have ownership of the ranking. They may not agree 100 percent, but they can live with it.
10	Very high probability of occurrence. Failure is almost certain. (1/10+).	7–8	High: Process not in statistical control. Have failures often (1/40 to 1/20).	
		9–10	Very high: Failures are inevitable	

Note: To use a criteria scale such as this, one must have a substantial amount of data to support statistical control and CpK values. This is a very powerful scale if one has the data; if not, do not try to generate the data to support the scale. Use a theoretical scale which is more qualitative but through the synergy of the team becomes just as powerful.

Table 7.2 Occurrence process and/or service guideline.*

*All the above guidelines and rankings may be changed to reflect specific situations.

Occurrence ratings also could be selected based on

- FITS scale–1 FIT equals approximately 1 occurrence per 10^9 Hrs
- CpK–If variable data are available and the process is in statistical control
- Cumulative failure data–If attribute data are available
- Subjective criteria–If no data are available (the evaluation becomes very subjective)

For failures that typically exist in the semiconductor industry, it is not unusual to encounter instances where only one data point of a test is known. Such is the case in "so many device-hours of testing resulting in a certain number of failures at one temperature."

Eachus (1992) explains the procedure to follow in this case, by assuming (1) the Arrhenius equation and (2) an activation energy in lieu of any known value. Then use the Chi-square distribution to ascertain with a certain probability *F* that the failure rate is less than a certain value given device-hours of testing and number of failures.

Another option in the semiconductor industry (because failure rates are inherently low), is to use a scale expressed as percent per thousand hours or failures per billion device hours (FITS). FITS scale–1 FIT approximately equals 1 occurrence per 10^9 hrs.

Detection Method; Process Verification/Validation; Existing Control (17). A method (procedure), test, or an engineering analysis. These are some of the first-level methods to detect or prevent a failure in the process, part, or in subsequent operations, and/or the customer. They can be very simple (brainstorming, audits, sampling based on statistical techniques) or very technical and advanced (finite element analysis, military standards, computer simulation, and laboratory tests). In either case, the focus is on the effectiveness of the control method/technique to catch the problem before it reaches the customer.

The only controls for the process FMEA that should be considered are those that will contribute to the estimation of the detection rating. Controls intended to prevent or reduce the occurrence of the cause of the failure should be considered when estimating the occurrence rating.

The objective is to detect a process deficiency as early as possible. That deficiency may be viewed as a weakness in the process to reveal, detect, or eliminate the problem from the process (Chien 1985). The idea of early detection in the process FMEA is to provide efficient manufacturing and/or product controls.

Because the process FMEA is done very early, it is sometimes very difficult to assess the detection rating. In these cases one may use historical information or similar types of information from similar processes and/or components. In some cases, it is possible to have no method, test, or technique to identify the failure. In that case, the entry in this column should state something like "None identified at this time."

Another way of focusing on the detection is to use the brainstorming technique to identify new methods and tests as they apply to the task at hand. Two of the leading questions in the brainstorming process should be

- How can this failure be discovered?
- In what way can this failure be recognized?

Some of the most effective ways to detect a failure are

- Proven simulation techniques
- Mathematical modeling
- Prototype testing
- Design of experiments
- Process verification testing
- Specific product testing
- Tolerance stack-up studies

Typical controls may include

- Probabilistic, reliability, and statistical modeling and testing as required.
- Reviewing test results, examining safety margins, evaluating material selections, and auditing tooling and manufacturing processes.

- Checklists for completeness of the documentation. A checklist may provide a last check of the functions, features, producibility, compliance to the appropriate standards, operator misuse, profitability, and safety of the manufacturing process.

A typical checklist may include the following.

- Define product in its use environment.
  –What are the product's uses?
  –What are the foreseeable environments of use?
  –Describe the skill and capability of foreseeable users.
- Identify safety and assess risk.
  –What are the hazards?
  –Estimate the probability of occurrence and seriousness of resulting harm for each hazard.
- Evaluate alternatives.
  –What alternative process features or production techniques are available, including warnings and instructions, that can be expected to reduce or eliminate safety issues?
  –Evaluate alternative process/product by considering the following:
    a. Characteristics and comparisons of different products
    b. Other safety issues that may be introduced by the alternative process
    c. Their effect on the usefulness of the product
    d. Their effect on the ultimate cost of the product

In the case of human errors a detection method may be developed based on MIL-STD-1472c and Woodson's (1981) list with the following criteria (partial list).

- Control and display integration
  –Controls and displays should be together.
  –Controls and displays with similar functions should be grouped.
  –Displays should reflect the proper direction for control movement.

- Visual displays
  - –Visual displays should provide only the information necessary for the operation of a system.
  - –Critical displays should be located in the operator's optimum viewing area.
  - –Indicator lights must follow certain standard color codes.
  - –Figure size must be based on operator viewing distance.
- Audio displays
  - –Audio signals must be of a frequency and amplitude that can be heard in the operating environment.
  - –The frequency response and range must be appropriate for the working environment.
- Controls
  - –Control movements must relate to standard norms and to the direction of movement of the equipment that they control.
  - –Controls should be arranged in the sequence in which they are used.
  - –Control color coding standards should be followed.
  - –Controls should be coded by shape, color, size, and location.
- Labels/warnings
  - –Labels/warnings should be readable and understandable under foreseeable operating conditions by the expected users.
  - –Labels and warning must, where appropriate,
    - –Identify the fact that there is a safety problem.
    - –Indicate the level of safety problem.
    - –Indicate the likelihood of the safety issue resulting in harm.
    - –Explain how to avoid the safety issue.
    - –Describe the consequences of the safety issue if the warning is not heeded.
- Anthropometry
  - –Equipment should be designed to accommodate the full range of potential users.
- Operating area criteria
  - –Controls must be placed within the reach of the operator.
  - –Design criteria must exist for standing/seating operator.

–Design criteria must exist for operator's seat and control console.

- Environmental process criteria
  –Heating, ventilating, air conditioning, and humidity standards for safe and efficient job performance
  –Proper illumination
  –Proper noise levels
  –Proper vibration and acceleration limits
- Maintainability process criteria
  –Accessibility criteria
  –Weight limitations
- Checklists
  –Specific checklists for specific functions

Detection (18). Detection is a rating corresponding to the likelihood that the current process controls will detect a specific root cause of a failure mode before the part leaves the manufacturing area. To identify a detection rating one must estimate the ability for each of the controls identified in item 17 to detect the failure before it reaches the customer. The assumption here is that the failure has occurred.

In addressing detection issues in the process FMEA, three items are very important.

1. Do not make the assumption that the detection should be low, just because the occurrence is low. The two ratings may or may not be correlated with each other for this particular item.
2. If 100 percent automatic gauging is listed as a control (for example, x-ray gauging in the steel industry) or 100 percent voltage output in motor testing (for example, in automotive and computer industry) the FMEA team must consider the effectiveness based on
   - Condition of the gauge
   - Condition of the testing equipment
   - Calibration of the gauge and testing equipment
   - Variation of gauge and testing equipment (based on repeatability and reproducibility study—R&R)
   - Likelihood that the system will fail or be bypassed

3. If 100 percent visual (as opposed to automatic, for example, process controller, brush recorders, artificial vision, and so on) inspection is listed, the FMEA team must consider the effectiveness based on
   - One hundred percent visual inspection is only 79 to 100 percent effective depending on inspector and conditions of inspection.
   - Who may perform the inspections? How is the consistency of evaluation going to be monitored?
   - The nature of the failure. Is the failure obscure, where a very high level of inspection ability is required–either through training and/or experience, or is the failure so obvious that anyone can identify it?

If the ability of the controls to detect the failure is unknown or the detection cannot be estimated, then the detection rating should be 10. A typical detection guideline is shown in Table 7.3.

Risk Priority Number (RPN) (19). This number is the product of severity, occurrence, and detection. The RPN defines the priority of the failure. By themselves the RPNs have no value or meaning. They are used only to rank (define) the potential process deficiencies.

In the process FMEA one must always remember that the goal is to reduce the RPN, but in a specific way. The specific way is through a reduction in

- Severity (if design actions have been taken)
- Occurrence
- Detection

The severity can be reduced only through a change in design. If that is attainable, then the failure is eliminated.

The occurrence can be reduced by improving engineering specifications and/or requirements in the process with the intent of preventing causes or reducing their frequency. The detection can be reduced by adding or improving evaluation techniques or increasing sample size, and/or adding detection equipment. The result will be improvement in the ability to detect the failure before it reaches the customer.

Rank			Resolution
1	Very high: Controls almost certainly will detect the existence of a defect.	Remote likelihood that the product or service will be delivered (1/10,000). The defect is functionally obvious and readily detected. Detection reliability at least 99.99 percent.	If the numerical value falls between two numbers *always* select the higher number. If the team has a disagreement in the ranking value the following may help. 1. If the disagreement is an adjacent category, average out the difference. For example, if one member says 2 and someone else says 6, the ranking in this case should be 4 (2 and 6 are adjacent categories. Therefore 2 + 6 = 8, 8/2 = 4). 2. If the disagreement jumps one category, then consensus must be reached. Even with one person holding out, total consensus must be reached. No average, no majority. Everyone in that team must have ownership of the ranking. They may not agree 100 percent, but they can live with it.
2–5	High: Controls have a good chance of detecting the existence of a failure.	Low likelihood that the product would be delivered with the defect. The defect is obvious (1/5000–1/500). Detection reliability at least 99.80 percent.	
6–8	Moderate: Controls may detect the existence of a defect.	Moderate likelihood that the product will be delivered with the defect. The defect is easily identified (1/200–1/50). Detection reliability at least 98.00 percent.	
9	Low: Controls more likely will not detect the existence of a defect.	High likelihood that the product would be delivered with the defect. The defect is subtle (1/20). Detection reliability greater than 90 percent.	
10	Very low: Controls very likely will not detect the existence of a defect.	Very high likelihood that the product and/or service will be delivered with the defect. Item is usually not checked or not checkable. Quite often the defect is latent and would not appear during the process or service (1/10+). Detection reliability 90 percent or less.	

Table 7.3 Detection process and/or service guideline.*

*All the above guidelines and rankings may be changed to reflect specific situations.

Recommended Action (20). No FMEA should be done without a recommended action. The recommended action may be specific action(s) or it may be further studying. The idea of the recommended action in the design FMEA is to reduce the severity, occurrence, detection, or all of these actions. In essence, the design FMEA is performed to eliminate design deficiencies and therefore eliminate failures.

To facilitate this goal the FMEA team must prioritize those failure modes with the highest RPN, the highest severity, the highest occurrence. Typical recommendations may be

- No action at this time
- Add built-in detection devices
- Provide alternatives to the design
- Add redundant subsystem

Responsible Area or Person and Completion Date (21). Identify the responsible person/area and the target completion date for the recommended action.

Action Taken (22). This is the follow-up. Just because something was recommended, does not mean that something was done. It is imperative that someone (usually the process engineer) will follow up on the recommendations to see if they have been addressed adequately, properly, and/or if they are in need of updating.

Note that all FMEAs are living documents and as such someone must be responsible to update them. Often the person who is responsible is the process engineer. That person has the responsibility to make sure that the process FMEA is a living document and reflects the latest relevant information and actions.

After the action has been taken, the effective date or completion date with a brief description of the action should be entered.

Revised RPN (23). After the actions are incorporated in the process, the FMEA team should reevaluate the consequences of severity, occurrence, and detection. The results should be reviewed by the FMEA team and a new RPN calculated and the failures ranked. This process is repeated as needed until such time as the FMEA team decides that all relevant information has been covered. If no actions are taken, these columns will remain blank.

Generally, the anticipated changes with the process FMEA are in the area of occurrence and detection. The severity remains the same. For the severity to change, the following must take place.

- As part of the root cause analysis, it was identified that the failure was caused by a design issue.
- The recommended action was to change the design based on the findings of the cause analysis.
- The design changes were implemented as recommended or modified.

At this point, the result is that the ratings (occurrence, severity, and detection) may all change, or some will change, or none will change.

Approval Signatures (24). Define the authority to carry out the FMEA. The names and titles will depend on the organization. Typical names may be those of the design and engineering manager.

Concurrence Signatures (25). Define the responsibility of carrying out the completion and implementation of the FMEA. The names and titles depend on the organization. Typical names may be those of the plant manager, manufacturing manager, and quality assurance manager.

Recommended Team

To perform a process FMEA, a team is necessary. The team makeup should be five to nine individuals with multidisciplined and multifunctional backgrounds. In addition, all members should have ownership of the problem (Stamatis 1992). A typical team may include the following:

- Quality engineer
- Reliability engineer
- Tooling engineer

- Process engineer (mandatory)
- Design engineer (mandatory)
- Responsible operators from all shifts (mandatory)

Other recommended participants may be

- Marketing representatives
- Material engineer
- Field service engineer
- Product engineer

Note that there is no such thing as *the* team. A team is made to reflect the needs and requirements that the problem and culture of the organization requires.

References

Bass, L. 1991. Cumulative supplement to *Products liability: Design and manufacturing defects.* Colorado Springs, Colo.: Shepard's/McGraw-Hill.

Blanchard, B. S. 1986. *Logistics engineering and management.* 3d ed. Englewood Cliffs, N.J.: Prentice Hall.

Blanchard, B. S., and E. E. Lowery. 1969. *Maintainability—Principles and practices.* New York: McGraw-Hill.

Chien, J. 1985. Detailed tests show how well industrial local network performs. *Data Communications* 14 (August): 119–131.

Chrysler Motors. 1986. Design feasibility and reliability assurance. In *FMEA.* Highland Park, Mich.: Chrysler Motors Engineering Office.

Eachus, J. 1982. Failure analysis in brief. In *Reliability and quality handbook,* by Motorola. Phoenix: Motorola Semiconductor Products Sector.

Ford Motor Company. 1988. *Potential failure mode and effect analysis.* Dearborn, Mich.: Ford Motor Company.

———. 1989. *Potential failure mode and effect analysis.* Dearborn, Mich.: Ford Motor Company.

——. 1992. *FMEA handbook.* Dearborn, Mich.: Ford Motor Company, Engineering Materials and Standards.

General Motors. 1988. *FMEA reference manual.* Detroit, Mich.: General Motors Corporation, Reliability and Technology Department.

MIL-STD-1472C. May 2, 1981. Washington, D.C.: Department of Defense.

Stamatis, D. H. 1992. *FMEA handbook.* Southgate, Mich.: Contemporary Consultants.

———. 1993. Value engineering: Maximizing value in specific areas. *Technology* (Engineering Society of Detroit) (April): 10–15.

Woodson, W. 1981. *Human factors design handbook.* New York: McGraw-Hill.

CHAPTER 8

Service FMEA

A service FMEA is a disciplined analysis/method of identifying potential or known failure modes and providing follow-up and corrective actions before the actual (first) service. A first service run is viewed as the act (service) that is performed for a specific customer as part of the everyday operation. This definition of the first service is important because it excludes trial and training runs. The threshold of the first service run is important, because up to that point, to modify and/or change the service generally is not a major event. At the point of the true first service, process and procedure validation is defined and the customer has a very important role in defining the service, process, product, procedure, and so on. After that point, however, the customer gets involved through the complaint letter, adjustment of services, or some other kind of formal notification, or perhaps discontinuance of the service due to dissatisfaction.

A service FMEA usually is accomplished through a series of interactions that include labor, machine, method, material, measurement and environment considerations. Of course, each one of these components has its own parts, which may react individually, or in tandem, or as an interaction, to create a failure. Because of this convolution, to perform a service FMEA is complicated and time-consuming. Often an iteration of the service is required to identify the root cause of the failure. This is shown in Figure 8.1.

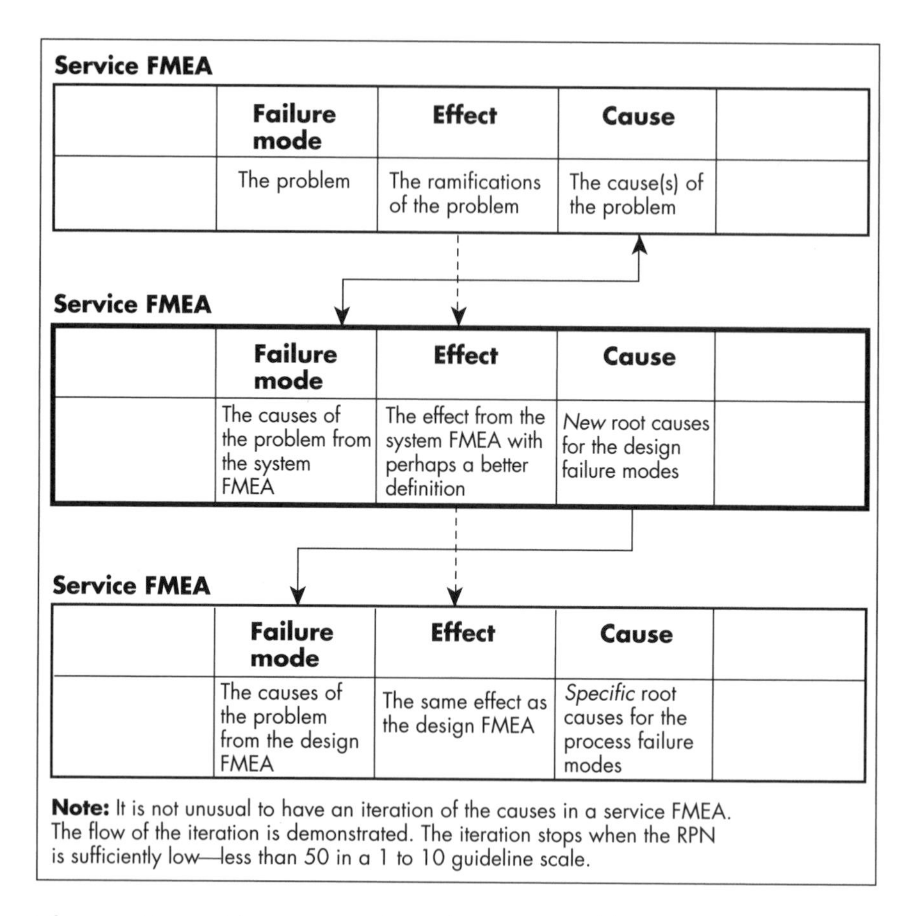

Service FMEA
Failure mode
Effect
Cause
The problem
The ramifications of the problem
The cause(s) of the problem
Service FMEA
Failure mode
Effect
Cause
The causes of the problem from the system FMEA
The effect from the system FMEA with perhaps a better definition
New root causes for the design failure modes
Service FMEA
Failure mode
Effect
Cause
The causes of the problem from the design FMEA
The same effect as the design FMEA
Specific root causes for the process failure modes
Note: It is not unusual to have an iteration of the causes in a service FMEA. The flow of the iteration is demonstrated. The iteration stops when the RPN is sufficiently low—less than 50 in a 1 to 10 guideline scale.

Figure 8.1 The relationship of a service FMEA in an iteration mode of failure identification.

The list of applications of a service FMEA is too long to list. A service FMEA, however, may be done in any situation for any industry that provides a service. Some examples include

- *Maintenance contractors*–May perform FMEAs to identify preventive maintenance cycles of repair, as well as possible trouble spots in the machinery under contract (Regalyi 1990; Bass 1991).
- *Financial institutions*–May perform FMEAs to identify the degree of effectiveness of their services, as well as to focus on issues that present uniqueness for the customer (in other words, loan

approvals, verification of funds transfer advice, bad loans, mispostings, transfer errors, encoder problems, wrong placement of magnetic ink character recognition [MICR] codes) (Latzko 1986).

- *Law firms*–May perform FMEAs to identify or track the logic of witness preparation or answers from the witness of the other side.
- *Organizations that deal with safety and hazardous issues*–FMEAs may be performed to identify not only the problems, the consequences, and the effects, but also to anticipate and plan accordingly for the failure. When used in conjunction with an FTA and/or hazard analysis, the service FMEA (in this case) becomes a powerful technique to resolve the safety and hazard issues (Bass 1986).
- *All engineering contractors*–May perform FMEAs to identify the problems and concerns that their service may provide to the customer (Blanchard and Lowery 1969; Blanchard 1986).
- *Hospitality industry (hotels/motels/resorts and restaurants)*–May perform FMEAs to identify specific problems and consequences in their service (in other words, employees not friendly, poor overall service, morning wake-up call not made, slow check-in/check-out, high employee turnover, poor housekeeping, cold food when served (should be hot) (Hall 1990).
- *Government and educational institutions*–May perform FMEAs to focus on poor service to their customer (in other words, traffic control signs, playground and play areas, information signs, sidewalks, budgetary issues, poor resource utilization, retention of students, scheduling human resources, classes too crowded, tuition too high, low/high enrollment) (Lefevre 1992; Spanbauer 1992).
- *Health care*–May perform FMEAs to define the consequences of known and/or potential problems before they happen (in other words, unplanned return to the operating room on same admission, medicine errors, death, patient/family dissatisfaction issues, postoperative complications (Sloan and Chmel 1991; Pozgar 1993).

The service FMEA is an evolutionary process (dynamic as opposed to static) involving the application of various technologies and methods to produce an effective process output. This result is a defect-free service.

The selection of appropriate technologies may include the customer's request, the utilization of existing system(s), standardized approaches, and/or procedures currently known or proposed, results of directed research, and/or a combination of all the above.

Effective service FMEA is basically realized through the active participation of customer service, service (product) development, research, quality assurance, marketing, operations, or a combination of all these entities. Thus, the focus of the service FMEA is to *minimize process failure effects on the service (system), regardless of what level of FMEA is being performed.*

This can be realized through a specific definition of the service specifications and a good understanding of what the service will provide. For the understanding of design specifications Griffiths (1990) and Stamatis (1992, 1992a) suggest a look at (partial list)

Benchmarking–A way to identify what the competition is doing and how to incorporate the best into the organization. The way to being a world-class organization.

Quality function deployment–The way to identify the needs, wants, and expectations of the customer. The voice of the customer.

Market research–The way to identify the market's need through mathematical modeling and surveying.

Focus groups–The way to identify how the customer will react to a service/product offered by an organization.

Total unduplicated research and frequency (TURF) analysis–A way to plan optimization of service/product lines or to provide guidance for possible line extensions in service and/or product. Generally, it offers reliable, cost-effective guidance to research and marketing decisions. TURF analysis may be conducted as a stand-alone service/product or integrated into more comprehensive service/product line (Cohen 1993).

Conjoint analysis–A way to decompose the total evaluation score into components relating to each attribute or to combinations of the attributes and to measure these components. This method is suitable for design of services, as well as to determine the optimum mix or portfolio of services/products (Sheth 1977).

Quality measuring systems (QMS)–A way to define what to measure. It can be useful in giving the people involved a better sense of their operations as well as an insight into a problem area that was not clearly understood (Pfeifer 1991).

By definition, a service dictates some kind of friendly action and/or conduct in the process of a given activity (in other words, friendly conduct in the process of providing any professional service). In understanding the service, however, the following may be helpful.

Service involves the utilization of six components: labor, machine, method, material, measurement, and environment. The goal of this is the production of an end item that meets or exceeds the safety and quality characteristics of the defined service (Welch and Geissler1992). An integral element of the service documentation should be the design specifications. It is difficult to do a thorough service FMEA without the completion or at least some information of a design specification as defined or expected from the customer.

It is very difficult to evaluate the entire service, especially in the early stages or initiation of the service. In most cases, the reality is that the service evaluation develops over time and as such the service FMEA becomes a living document (dynamic as opposed to static) to reflect the changes of the service.

Generally, there are two basic types of service evaluation techniques that are utilized in the early stages.

1. *Process capability studies*–Such studies are used to determine the inherent capability of specific elements of the service. Examples include machine acceptance capability, process potential study (short-term capability), and long-term capability. The questions usually are "Can this service be provided?" and "How can the organization provide this service?"

2. *Mandatory service evaluation*–As previously pointed out, it is difficult to evaluate *all* service parameters. Thus, each company establishes mandatory evaluation points for specific variables that are critical to the service and/or the customer. They may be helped in this identification by
    - Customer requirements
    - Government regulations
    - Internal guidelines
    - Design specifications

- Industry standard/guidelines
- Generally accepted practices

Some of the evaluation points may be

- *Certification of personnel.* Certification may be necessary for critical skills (in other words, cashiers, loan officers, nurses).
- *Tool verification*–Tools, jigs, and fixtures may be required to be validated (in other words, cashing machines, CAT scan machines, x-ray machine, check-decoding machines).
- *Critical process*–Most critical processes as defined by safety, customers, general practices, or government regulations require evaluation and prior approval (for example, practically all drug and medical device processes; authorization for deposit or withdrawal of funds).
- *Test operation*–Most complex testing operations require review and approval to ensure accuracy.

The goal, purpose, and/or objective of the service FMEA is to define, demonstrate, and maximize solutions in response to quality, reliability, maintainability, cost, and productivity as defined by the design specifications and the customer.

To accomplish this objective the service FMEA must base its requirements on solid needs, wants, and expectations of the customer. As a general rule that information may be the result of a QFD (preferred), an internal need for improvement, the results of benchmarking (Trace 1993), or some other input.

In any case, one of the first steps in conducting the FMEA should be to include a feasibility study and/or a risk-benefit analysis directed toward defining a set of useful solutions to the problem(s) being addressed. The objective of this early (not definitive) stage is to maximize the service quality, reliability, cost, productivity, and maintainability, regardless of what level the FMEA is being performed. This can be accomplished by the following considerations.

1. Transform an operational need as defined by the design specification into a description of service performance parameters and as perfect as possible service configuration through the use of an interactive service of functional

analysis, synthesis, optimization, definition, test, and evaluation.

2. Integrate related technical parameters and ensure compatibility of all physical, functional, and program interfaces in a manner that optimizes the total service definition and delivery of that service.
3. Integrate reliability, maintainability, human factors, safety, security, structural integrity, producibility, and other related specialties into the total service effort.

The outcome of the service FMEA is a service (it may change with new or modified information) with a baseline configuration and functional specifications toward translating the established requirements into detailed qualitative and quantitative service characteristics. Some of the generic concerns in a service FMEA include

General concerns

- Service operational requirements defined
- Effectiveness factors established
- Service maintenance concept defined

Support elements

In this area one must do a thorough investigation as to whether or not the requirements are known and/or can be optimized for

- Test and support equipment
- Personnel and training
- Repair and spare parts

Service features

- Standardization
- Test provisions
- Interchangeability
- Accessibility
- Controls
- Technical data, procedures

- Transportability
- Producibility
- Safety
- Reliability
- Software
- Traceability

Specific questions in the course of performing a service FMEA may be

1. What is the true performance and effectiveness of the service?
2. What does the service do and what are its intended uses?
3. What is the true effectiveness of the support capability?
4. Are the initially specified requirements appropriate for the service? Are they being met?
5. How does the service perform its function?
6. What materials, and/or other services are used in the delivery of the service?
7. How, and under what conditions, does the service interface with other services (current or projected)?
8. What by-products are created by the service or by the delivery of this service?
9. How is the service used, maintained, modified, and discontinued at the end of its useful life?
10. What are the operational steps in the delivery of the service?
11. What energy sources are involved and how?
12. Who will use or be in the vicinity of the service, and what are the capabilities and limitations of these individuals?
14. Is the service cost-effective?

Finally, when conducting a service FMEA, it is assumed that the design specifications are the best they can be. If this assumption is not made, the FMEA team will end up doing the design specifications and service FMEAs simultaneously and will move in a circular pattern not accomplishing its task. The only way to address the design specifications in the service FMEA is when the root causes of the failure modes in the service are caused by the design specifications.

Step-by-Step Service FMEA Analysis

There are two requirements to perform a service FMEA. The first requirement is identification of the appropriate form. The second requirement is identification of the rating guidelines.

The form for the service FMEA is not universal or standardized. Each company has its own form that reflects the needs of the organization and the concerns of the customer.

This section addresses a form to illustrate the generally accepted items that should be addressed as part of a service FMEA. Appendix E includes various FMEA forms that apply to service applications. Remember, there is no such thing as *the* service FMEA form.

The rating guidelines also are not universal or standardized. Each company has its own guidelines to reflect the needs of the organization, the product, and the concerns of the customer.

Generally, there are two ways that the rating guidelines can be formulated—qualitative and quantitative. In either case the numerical values can be from 1 to 5 or 1 to 10, with the 1 through 10 range being the most common. Again, there is no common rating guideline for the system FMEA. This section addresses the two different guidelines.

Figure 8.2 shows the most common service FMEA form. The form is divided into three parts. The first part, items 1 through 9 reflect the introduction of the form. None of the items are mandatory, but they contribute additional information to the task of the service FMEA and provide essential information that may be needed in the course of writing and/or completing the FMEA.

The second part of the form includes items 10 through 23. These are mandatory items for any service FMEA. The order of the columns may be changed, more columns may be added, but none of the columns presented may be removed. Items 10 through 23 may be viewed as the body of the service FMEA.

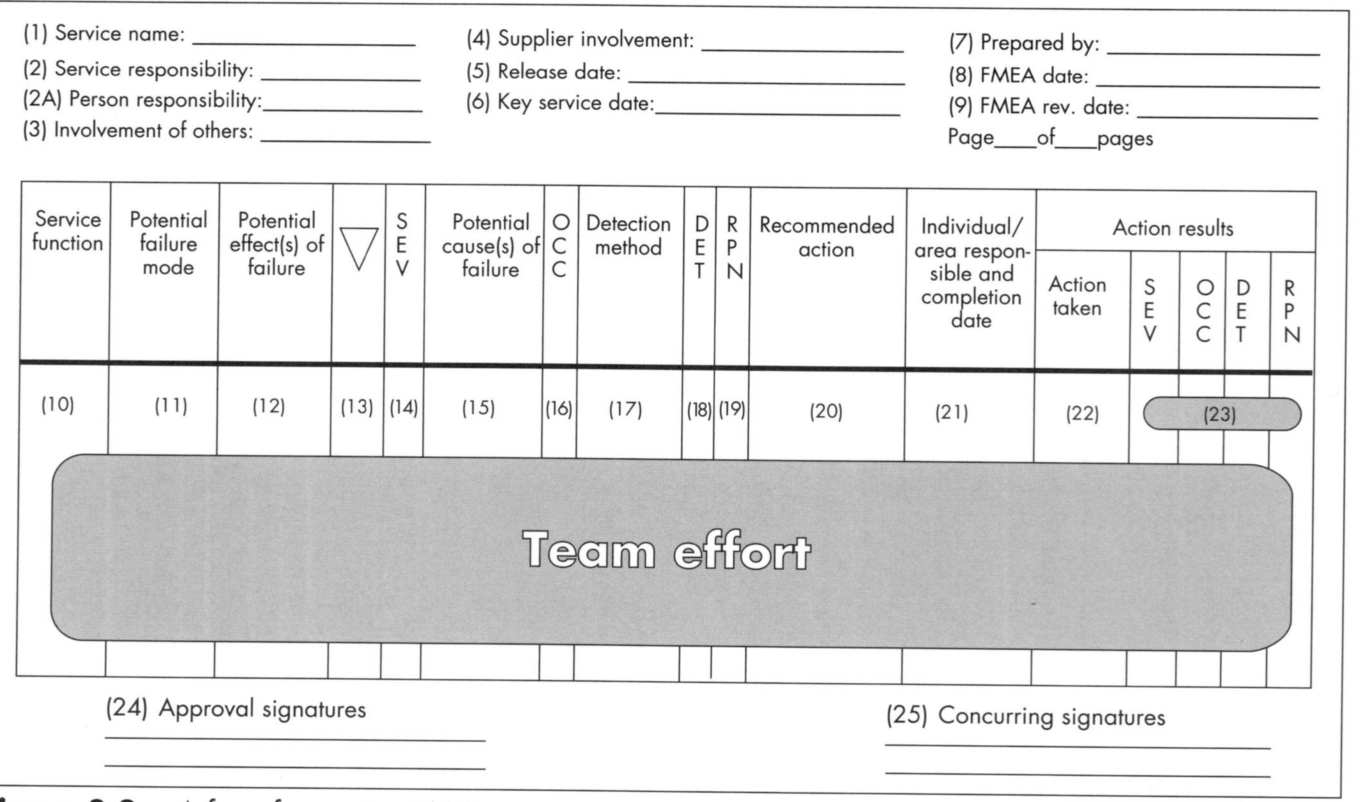

(1) Service name: ______
(2) Service responsibility: ______
(2A) Person responsibility: ______
(3) Involvement of others: ______
(4) Supplier involvement: ______
(5) Release date: ______
(6) Key service date: ______
(7) Prepared by: ______
(8) FMEA date: ______
(9) FMEA rev. date: ______
Page____of____pages

Service function	Potential failure mode	Potential effect(s) of failure	▽	SEV	Potential cause(s) of failure	OCC	Detection method	DET	RPN	Recommended action	Individual/area respon-sible and completion date	Action results				
												Action taken	SEV	OCC	DET	RPN
(10)	(11)	(12)	(13)	(14)	(15)	(16)	(17)	(18)	(19)	(20)	(21)	(22)	(23)			

Team effort

(24) Approval signatures
(25) Concurring signatures

Figure 8.2 A form for service FMEA.

The third part of the form, items 24 and 25, includes the signatures. Although they are not mandatory, they do reflect the authority and responsibility of the team to undertake the project of writing the service FMEA. The signatures may be viewed as the closure of the FMEA. All numbers in parentheses are coded numbers for the discussion of the form.

Service Identification (1). Identify the service name or reference numbers or service codes as appropriate.

Service Responsibility (2). Name the primary responsibility for the service (machine, material, and so on). Enter the name of the activity responsible for the service, if appropriate. This is used strictly for a cross-reference point to other services.

Person Responsibility (2A). Sometimes it is necessary to name the person who is responsible for the service FMEA.

Involvement of Other Areas (3). Identify other persons or activities (within the organization) that are affected or are involved in the service.

Involvement of Suppliers or Others (4). Name other persons, suppliers, and/or plants (outside the organization) that affect the service and are involved in the definition and/or the delivery of the service.

Release Date (5). Identify the date (Mo–Day–Yr) that the service is scheduled to be released.

Key Service Date (6). Identify milestone dates (Mo–Day–Yr) (in other words, dates for specific reviews, date for initial trial, and so on).

Prepared by (7). Generally, the name of the responsible person for the service FMEA is identified. Sometimes, additional information, with an attachment, also is recorded such as

- Telephone number of the system design engineer
- Address of the system design engineer
- Organizational activity (in other words, division, department, and so on)
- Team members (name, telephone, address, and so on)

FMEA Date—Original (8). Record the date (Mo–Day–Yr) of the initiation of the service FMEA. The starting date.

FMEA Date—Revision (9). Record the date (Mo–Day–Yr) of the latest revision.

Service Function (10). The facilitator writes the intent, purpose, goal, or objective of the service. The service function must be derived from the design specifications and describe what the service is now, not what it should be.

Generally, the service function is identified with a process flow diagram followed by a task analysis. The process flow diagram identifies sequentially the flow of operations among personnel and the interaction among personnel and major equipment components.

The task analysis serves as the basis of workload analysis by defining the specific sequence of tasks that each person in the service must perform. This step is important because inefficient distribution of workload can result in increased human error and subsequent safety or critical problems (Bass 1991).

Task analysis and task identification are not the same, nor can they can be used interchangeably. A task analysis defines

- What initiates the task
- The equipment used to perform the task
- The human response
- The task feedback
- The characteristics of the task output, including performance requirements

Task identification defines the task through one or more of the following techniques.

- System analysis
  –Functional flow block diagrams
  –Decision/action diagrams
  –Functional allocation
  –Time lines
  –Time and motion analysis

–Human reliability analysis
–Operational sequence diagram

For the service function to be effective it must be identified in detail through a statement that is concise, exact, and easy to understand (no jargon). The statement that is used to describe the function should be described in specific terms. To facilitate this, the writer of the FMEA should try to think of active verbs and appropriate nouns. The active verbs define performance and performance defines function. The combination of the active verb with the noun defines the relationship, consequently, the definition of the service becomes much easier.

Examples include

- Provide 24-hour service
- Service all TV models
- Repair roofs
- Provide tutoring in the home

Another way to facilitate the formation of the function is to ask questions such as "What is the purpose, objective, function, goal of the service?" "What is the service supposed to do?" If there are more than one purpose or function it is imperative that each should be identified separately because it probably will have different potential failure modes.

Potential Failure Mode (11). The problem. The concern. The opportunity to improve. The error/mistake. The failure. The reject. The defect. As mentioned earlier, a service defect (nonconformity) exists when the service does not meet the defined criteria of the design and/or the customer. Peters (1982) identified some of those criteria.

- *Usability*–Is the service usable? Does the service contribute utility in the organization? If yes, how? Can it be improved? If not, should it? Why not?
- *Signature, personality, distinction*–Is the service unique? How is it viewed by the customers and/or the competition? Are aesthetic considerations accounted for? If yes, how? If not, why not?

- *Attitude*–What is the attitude about the service from the customer's, supplier's, and employee's perspective?

The contribution of failures based on these criteria for a given service has been identified by Peters (1992) through a regression analysis as

- Reliability (30 percent). The ability to perform the promised service dependably and accurately
- Responsiveness (25 percent). The willingness to help customers and provide prompt service
- Assurance (20 percent). The knowledge and courtesy of employees and their ability to convey trust and confidence
- Empathy (16 percent). The caring, individualized attention provided to the customer
- Tangibles (7 percent). The appearance of physical facilities, equipment, personnel, and communication materials

Specifically, when one considers the potential failure mode one must think of the loss of a service function—a specific failure. The more specific one is, the better opportunity one will have to identify the effects and causes of the failure. Service failures occur when a service does not adequately protect against risks of injury, fails to perform intended functions safely (as defined by design specifications), or fails to minimize avoidable consequences in the event of an accident, avoidance of the service, and/or fails to deliver the expected service.

Generally, there are two categories of service failure modes. They are

- Evaluation (testing and/or inspection)
  –Accept or reject bad or good service respectively
- Process
  –Relational concerns, misoriented services and/or missing services

For each service function identified in item 10 one must list the corresponding failure of the function. There can be more than one failure from one function. To help identify the potential failure mode think of the negative or loss of the function. Examples include

- Bad service
- Poor communication
- Poor customer service
- Cashier not knowledgeable about returns

Another way of identifying the anticipated failure mode is by asking questions such as (partial list)

- How could this process fail to complete its intended function?
- Why can this part be rejected at this operation?
- What does the customer find unacceptable?
- How would the part not conform to specifications at this operation?

The emphasis is on the facilitator to try to anticipate how the service being considered could possibly fail, not whether or not it will fail. Another way of identifying failure modes is through a review of historical documentation, customer complaints, and any other applicable documentation.

Potential Effect(s) of Failure (12). A potential effect of the failure is the consequence of its failure on the next process, operation, product, customer, and/or government regulations. The questions usually asked are: "What does the customer experience as a result of the failure mode described?" or "What happens or what is (are) the ramification(s) of this problem or failure?" The consequences may be to the design itself, the product, the customer, and/or government regulations. Often, the failure effect is evaluated from a customer's perspective or experience.

To identify the potential effects, some of the documents one may review include

- Historical data
- Similar current or past FMEAs

- Customer complaints
- Field service data
- Reliability data
- Feasibility studies

No matter how the potential effect(s) is (are) identified the ramifications of the loss to the process function must be determined. Consideration must be given to the service itself, other processes, the product, safety, government regulations, machines and equipment, and the customer (both the next and the ultimate). If safety considerations may be an issue, this is the column where the appropriate notation should be made. Examples of potential effect of failure may be

- Subsequent operation: "Nobody knows anything about it"
- Other operation(s): None
- Task: Task function incomplete
- Service: Poor performance
- Customer: Complete dissatisfaction; service incomplete
- Government: May not comply with STD-XXX

Note: A special consideration for the effects of the failure is that the maximum effect of the service FMEA can only be attained through truly open communication of the team that is conducting the FMEA. This can be facilitated through multidisciplined and multifunctional team members.

Critical Characteristics (13). Critical characteristics usually are associated with design FMEAs because in the design stage the hardware begins to be formalized. In the service FMEA, however, the critical characteristics gain paramount importance because they define the service, process requirements, sequences, tooling, and anything that can affect the customer or government regulations.

The critical characteristic column applies *only* when compliance with the government regulations, safety and design specifications for the service, and/or process are of concern.

The identification of the criticality or significance in the service FMEA is only to designate special controls for the process and/or service FMEA. From this point they are transferred to the control plan.

Examples of possible critical items may be

- Dimensions
- Specifications
- Tests
- Processes
- Procedures
- Usage

Critical characteristics are identified when (1) service requirements can affect safety, (2) service requirements can affect compliance with government regulations, and (3) service requirements are necessary for special actions/controls.

The entry to this column is a “Y” for yes, or “N” for no, or a notation symbol (in other words, inverted delta). Its purpose is to flag a potential critical characteristic that may or may not exist. A good indication of criticality is when severity is rated 9 or 10 with occurrence and detection higher than 1.

Severity of Effect (14). Severity is a rating indicating the seriousness of the effect of the potential service failure mode. The severity always applies to the effect of a failure mode. In fact, there is a direct correlation between effect and severity. For example, if the effect is critical, the severity is high. On the other hand, if the effect is not critical, the severity is very low.

Severity is reviewed from the perspective of the system, the service, other systems/services, the customer, and/or government regulations. For evaluation purposes there usually is a rating table that reflects the issues of the organization in conjunction with the customer and/or the government regulations. An example of such a rating may be seen in Table 7.1.

In the service FMEA, the severity rating should be based on the worst effect of the failure mode. When this is complete rank the failure modes on the basis of the severity of their effects.

Blanchard (1986) suggests the severity for the service FMEA may be viewed from the following perspective.

Category 1 *Catastrophic*–In this category, failure of the service may contribute to a disastrous result (for example, a last-minute witness on a murder case or an automatic teller machine gives out more money than it is coded for).

Category 2 *Critical*–In this category, failure of the service may contribute to a major damage (for example, the deposit coupon of the mortgage payment was not read correctly by the computer).

Category 3 *Marginal*–In this category, failure of the service may contribute to a minor damage (for example, the waitperson was not friendly).

Category 4 *Negligible*–In this category, failure of the service may contribute to a nuisance rather than anything else (for example, vending machine does not provide change).

Potential Cause(s) of Failure (15). The cause of a service failure mode is the service deficiency that results in the failure mode. It must be emphasized repeatedly that when one focuses on the cause(s) one must look at the failure's *root cause,* not the symptom .

To do a good job of proper potential cause(s) of failure identification, one must understand the service and ask the appropriate questions. Specificity is of paramount importance. The more one focuses on the root cause, the better one understands the failure. For example, "Would an inadequate promotion campaign cause the low turnover?" "Would inefficient training cause misrouting of the documents?" Some of the techniques that may be used are brainstorming, cause-and-effect analysis, analysis of the functional diagram, and affinity charts.

The basic question to ask is: "In what way can this service fail to perform its intended function?" Another method is to ask five "whys" in a row. This is because it becomes a progressively more difficult and thought-provoking assignment to identify the whys. The early questions are superficial, but the later ones are more substantive. Other questions that may be asked are: "What circumstances could cause the failure?" "How or why can the service fail to meet its customer specifications?"

A failure mode can be caused by one or more individual components or by (partial list)

- Hardware failure due to inadequate product design
- Improper selection of component parts
- Improper use of processes
- Inadequate control procedures
- Failure to enforce process and quality controls
- Improper installation, maintenance
- Lack of safety devices, environmental factors
- Misuse, abuse
- Alteration of the service/product
- Improper operating instructions
- Human error
- Improper training
- Improper choice of materials
- Stress concentrations
- Interaction with other services/components
- Interaction with systems
- Interaction with the government
- Interaction with the customer

At this point, it must be emphasized that a major benefit of the service FMEA is identification of potential failure modes caused by the service itself and/or process interactions. These interactions may also involve human factors and must be reviewed thoroughly.

The relationship between the failure mode and the cause(s) is not linear or one-to-one. Do not be surprised if there are several causes for one failure mode. (Sometimes a one-to-one relationship exists.) List as many causes as possible. These causes will identify flaws and opportunities for improvement of the service. Therefore, the more causes identified in the service FMEA, the easier the corrective action becomes.

Examples of failure causes

- Poor instructions
- Not appropriately trained
- Surprise in the process
- Human error

Note: If the effect of the failure is rated 8 through 10, special effort should be made to identify as many root causes as possible.

Occurrence (16). Occurrence (frequency) is the rating value corresponding to the estimated expected frequencies and/or cumulative number of failures that could occur for a given cause over the length of the service with the existing controls. (Usually this is given as part of the specification.) To identify the frequency for each of the causes one may use reliability mathematics (beyond the scope of this book), use the expected frequencies, or use a cumulative number of component failures (CNF) per 100 or 1000 components (CNF/100 or CNF/1000, respectively) over the design life of the component under study. Design life was explained in the design FMEA section.

Another way to help identify occurrences is the target (goal) period or useful life after which the service is discarded because it ceases to function as designed (normal life). Thus, it is too expensive to reinstall.

If expected frequencies and/or cumulative number of failures cannot be estimated, it is acceptable for the service FMEA to look at similar or surrogate services and/or processes for similar information.

Generally, the service FMEA operates under the assumption of the single-point failures (in other words, if a single service failure occurs the system fails). A single-point failure was defined in chapter 7. The single-point failure can help minimize service disruption after it is identified. Please note, this is not to suggest that every single service failure is catastrophic, rather that each service failure should be addressed because it contributes to the dissatisfaction of the customer.

When the occurrence/frequency is calculated, it is imperative that it must be for every single cause of the failure. If it cannot be estimated, then the occurrence should be entered as 10. It must also be a consensus agreement of the entire team. A typical occurrence guideline is shown in Table 7.2.

Detection Method; Existing Control (17). A method (procedure), test, or analysis. These are some of the first-level methods to detect or prevent a failure in the service, process, and/or the customer (Blanchard 1969). They can be very simple (in other words, brainstorming, audits, sampling based on statistical techniques) or very technical and advanced (in other words, military standards and computer simulation). In either case, the focus is on the effectiveness of the control method/technique to catch the problem before it reaches the customer.

The only controls for the service FMEA that should be considered must contribute to the estimation of the detection rating. Controls intended to prevent or reduce the occurrence of the cause of the failure should be considered when estimating the occurrence rating.

The objective of the detection is to identify a service deficiency as early as possible. That deficiency may be viewed as a weakness in the process to reveal, detect, or eliminate the problem from the service (Chien 1985). The purpose of early detection in the service FMEA is to provide efficient service controls.

Because the service FMEA is completed early, it is sometimes difficult to assess the detection rating. In these cases one may use historical information, or similar types of information from similar services and/or processes. Occasionally, it is possible to have no method, test, or technique to identify the failure. In that case, the entry in this column should state something like "None identified at this time."

Another way of focusing on detection is to use the brainstorming technique to identify new methods and tests as they apply to the task at hand. Two of the leading questions in the brainstorming process should be

- How can this failure be discovered?
- In what way can this failure be recognized?

Some of the most effective ways to detect a failure are

- Proven simulation techniques
- Mathematical modeling

- Trial testing
- Design of experiments
- Process verification testing

Typical controls may include

- Probabilistic, reliability, and statistical modeling and testing as required.
- Reviewing test results, examining safety margins, evaluating material selections, and auditing of the service and processes.
- Checklists for completeness of the documentation. A checklist may provide a last check of the functions, features, producibility, compliance to the appropriate standards, operator misuse, profitability and safety of the services, and its effect(s) on the process.

A typical checklist may include the following:

- Define service in its use environment.
  - –What are the service's uses?
  - –What are the foreseeable environments of use?
  - –Describe the skill and capability of foreseeable users.
- Identify safety and assess risk.
  - –What are the hazards?
  - –Estimate the probability of occurrence and seriousness of resulting harm for each hazard.
- Evaluate alternatives.
  - –What alternative service features or techniques are available that can be expected to reduce or eliminate safety issues?
  - –Evaluate alternative services/process by considering the following:
    - –Characteristics and comparisons of different services
    - –Other safety issues that may be introduced by the alternative services
    - –Their effect on the usefulness of the service
    - –Their effect on the ultimate cost of the service

In the case of human errors, a detection method may be developed based on similar guidelines given in the process FMEA section based on MIL-STD-1472c and Woodson (1981).

Detection (18). Detection is a rating corresponding to the likelihood that the current process controls will detect a specific root cause of a failure mode before the service is completed. To identify a detection rating one must estimate the ability for each of the controls identified in item 17 to detect the failure before it reaches the customer. The assumption is that the failure has occurred.

In addressing detection issues in the service FMEA, three items are very important.

1. Do not make the assumption—it happens quite often—that the detection should be low, just because the occurance is low. The two ratings may or may not be correlated with each other for this particular item.
2. If 100 percent automatic control is listed as a control the FMEA team must consider the effectiveness based on
   - Condition of the control
   - Condition of the testing equipment
   - Calibration of the gauge and testing equipment
   - Variation of gauge and testing equipment (based on repeatability and reproducibility study—R&R)
   - Likelihood that the system will fail or be bypassed
3. If 100 percent visual (as opposed to automatic—process controller, brush recorders, artificial vision, and so on) inspection is listed, the FMEA team must consider the effectiveness based on
   - One hundred percent visual inspection is only 79 to 100 percent effective, depending on inspector and conditions of inspection.
   - The number who may perform the inspections—How is the consistency of evaluation going to be monitored?
   - The nature of the failure. Is the failure obscure where a very high level of inspection ability is required (through training and/or experience), or is the failure so obvious that anyone can identify it?

If the ability of the controls to detect the failure is unknown, or the detection cannot be estimated, then the detection rating should be 10. A typical detection guide is shown in Table 7.3.

Risk Priority Number (RPN) (19). This number is the product of severity, occurrence, and detection. The RPN defines the priority of the failure. By themselves the RPNs have no value or meaning. They are used only to rank (define) the potential service deficiencies.

In the service FMEA one must always remember that the goal is to reduce the RPN, but in a specific way. The specific way is through a reduction in

- Severity (if design actions have been taken)
- Detection
- Occurrence

The severity can be reduced only through a change in design. If that is attainable, then the failure is eliminated.

The occurrence can be reduced by improving task specifications and/or requirements in the service/process with the intent of preventing causes or reducing their frequency. The detection can be reduced by adding or improving evaluation techniques, increasing sample size, and/or add detection equipment. The result will be improvement in the ability to detect the failure before it reaches the customer.

Recommended Action (20). No FMEA should be done without a recommended action. The recommended action may be specific action(s) or it may be further studying. The purpose of the recommended action in the service FMEA is to reduce the severity, occurrence, detection, or all of these factors. In essence the service FMEA is done to eliminate deficiencies and thus eliminate failures.

To facilitate this goal, the FMEA team must prioritize those failure modes with the highest RPN, the highest severity, the highest occurrence. Typical recommendations may be

- No action at this time
- Add built-in detection devices
- Provide alternatives to the design/service
- Add redundant subsystem

Responsible Area or Person and Completion Date (21). This section includes the responsible person/area and the target completion date for the recommended action.

Action Taken (22). This is the follow-up. Just because something was recommended, does not mean that something was done. It is imperative, that someone (usually the department head) will follow up on the recommendations to determine if they have been addressed adequately, properly, and/or if they are in need of updating.

Note that all FMEAs are living documents and as such someone must be responsible to update them. Often the person who is responsible is the department head. She or he has the responsibility to make sure that the service FMEA is a living document and it reflects the latest relevant information and actions.

After the action has been taken, the effective date or completion date with a brief description of the action should be entered.

Revised RPN (23). After the actions are incorporated in the process, the FMEA team should reevaluate the consequences of severity, occurrence, and detection. The results should be reviewed by the FMEA team and a new RPN is calculated and the failures are ranked. This process is repeated as needed until such time as the FMEA team decides that all relevant information has been covered. If no actions are taken, then these columns will remain blank.

As a general rule, the anticipated changes with the service FMEA are in the area of occurrence and detection. The severity stays the same. For the severity to change the following must take place

1. As part of the root cause analysis, it must be identified that the failure was caused because of a design/system issue.
2. The recommended action was to change the design based on the findings of the cause analysis.
3. The design changes were implemented as recommended or modified.

At this point the result is that the ratings (occurrence, severity, and detection) may all change, or some will change, or none will change.

Approval Signatures (24). Define the authority to carry out the FMEA. The names and titles will depend on the organization. Typical names may be the those of branch (department) manager, marketing manager, and area supervisor.

Concurrence Signatures (25). Define the responsibility of carrying out the completion and implementation of the FMEA. The names and titles will depend on the organization. Typical names may be those of the department head, marketing manager, and quality assurance manager.

Recommended Team

A team is necessary to complete a service FMEA. The team makeup should consist of five to nine individuals with a multidisciplined and multifunctional background. In addition, all members should have ownership of the problem (Stamatis 1992).

Selecting a service FMEA team is both important and difficult. Team members should include those

- Who have the time to devote to the project
- With upward mobility
- With administrative skills
- Who have the respect of their peers
- With knowledge of the service
- With experience in similar services
- Who are willing to participate
- Who are politically astute in the organization

A typical service FMEA team includes the following:

- Department head (mandatory)
- Department supervisor (mandatory)
- Personnel involved with the service (mandatory)

Other recommended participants may be

- Marketing representatives
- Material manager
- Field service manager

Once again, remember there is no such thing as *the* team. A team is made to reflect the needs and requirements that the problem and culture of the organization requires.

References

Bass, L. 1986. *Products liability: Design and manufacturing defects.* Colorado Springs, Colo.: Shepard's/McGraw-Hill.

———. 1991. Cumulative supplement to *Products liability: Design and manufacturing defects.* Colorado Springs, Colo.: Shepard's/McGraw-Hill.

Blanchard, B. S. 1986. *Logistics engineering and management.* 3d ed. Englewood Cliffs, N.J.: Prentice Hall.

Blanchard, B. S., and E. E. Lowery. 1969. *Maintainability—Principles and practices.* New York: McGraw-Hill.

Chien, J. 1985. Detailed tests show how well industrial local network performs. *Data Communications* 14 (August): 119–131.

Cohen, E. 1993. Turf analysis. *Quirk's Marketing Research Review* (July/August): 10–13.

Griffiths, D. N. 1990. *Implementing quality with a customer focus.* Milwaukee: ASQC Quality Press.

Hall, S. S. J. 1990. *Quality assurance in the hospitality industry.* Milwaukee: ASQC Quality Press.

Latzko, W. J. 1986. *Quality and productivity for bankers and financial managers.* Milwaukee: ASQC Quality Press.

Lefevre, H., ed. 1992. *Government quality and productivity: Success stories.* Milwaukee: ASQC Quality Press.

MIL-STD-1472C. May 2, 1981. Washington, D.C.: Department of Defense.

Peters, T. 1992. *Liberation management.* New York: Alfred A. Knopf.

Pfeiffer, J. W., ed. 1991. *Theories and models in applied behavioral science: Management leadership.* Vols. 2 and 3. San Diego: Pfeiffer.

Pozgar, G. D. 1993. *Legal aspects of health care administration.* Gaithersburg, Md.: Aspen Publishers.

Ragalyi, J. 1990. The effect of preventive maintenance on machine productivity. Master's thesis, Central Michigan University.

Sheth, J. N., ed. 1977. *Multivariate methods for market and survey research.* Chicago: American Marketing Association.

Sloan, M. D., and M. Chmel. 1991. *The quality revolution and health care: A primer for purchasers and providers.* Milwaukee: ASQC Quality Press.

Spanbauer, S. J. 1992. *A quality system for education.* Milwaukee: ASQC Quality Press.

Stamatis, D. H. 1992. *Customer satisfaction manual.* Southgate, Mich.: Contemporary Consultants.

———. 1992a. *Benchmarking manual.* Southgate, Mich.: Contemporary Consultants.

———. 1993. *FMEA training manual.* Southgate, Mich.: Contemporary Consultants.

Trace, S. 1993. Benchmarking: How to be an industrial spy. *Continuous Improvement* (Solution Specialists, Alto, Mich.) (June): 1–3.

Welch, C., and P. Geissler. 1992. *Bringing total quality to sales.* Milwaukee: ASQC Quality Press.

Woodson, W. 1981. *Human factors design handbook.* New York: McGraw-Hill.

CHAPTER 9

FMEA and the Electromechanical Industry*

This chapter provides an overview of the FMEA and the electromechanical (EM) industry and tries to identify some of the special concerns in its utilization.

The FMEA is a method of reliability analysis intended to identify failures that have significant consequences affecting the system performance in the application considered. These failures may be potential or known (through warranty failures, internal rework records, inspection records, customer feedback and/or complaints, and so on). The potential failures may be suspect based on similar designs, processes, products, services, and so on.

In general terms, failures of any component will affect system performance adversely (Eachus 1992). When one studies the system reliability, safety, and availability, however, both qualitative and quantitative analyses are required as they complement each other. Quantitative analysis methods allow calculation or prediction of performance indices of the system while satisfying a specific task, or in long-term operation under specific conditions. Typical indices denote reliability, safety, availability, maintainability, failure rates, mean time between failure (MTBF), and so on.

On the other hand, qualitative methods, may be used to identify the failures, categorize them, understand them better, and help in the priority of quantification process. Typical tools used in such cases are

*Portions of this chapter are based on the International Electrotechnical Commission IEC Standard Publication 812 (1985). *Analysis Techniques for System Reliability—Procedure for Failure Mode and Effects Analysis*. Bureau Central de la Commission Electrotechnique Internationale. Geneva, Switzerland.

brainstorming, affinity charts, force field analysis, cause-and-effect charts, Pareto charts, and so on.

Generally, the FMEA in the EM industry is based on a specific component or subassembly level where the basic failure criteria (primary failure modes) are available. Starting from the basic element failure characteristics and the functional system structure, the FMEA determines the relationship between the element failures and the system failures, malfunctions, operational constraints, and degradation of performance or integrity. To evaluate secondary and higher-order system and subsystem failures, the sequences of events in time may also have to be considered. A process flowchart or a block diagram may be used to facilitate this sequence.

FMEA is a method primarily adapted for material and equipment failures. It can be applied to categories based on different technologies (hydraulic, mechanical, electrical, and so on) and combinations of technologies.

In a narrow sense, the FMEA is limited to a qualitative analysis of failure modes of hardware and does not include human errors/performance and software errors, despite the fact that current systems usually are subject to both. In a wider sense, these factors can be included. Indeed one can perform FMEA for a system, design, process, service (in other words, customer service, software applications, and so on). See chapter 10 for more information on this.

The severity of the consequences of a failure is described by criticality. Criticality is designated by categories or levels that are functions of the dangers and losses of system capabilities and sometimes of the probability of their occurrence. (These categories sometimes are defined by the customer or are given by a standard, such as MIL-STD 1629A.) This probability is best identified separately. A logical extension of the FMEA is consideration of the criticality and probability of occurrence of the failure modes. This criticality analysis of the identified failure modes is widely known as failure mode effect and critical analysis (FMECA).

The FMEA in the EM industry is an important technique for a reliability assurance program which can be applied to a wide range of problems and may be encountered in technical systems with varying depths and modifications to suit the purpose (Kececioglu 1991). The analysis is carried out in a limited way during conception, planning, and definition phases and conducted more fully in the design and development phase, followed by the process phase and occasionally the product phase. In the case of service application, the FMEA may be used or developed during the implementation phase or concurrently with the problem. In any case, the FMEA is an inductive method of performing a qualitative system reliability or safety analysis from a low to high level (Blanchard 1988; Bass 1991). To accomplish this, the FMEA uses a variety of tasks and activities to derive appropriate results.

The application of the FMEA within the framework of the specific project is very important and one must plan how and for what purpose the FMEA will be used. Always remember that the requirements for FMEA originate with the need, wish, and expectancy to understand a problem's behavior and its implications and ultimately to remove the root cause for that unwanted behavior. Look for continual improvement. Because behaviors vary, the FMEA can vary widely from one project to another and from company to company.

Furthermore, the FMEA is a technique for design review support and for assurance and assessment, which should be employed from the first steps of system and subsystem design. FMEA is appropriate to all levels of system, design, process, service, and software development. Special training of personnel performing FMEA is required; the FMEA team must have the close collaboration of systems engineers, designers, operators, manufacturing engineers, and anyone who is close to the project. The FMEA must be updated as the project progresses and as the system, design, process, software, and service are modified. By the end of the project, FMEA is used to check the overall system, design, process, software, and service and may be essential for demonstration of conformity of a design system to required standards, regulations, and user's requirements.

Information from the FMEA identifies priorities for process controls and inspection tests during manufacturing and installation, and for qualification, approval, acceptance, and start-up tests. It provides essential information for diagnostic and maintenance procedures, and it should be identified in the reliability program and/or the control plan. This identification will make the FMEA even more effective.

In deciding on the extent and manner in which FMEA should be applied to an item, one should consider the specific purposes for which FMEA results are needed, the time phasing with other activities, and the importance of establishing a predetermined degree of awareness and control over unwanted failure modes and effects. This leads to the planning of FMEA in qualitative terms at specified levels (item, component, code, subsystem, system, process, task) to relate to the iterative design and development process.

Uses of FMEA

Some of FMEA's benefits are

- To identify failures that, when they occur alone, have unacceptable or significant effects, and to determine the failure modes which may seriously affect the expected or required operation. Such effects may include secondary failures.
- To determine the need for
  - –Redundancy
  - –Designing features which increase the probability of fail-safe outcomes of failures
  - –Further derating and/or design simplification (This may be done in conjunction with concurrent engineering and/or the poka-yoke method of designing.)
  - –Improvement of task, failure, and so on
- To determine the need for selecting alternative materials, parts, devices, components, and tasks (This may be done in conjunction with DOE—classical or Taguchi.)
- To identify serious failure consequences and hence the need for design review and revision
- To provide the logic model required to evaluate the probability of anomalous operating conditions of the system
- To disclose safety hazard and liability problem areas, or noncompliance with regulatory requirements
- To ensure that the test program prototype can detect potential failure modes
- To establish duty cycles which anticipate and avoid wear-out failures
- To focus upon key/areas in which to concentrate quality, inspection, and manufacturing process controls

- To avoid costly modifications by the early identification of design deficiencies
- To establish the need for data recording and monitoring during testing, checkout, and use
- To provide information for selection of preventive or corrective maintenance points and development of troubleshooting guides, built-in test equipment, procedures for testing, and/or inspection and suitable test points
- To facilitate or support the determination of test criteria, test plans, and diagnostic procedures (for example, performance testing, reliability testing)
- To identify circuits requiring worst case analysis (frequently required for failure models involving parameter shifts)
- To support the design of fault isolation sequences and to support the planning for alternative modes of operation and reconfiguration
- To facilitate communication between
  –General and specialized engineers
  –General and specialized attorneys
  –General and specialized health care personnel
  –Operators (doers) and management
  –Equipment manufacturer and suppliers and customers
  –System user and the designer or manufacturer
  –System, design, process, product, service personnel
- To enhance the analyst's knowledge and understanding of the behavior of the equipment, task, process, software, service, product, system, and design studied
- To provide a systematic and rigorous approach to the study of system facilities

Limitations of FMEA

FMEA is extremely efficient when it is applied to the analysis of elements that cause a failure of the entire system; however, FMEA may be difficult and tedious for the case of complex systems that have multiple functions consisting of a number of components. This is because of the quantity of detailed system information which must be considered. This difficulty can be increased by the number of possible operating modes, as well as by considerations of the repair and maintenance policies.

Another limitation is that the results of human error usually are not included. Studies of machine interactions are the subject of specific methods (for example, task analysis). Generally, human errors appear during operation systems in a sequential mode and the study of their impact has to be made by methods such as cause-consequence analysis. Nevertheless, the FMEA can identify components most sensitive to human factors. A further limitation is apparent when the effects of the environment are significant. The consideration of these effects requires a thorough knowledge of the characteristics and performance of the different components of the system.

Note that human error and environmental effects constitute a major source of common mode or common cause failure, especially in the process, service, and software FMEA.

The Principles of FMEA

Terminology

The terminology is the same as the generic FMEA.

Concepts

All FMEAs require

- The system breakdown into elements—the smallest component or individual task
- Diagrams of the system functional structure and identification of the various data that are needed to perform the FMEA
- The failure mode concept
- The criticality concept (if criticality analysis is required)

Definition of the System Functional Structure

The analysis is initiated by selecting lowest level of interest (usually the part, circuit, or module/task level) at which sufficient information is available. At this lowest level, the various failure modes that can occur for each item at that level are tabulated. The corresponding failure effect for each (taken singly and in turn), is interpreted as a failure mode for consideration of the failure effect at the next higher functional level. Successive iterations result in the identification of the failure effects in relation to specific failure modes.

It is important to determine the breakdown level that will be used for the analysis. For example, systems can be broken down into subsystems, least replaceable items, or detailed parts (components). The same can be said about a process, which can be broken into the areas of labor, machine, method, material, measurement, and environment. These areas can be broken into smaller items. In the case of the service (customer service) FMEA one must break down each task into a single unit relevant to the entire job. Some good tools for such a breakdown may be the use of the process flowchart, task analysis, brainstorming, or cause-and-effect analysis. An example of a design FMEA using the cause-and-effect diagram with certain criteria is shown in Figures 9.1 and 9.2 and Tables 9.1 and 9.2.

Where relevant, nonelectrical items must be considered. When quantitative results are required, the level chosen must be one at which it is possible to obtain adequate and dependable failure rate data on each failure mode or error mode; or to make reasonable identified assumptions of such failure rates. The chosen breakdown level requires a dependable and detailed knowledge of the failure modes of the elements. Apart from this requirement, it is neither possible nor desirable to set strict rules about the choice of the breakdown level.

Information Necessary to Perform the FMEA

System Structure

The following information is required

- The different system elements with their characteristics, performances, roles, and functions

The development of the FMEA
Step 1: The criteria

Project number:

Description: Industrial-grade, all-plastic connector for non-metallic conduit

Products designed must meet the following minimum requirements.

1. Complete line of straits, 90-degree and 45-degree connectors for conduit sizes: 3/8", 1/2", 3/4", 1", 1-1/4", 1-1/2", 2".
2. Compatible with UL-listed type B nonmetallic conduit and UL-recognized flexible corrugated tubing (type EFC style)
3. Resistance to chemical found in the following:
   - Machine tool-related environments
   - Food processing-related environments
   - Automotive-related environments
   - Determine suitability for use in marine environments
4. Suitable and marked for outdoor use (UV/sunlight resistant)
5. Consistently meets UL requirements for pullout and liquid tightness on both LTC and EFC styles
6. Meets T&B requirements for impact resistance
7. Install connector on conduit without disassembly
8. Conduit should not rotate as gland nut is tightened
9. 90-degree connector to easily allow wire pulling similar to the established 2680 series
10. Include sealing ring (not standard product) and metallic locknut
11. Connectors to be black in color
12. UL listing and CSA certification required. It is desirable to meet NEMA 4, NEMA 6, and NEMA 12 specs.

Figure 9.1 Criteria for a product.

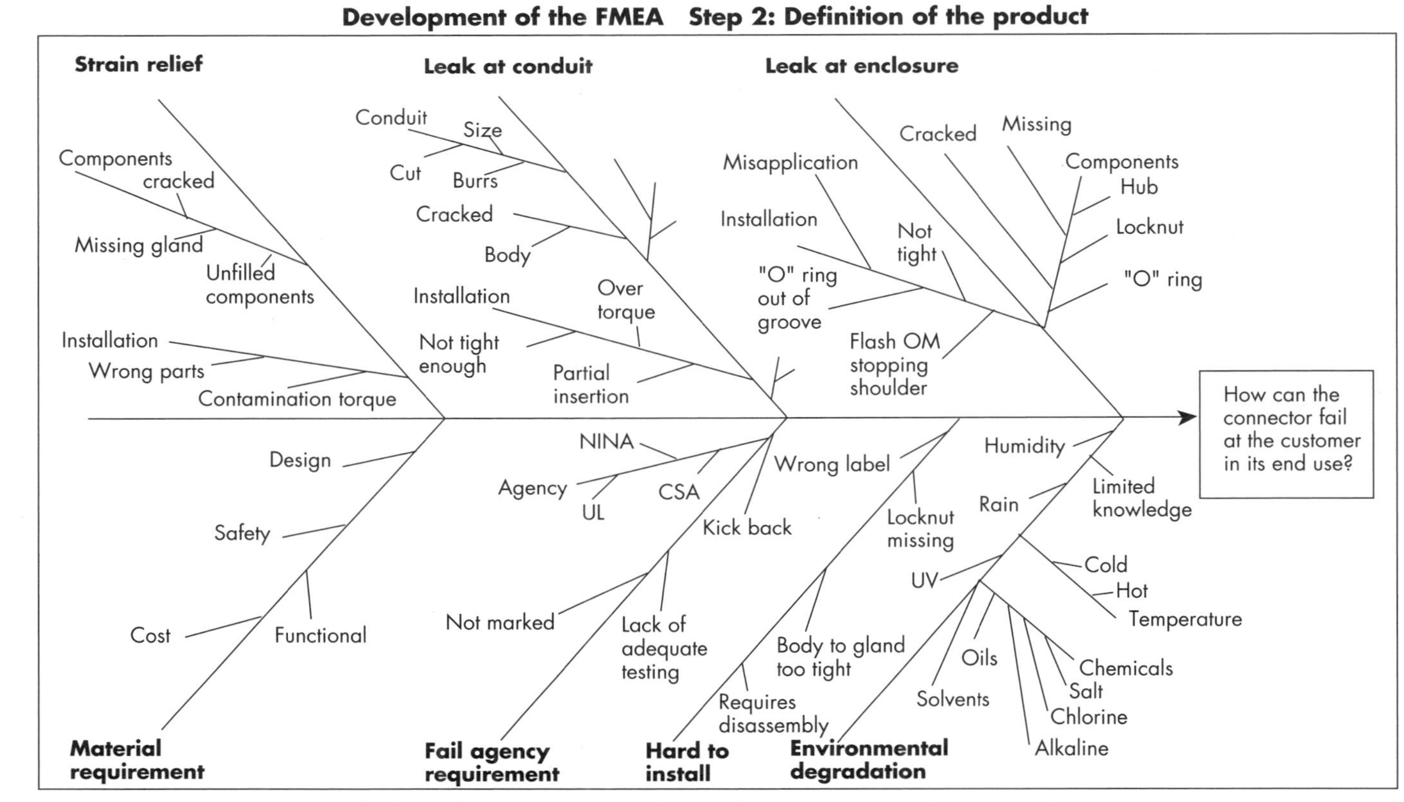

Figure 9.2 Cause-and-effect diagram. (Based on information from Figure 9.1.)

Step 3: Fill in the Design Form

Product: Industrial grade APC connector Page 1 of 5

FMEA date (original): 11/21/89 Rev.: Orig. Scheduled production release: ______

Project no. ______

Prepared by: ______ Design team ______

Approved by: ______

Product requirement	Potential failure mode	Potential effects of failure	SPC SYM	Potential causes of failure	Existing conditions					Recommended actions and status	Resulting					Responsible activity
					Current controls	OCC	SEV	DET	RSK PRT NO.		Actions taken	OCC	SEV	DET	RSK PRT NO.	
Seal at the enclosure	Leakage at enclosure	1. Equipment failure (physical) 2. Fire 3. Equipment failure (electric) 4. Rework/ Maintenance		**"O" Ring** ...missing	Visual	2	8	5	96	Review design of "O" ring for color and fit						Design team
				...Size	Cert.	1	6	9	54							
				...Cracked	Visual	1	3	9	27							
				...Out of groove	Visual	2	6	3	36							
				Body ...Cracked hub	Visual	1	2	10	100							
				...Undersize hub	Gauge	1	4	9	36							
				Flash on stopping shld.	Visual	1	4	9	36							

Table 9.1 Design FMEA. (Based on information from Figures 9.1 and 9.2.)

Project no. ____

Product: Industrial grade APC connector Page 2 of 5

Prepared by: ____ Design team ____

FMEA date (original): 11/21/89 Rev.: Orig. Scheduled production release: ____

Approved by: ____

Product requirement	Potential failure mode	Potential effects of failure	SPC SYM	Potential causes of failure	Existing conditions					Recommended actions and status	Resulting					Responsible activity
					Current controls	OCC	SEV	DET	RSK PRT NO.		Actions taken	OCC	SEV	DET	RSK PRT NO.	
Seal at the conduit	Leakage at conduit	1. Equipment failure (physical)		**Conduit**												
				...Size	Industry standard	5	6	8	240	Look for new vendor						Design team
				...Burrs	Stuffer	2	3	9	5							
		2. Fire														
				Body												
		3. Equipment failure (electric)		...Scratched	Visual	1	3	9	27							
				...Cracked	Visual	1	3	9	27							
				...Dimensional	Control chart	1	4	9	36							
		4. Rework/ Maintenance		**Installation**												
				...Partial insertion	Stuffer	4	3	9	108	Review design to allow wider range of cond. I.D.						Design team

Table 9.1 (continued)

Product: Industrial grade APC connector Page 3 of 5 Project no. ____

FMEA date (original): 11/21/89 Rev.: Orig. Scheduled production release: ____ Prepared by: ____ Design team ____

Approved by: ____

Product requirement	Potential failure mode	Potential effects of failure	SPC SYM	Potential causes of failure	Existing conditions					Recommended actions and status	Resulting					Responsible activity
					Current controls	OCC	SEV	DET	RSK PRT NO.		Actions taken	OCC	SEV	DET	RSK PRT NO.	
Strain relief	Strain relief and pullout resistance	1. Loss of conductor protection		**Parts cracked** ...Over torque	Stuffer	1	8	1	8							
				...Vibration	None	1	8	2	16							
		2. Equipment failure (electrical)		...Abuse	None	2	8	1	16							
				Dimensional ...Gland/ body thread	Control Chart	1	8	2	16							
		3. Rework/ Maintenance		...Unfilled parts	Visual	1	8	1	8							
		4. Equipment damage (mechanical)		**Installation** ...Not tight	Stuffer	3	8	2	48	Review installation instructions						Design team
		5. Fire		...Contaminant	Stuffer	2	8	2	32							

Table 9.1 (continued)

Step 4: Fill in the Process Form

Product: Industrial grade APC connector   Page 4 of 5   Project no. ______

FMEA date (original): 11/21/89   Rev.: Orig.   Scheduled production release: ______

Prepared by: ______ Design team ______

Approved by: ______

Product requirement	Potential failure mode	Potential effects of failure	SPC SYM	Potential causes of failure	Existing conditions					Recommended actions and status	Resulting					Responsible activity
					Current controls	OCC	SEV	DET	RSK PRT NO.		Actions taken	OCC	SEV	DET	RSK PRT NO.	
Ease of installation	Hard to install (without disassemble)	1. Ineffiecient installation		**Assemble** ...Over-tight Disassembled con.	Note on drawing Note on drawing	9 5	3 4	1 1	27 20							
Environ-mental integrity	Environ-mental outdoor/ industrial degradation	1. Equipment failure 2. Rework/ maintenance 3. Equipment damage		**Weather** **Chemicals**	None Stuffer	1 1	8 9	8 8	64 72	Review M&E Conduct design experiments						Production Manager Design team

Table 9.1 (continued)

Product: Industrial grade APC connector Page 5 of 5

FMEA date (original): 11/21/89 Rev.: Orig. Scheduled production release: ______

Project no. ______

Prepared by: ______ Design team ______

Approved by: ______

Product requirement	Potential failure mode	Potential effects of failure	SPC SYM	Potential causes of failure	Existing conditions					Recommended actions and status	Resulting					Responsible activity
					Current controls	OCC	SEV	DET	RSK PRT NO.		Actions taken	OCC	SEV	DET	RSK PRT NO.	
Meet agency requirement	Fail agency require-ment	1. Delist/ decertified 2. Recall 3. Requalifi-cation 4. Loss of business 5. Customer rework		**Failure to meet agency performance requirements** **Lack of proper identification**	Drawings specs./ process/ control Drawings	1 1	7 6	9 1	63 6							
Internal business requirement	Not meeting require-ment (cost/ functional design/ safety)	1. Loss of market share 2. High cost		**Design** …product/ process/ material	Design review	1	10	1	10							

Table 9.1 (continued)

Part name: Industrial grade connector Page 1 of 7

Part number: ______ Outside supplier affected:

FMEA date: ______ (Rev.): 0 Approved by (design review team) ______

Part I.D.	Process function	Potential failure mode	Potential effects of failure	SPC SYM	Potential causes of failure	Existing condition					Recommended actions and status	Responsible person	Resulting				
						Current controls	OCC	SEV	DET	Risk NO.			Actions taken	OCC	SEV	DET	Risk NO.
	Incoming inspection	Wrong material	Scrap		Shipped incorrectly Labeled wrong	Visual Certification Moisture analysis	1 1 1	8 8 8	4 4 4	32 32 32							
	Incoming inspection	Material not to specs	Scrap/failed parts		Mfg. process degraded/ contaminated material	Lab tests	1	4	9	36							
	Incoming inspection	Wrong moisture content	Brittleness/ flash		Mfg. control Bag breakage Poor sealing	Moisture analysis	3	5	1	15							
	Material preparation	Wrong material	Scrap floor		Labels Error on order form	None	1	8	10	80							

Table 9.2 Process FMEA. (Based on information from Figures 9.1 and 9.2 and Table 9.1.)

Part name: Industrial grade connector   Page 2 of 7

Part number: ______   Outside supplier affected:

FMEA date: ______ (Rev.): 0   Approved by (design review team) ______

Part I.D.	Process function	Potential failure mode	Potential effects of failure	SPC SYM	Potential causes of failure	Existing condition: Current controls	OCC	SEV	DET	Risk NO.	Recommended actions and status	Responsible person	Resulting: Actions taken	OCC	SEV	DET	Risk NO.
	Material preparation	Wrong moisture level	Brittleness/ flash		Poor analysis	None	6	5	9	270							
					Material not inspected	None	6	5	9	270							
					Wrong dryer temperature	Dessicant beds in dryers	6	5	9	270							
	Material preparation	Wrong mix pro- portions sealed	Dimensional stability cycle changes		Guessing	None	1	8	10	80							
					Bad scales	Calibration	3	2	10	60							
					Did not check router	None	1	2	10	20							
	Material preparation	Wrong material mix	Unsafe conditions		Inventory control	None	1	10	10	100							
					Wrong labels	None	1	10	10	100							
					Regrind handling	None	1	10	10	100							

Table 9.2 (continued)

Product: Industrial grade APC connector Page 3 of 7

FMEA date (original): 11/21/89 Rev.: Orig. Scheduled production release: ____________

Project no. ____________

Prepared by: ____________ Design team ____________

Approved by: ____________

Product requirement	Potential failure mode	Potential effects of failure	SPC SYM	Potential causes of failure	Existing conditions					Recommended actions and status	Resulting					Responsible activity
					Current controls	OCC	SEV	DET	RSK PRT NO.		Actions taken	OCC	SEV	DET	RSK PRT NO.	
Meet agency requirement	Fail agency requirement	1. Delist/ decertified 2. Recall 3. Requalification 4. Loss of business 5. Customer rework		**Failure to meet agency perform. requirements**	Drawings specs./ process/ control	1	7	9	63							
				Lack of proper identification	Drawings	1	6	1	6							
Internal business requirement	Not meeting requirement (cost/ functional design/ safety)	1. Loss of market share 2. High cost		**Design** ...product/ process/ material	Design review	1	10	1	10							

Table 9.2 (continued)

Part name: Industrial grade connector Page 4 of 7

Part number: ______________ Outside supplier affected:

FMEA date: ______________ (Rev.): 0 Approved by (design review team) ______________

Part I.D.	Process function	Potential failure mode	Potential effects of failure	SPC SYM	Potential causes of failure	Existing conditions					Recommended actions and status	Responsible person	Resulting				
						Current controls	OCC	SEV	DET	Risk NO.			Actions taken	OCC	SEV	DET	Risk NO.
	Robot extracts parts	Failed to pick up	Shut down operation		No part in mold	Sensors	1	8	1	8							
					Improper setup	Setup sheet	1	8	1	8							
					Robot malfunction	Sensors	1	8	1	8							
	Robot extracts parts	Failed to degate parts	Shut down operation		Robot malfunction	Sensors	1	8	1	8							
					Low air pressure	Air gauge	1	8	1	8							
					Dull cutters	Maintenance inspection	1	8	1	8							
	Robot positions parts on assembly machine	Failed to placed parts on assembly machine	Shut down operation		Assembly machine misaligned	Sensors	1	7	2	14							
					Parts not degated	Sensors	1	7	2	14							
					Incorrect orientation	Sensors	1	7	2	14							
					Flash on parts	Sensors	?	?	?	?							

Table 9.2 (continued)

Part name: Industrial grade connector Page 5 of 7

Part number ______________ Outside supplier affected:

FMEA date: ______________ (Rev.): 0 Approved by (design review team) ______________

Part I.D.	Process function	Potential failure mode	Potential effects of failure	SPC SYM	Potential causes of failure	Existing condition					Recommended actions and status	Responsible person	Resulting				
						Current controls	OCC	SEV	DET	Risk NO.			Actions taken	OCC	SEV	DET	Risk NO.
	Assembly machine	Failed to orientate parts correctly	"O" ring installed		Malfunction in pickup operation	Gripping cup	9	1	1	9							
			Cross thread parts		Screwdriver	Over torque/	3	3	1	9							
			No assembly		malfunction	height senor	2	3	1	6							
					No parts	Sensor	2	3	1	6							
	Assembly machine	Gland threaded too far	Customer disassemble parts		Screwdriver malfunction	Sensor	1	3	2	6							
					Setup	Setup sheet	1	3	2	6							
		Gland threaded not enough	Customer assembling parts		Screwdriver malfunction	Sensor	1	3	2	6							
					Setup	Setup sheet	1	3	2	6							
			Loose parts in bag		Handling/ transportation	None	1	9	2	18							

Table 9.2 (continued)

Part name: Industrial grade connector   Page 6 of 7

Part number: ______   Outside supplier affected:

FMEA date: ______ (Rev.): 0   Approved by (design review team) ______

Part I.D.	Process function	Potential failure mode	Potential effects of failure	SPC SYM	Potential causes of failure	Existing condition					Recommended actions and status	Responsible person	Resulting				
						Current controls	OCC	SEV	DET	Risk NO.			Actions taken	OCC	SEV	DET	Risk NO.
	Assembly machine	Missing "O" ring	Reject part		Bowl feeder malfunction	Level control	1	7	1	7							
					Bowl feeder empty	Track sensor	1	7	1	7							
					Wrong size "O" ring	Setup sheet	1	7	1	7							
	Assembly machine	Damaged "O" ring	Reject part		Degraded parts	Incoming inspection	1	8	8	64							
			Parts leak in the field		Machine malfunction	None	2	8	8	128							
	Assembly machine	Partially installed "O" ring	Part falls from assembly		Machine malfunction	Sensor ?	1	5	8	40							
	Packaging	No bags	Parts drop to floor		Bag roll emptied	Bell	1	3	1	3							
					Bag jammed	Sensor	1	3	1	3							

Table 9.2 (continued)

Part name: Industrial grade connector Page 7 of 7

Part number: ______ Outside supplier affected:

FMEA date: ______ (Rev.): 0 Approved by (design review team) ______

Part I.D.	Process function	Potential failure mode	Potential effects of failure	SPC SYM	Potential causes of failure	Existing condition					Recommended actions and status	Responsible person	Resulting				
						Current controls	OCC	SEV	DET	Risk NO.			Actions taken	OCC	SEV	DET	Risk NO.
	Packaging	No locknuts	Customer dissatis-faction		No part Locknut jammed	None None	3 3	7 7	8 8	168 168							
	Packaging	Wrong size locknut	Customer dissatis-faction		Material mix inventory	First article inspection	1	7	8	56							
	Packaging	Bag not fully sealed	Shut down operation		Mechanical failure	Sensor	3	6	8	144							
	Packaging	Registra-tion	No instruction on bag		Print location index	Sensor	1	5	3	15							

Table 9.2 (continued)

- The connections between elements, tasks, components
- Redundancy level and nature of the redundant systems
- Location of the system within the entire facility (if possible)

Data pertaining to functions, characteristics, and performances are required for all levels considered, up to the highest level.

System Initiation, Operation, Control, and Maintenance

The status of the different operating conditions of the system should be specified, as well as the changes in the configuration or the position of the system and its components during the different operational phases. The minimum performances demanded of the system should be defined and such specific requirements as availability or safety should be considered in terms of specified levels of performance and levels of damage or harm.

It is necessary to know the following:

- The duration of each task
- The time interval between periodic tests
- The time available for corrective action before serious consequences occur to the system
- The entire facility, the environment, and/or the personnel repair conditions including corrective actions and the time, equipment, and/or personnel to achieve them

Further information is required on

- Operating procedures during system start-up
- Control during operational phases
- Preventive and/or corrective maintenance
- Procedures for routine testing, if employed

System Environment

The environmental conditions of the system should be specified, including ambient conditions and those created by other systems in the facility. The system should be delineated as to its relationships, dependencies, or interconnections with auxiliary or other systems and human interfaces.

Usually at the design stage these facts are not (all) known and therefore approximations and assumptions will be needed. As the project progresses, the data will have to be augmented and the FMEA modified to allow for new information or changed assumptions or approximations.

FMEA or any other analysis requires certain modeling of the system (in other words, a simplification of the relevant information on the system). Some assumptions may be made about the nature of failure modes, and the seriousness of their consequences. For example, in safety situations conservative hypotheses may be made concerning the impact of certain failures on the system.

An FMEA conducted on hardware may result in decisions on effects, criticality, and conditional probabilities that involve identifying software elements and their nature, sequence, and timing. When this is the case, the facts must be clearly identified because any subsequent alteration or improvement of the software may modify the FMEA and the assessments derived from it. Approval of software development and change may be conditional upon revision of the FMEA and the related assessments.

Representation of System Structure

Symbolic representations of the system structure and operation, especially diagrams, can be used. Usually block diagrams are adopted highlighting all the functions essential to the system.

In the diagram, the blocks are linked together by lines that represent the inputs and outputs for each function. Usually, the nature of each function and input must be precisely described. There also may be several diagrams to cover different phases of system operation.

Generally graphical presentations, including those closely related to analytical methods (such as failure trees or cause-consequence diagrams) contribute to a better understanding of a system, its structure and its operation. Their use, however, raises the problem of the relationship between FMEA and these methods.

Failure Modes

A failure mode is the effect by which a failure is observed in a system component. It is important that all possible or potential failure modes of a system be listed as this is the essential basis of the FMEA.

Component or equipment manufacturers should take part in the identification of the failure modes of their products because of the following:

- For new components, reference can be made to other components with similar functions and structures and to tests performed on them.
- For commonly used components already in service, records on their performance, reported failures, and laboratory tests can be consulted.
- Complex components that can be broken down into elements can be analyzed qualitatively, treating each as a system.
- Potential failure modes can be deduced from functions and physical parameters typical of the component operation.

Classification of failure modes should be performed. Two common ways of classifying failure modes are

1. Identification of general failure modes, such as
    - Premature operation
    - Failure to operate at a prescribed time
    - Failure to cease operation at a prescribed time
    - Failure during operation
2. By listing, as completely as possible, all generic failure modes. Some of these failure modes follow.
    - Structural failure (rupture)
    - False actuation
    - Physical binding or jamming
    - Fails to stop
    - Vibration
    - Fails to start
    - Fails to remain in position
    - Fails to switch
    - Fails to open

- Premature operation
- Fails to close
- Delays operation
- Erroneous input—increase
- Internal leakage
- Erroneous input—decreased
- Loss of input
- Erroneous output—increased
- Loss of output
- Erroneous output—decreased
- Shorted (electrical)
- Fails out of tolerance (high)
- Open (electrical)
- Fails out of tolerance (low)
- Erratic operation
- Intermittent operation
- Leakage (electrical)
- Inadvertent operation
- Erroneous indication
- Restricted flow
- Communications
- No power
- Code errors
- Restricted flow
- Security issues

Common Cause Failures

In a reliability analysis, it is not sufficient to consider only random and independent failures. Some common cause failures can occur, which cause system performance degradation or failure through simultaneous deficiency in several system components, due to single source such as design error, human error, and so on. An FMEA analysis does just that.

A common cause failure is the result of an event that (because of dependencies) causes a coincidence of failure states in two or more components (excluding secondary failures caused by the effects of a primary failure).

A common cause can be subjected to qualitative analytical techniques using FMEA. FMEA is a methodology to successively examine each failure mode and associated causes and to identify all periodic tests, preventive maintenance measures, and so on. It makes possible a study of all the causes, including potential common cause failures.

These causes can be classified into five main categories.

1. Environmental effects (normal, abnormal, and accidental)
2. Design deficiencies
3. Manufacturing defects
4. Assembly errors
5. Human errors (during operation and/or maintenance)

A checklist based on these categories may be developed and used to identify in a detailed manner all possible causes that may include common cause failure. Chapter 10 provides a structure to help develop a specific checklist given a set of parameters.

The tendency is to build redundant systems to avoid failures. One must be careful because redundancy alone does not solve or eliminate all the common cause failure problems. What is necessary and highly encouraged is to combine several methods in dealing with these failures (functional diversity, redundancies of different types, physical separation, tests, and so on).

Human Factors

Some systems must be designed to allow for human error (for example, by providing mechanical interlocks on railway signals, passwords for computer usage or data retrieval). Where such provisions exist in a system, the effect of failure of the provisions will depend on the type of error. Some modes of human error also should be considered for an otherwise fault-tree system, to check the effectiveness of the provisions. Although incomplete, even a partial listing of these modes is beneficial.

Software Errors

There will be effects from malfunctions due to software errors or inadequacies. Criticality will be determined by both hardware and software design. The postulation of such errors or inadequacies and the analysis of their effects is possible only to a limited extent and is beyond the scope of the FMEA; however, the effects upon associated hardware of possible errors in software may be estimated. For specific guidelines in this area see chapter 10.

Criticality Concept

The degree of concern appropriate to any failure situation is clearly related both to its probability of occurrence and the seriousness of its effects. The criticality concept quantifies analysis and compliments FMEA. There are no general criteria for criticality applicable to a system, because this concept is fundamentally linked to that of the severity of consequences and their probability of occurrence. The severity concept itself can be defined in various ways depending on whether the objective is related to safety of life, consequential damage or loss, or service availability.

The criticality concept adds greatly to the benefits of the FMEA process by considering

- Items to be given more intensive study to eliminate a particular hazard, to increase the probability of a fail-safe outcome, or reduce the failure rate or extent and risk of resultant damage
- Items requiring special attention during manufacture and stringent quality assurance or special control of handling
- Special requirements in purchasing specifications concerning design, performance, reliability, safety, or quality assurance
- Acceptance standards for subcontractors' products including parameters that should be stringently tested
- Any special procedures, safeguards, protective equipment, monitoring devices, or warning systems
- The most cost-effective application of accident prevention resources

In order to define criticality, there must be a value scale to judge the severity of the consequences in terms of the criteria considered. The following is an example of definition, based on a classification of consequence severity of four levels (MIL-STD1629A 1980).

Criticality Level and Criticality Conditions

1. Any event that could cause degradation of system performance function(s) resulting in negligible damage to either system or its environment and no damage to life or limb
2. Any event that degrades system performance function(s) without appreciable damage to system, life, or limb
3. Any event that potentially could cause the loss of primary system function(s) resulting in significant damage to the said system or its environment and negligible hazard to life or limb
4. Any event that potentially could cause the loss of primary system function(s) resulting in significant damage to the said system or its environment and significant hazard to life or limb

The actual number of the selected levels is arbitrary. In this example, the levels are based on the combination of criteria considered relevant and concerning, respectively,

- Harm to personnel (injuries, death)
- Loss of system function(s)
- Environmental impact and material damage

The terms *catastrophic, critical, major,* and *minor* are widely used, but their definition in IEC Publication 271 may or may not suit particular FMEA usage. Words such as these could be specifically defined in individual cases.

Procedure

The wide variation in complexity of system designs and applications may require the development of highly individualized FMEA procedures consistent with the information available. The following are the fundamental steps used in FMEA cases in the EM industry.

1. Definition of the system and its functional and minimal operating requirements
   a. A complete definition of a system includes its primary and secondary functions, its use, expected performance, system constraints, and explicit conditions that constitute a failure.
   b. In addition, it may be necessary to define the acceptable functional performance of the system as a whole and of its constituent elements, as well as those performance characteristics considered unacceptable. Part of this definition should also account for regulatory requirements, especially those governing production, use, and by-products.
   c. The functional requirements should include a definition of acceptable performance for all desired or specified characteristics, in all operating and nonoperating modes, for all relevant periods of time, and for all environmental conditions.
   d. The environmental conditions such as temperature, humidity, radiation, vibration, and pressure should be clearly defined, specifically for the environment that the system will operate in (exposed and/or stored). For cybernetic systems consideration also should be given to further factors, psychological, physiological, and environmental, insofar as they affect human performances and system design or operation.
2. Development of functional and reliability block diagrams and other diagrammatic or mathematical models and descriptions
   a. Diagrams showing the functional elements of the system are necessary both for technical understanding of the functions and the subsequent analysis. The diagrams should display any series and redundant relationships among the elements and the functional interdependencies between them. This allows the functional failures to be tracked through the system. More than one diagram may

be needed to display the alternative modes of system operation. Separate logic diagrams may be required for each operational mode. As a minimum, the block diagram should contain

1. Breakdown of the system into major subsystems including functional relationships
2. All appropriately labeled inputs and outputs and identification numbers by which each subsystem is consistently referenced
3. All redundancies, alternative signal paths, and other engineering features that provide fail-safe measures
4. Establishment of basic principles and corresponding documentation in performing the analysis

Basic principles for selecting the system levels for analysis depend on the results desired and the availability of design information. The following may be of help.

- The highest system level is selected from the design concept and specified output requirements.
- The lowest system level at which the analysis is effective is that level for which information is available to establish definition and description of functions. The lowest system level is influenced by previous experience. Less-detailed analysis can be justified for any system having a mature design, good reliability, maintainability, and safety record. Conversely, greater detail and a correspondingly lower system level is indicated for any newly designed system or system with unknown reliability history.
- The specified or intended maintenance and repair level may be a valuable guide in determining lower system levels. The lowest system level at which system maintenance will be performed should first be identified. An analysis is then made of the level immediately above the lowest system level at which maintenance will be performed. On critical system elements, the analysis is performed down to the least replaceable element.

As for documentation, it is recommended that the FMEA be done in a form that is designed to meet the requirements of the system and is consistent with the set objectives. No standard form exists. Each company must design its own with its specific objectives in mind. (For a variety of FMEA forms see Appendix E.)

- **Identification of failure modes, their causes and effects, their relative importance, and their sequence**

The operation of a successful FMEA is dependent on the performance of certain critical system elements. The key to evaluation of system performance is the identification of critical elements. The procedures for identifying failure modes, their causes, and effects can be effectively enhanced by the preparation of a list of failure modes anticipated in view of

- System usage
- Particular system element involved
- Mode of operation
- Pertinent operation specifications
- Time constraints
- Environment

It is important to remember that in the FMEA the definitions of failure modes, causes, and effects depend on the level of analysis and they may be interchanged depending on the level addressed. For example, a failure may be an effect, and a cause may be a failure depending on the level of analysis. Furthermore, as the analysis progresses, the failure effects identified at the lower level may become failure modes at the higher level. Similarly, the failure modes at the lower level may become the failure causes at the higher level and so on.

- **Identification of failure detection and isolation provisions and methods**

The methods of detection of the failure mode are described. Failure modes other than the one being considered which give rise to an identical indication are analyzed and listed. The need for separate failure detection of redundant elements during operation should be considered.

- **Identification of design and operating provisions against particularly undesirable events**

The relative significance of the failure should be recorded on the FMEA form. The idea is that the form will clearly show the true behavior of the equipment in the presence of an internal malfunction. Other provisions include

- Redundant items that allow continued operation if one or more elements fail
- Alternative means of operation
- Monitoring or alarm devices
- Any other means permitting effective operation or limiting damage

When the functional elements (either the hardware or software) are rearranged or reconfigured in the design, the capability will change. Following this, the relevant failure modes should be reexamined before repeating the FMEA.

Special remarks also may be incorporated in the FMEA form to denote

- Any unusual conditions
- Effects of redundant element failures
- Recognition of especially critical design features
- Any remarks to amplify the line entry
- References to other FMEAs or entries for sequential failure analysis
  –Determination of event criticality (FMECA only)
  –Evaluation of failure probability (FMECA only)
  –Search for specific combinations of multiple failures to be considered (optional)
  –Recommendation

Note that one may conduct an FMEA with full benefits without completing an FMECA.

References

Bass, L. 1991. Cumulative supplement to *Products liability: Design and manufacturing defects.* Colorado Springs, Colo.: Shepard's/McGraw-Hill.

Blanchard, B. S. 1986. *Logistics engineering and management.* 3d ed. Englewood Cliffs, N.J.: Prentice Hall.

Eachus, J. 1982. Failure analysis in brief. In *Reliability and quality handbook,* by Motorola. Phoenix: Motorola Semiconductor Products Sector.

Kececioglu, D. 1991. *Reliability engineering handbook.* Vols. 1 and 2. Englewood Cliffs, N.J.: Prentice Hall.

MIL-STD-1629A. 1980. *FMEA.* 24 November. Washington, D.C.: Department of Defense.

CHAPTER 10

FMEA and Computers: Hardware and Software

Chapter 2 provided a general overview of what the FMEA is and how it works. Chapters 4 through 7 discussed the specific mechanics of the FMEA. This chapter focuses on the computer industry. The focus is as specific as possible without being too rigid. Thus, this chapter will identify the entire concept of hardware and software and will address specific issues dealing with the FMEA.

As discussed earlier, the fundamental reason for conducting an FMEA is to prevent known and potential failures from reaching the customer. Indeed, if an organization wants to be world-class it has to be a market-driven organization with the emphasis of satisfying the customer through process improvement.

This section addresses this prevention mode of operation using the FMEA approach. It will not, however, repeat the methodology that is identical to that for system, design, process, and service. Rather it will focus on the thought process for identifying possible problems.

Failures have been defined as something that fails to meet customer expectations. In the computer industry that may be interpreted as

- Day-to-day problems
- Process problems (Writing a software program is a process)
- Communications
- Rework defect removal
- Coding
- Creative analysis

- Meetings with functional (users) customers
- Paperwork
- Integration
- Clerical support
- Field failures
- Scheduling
- Late delivery
- Lost order
- Customer dissatisfaction
- Software error
- Typing errors

Although all of these may not be present in all situations, they do represent a major portion of the problems that are being faced in the industry. Figures 10.1 and 10.2 represent failures that could have been avoided if proper planning and an FMEA had been conducted.

To prevent these irregularities from happening repeatedly, the focus must be on three basic concepts.

1. What is the cause of the error?
2. What will prevent it in the future?
3. Implement the preventive actions.

The moral of these three concepts is that everyone should learn from every error.

The learning process will begin with appropriate planning and appropriate definition of the needs, wants, and expectations of the defined customer. To make sure that this learning process starts with a chance of being completed one must assemble a team, and the team must define the work items under three categories.

1. Product strategy
2. Objectives and goals of the project
3. Statement of requirements

Look at these work items from a specific functional perspective.

- AT&T's entire long distance network was once shut down.
- The bank of New York once had to borrow $21 billion in emergency overnight funds from the Federal Reserve, incurring a cool $5 million in interest charges.
- Because of a decimal point error, Wells Fargo Bank in California overstated the income of 22,000 employees in statements to the IRS.
- International lenders could lose up to $650 million because of inadequate software used to process student loans.
- According to the General Accounting Office (GAO) only 2 percent of a sample group of $6.77 million in software projects was used as delivered.

2 percent used as delivered	$119,000
3 percent useable after changes	$198,000
29 percent paid but never delivered	$1,950,000
47 percent delivered but never used	$3,200,000
19 percent used after extensive rework	$13,000,000

- Technical failures per 1000 lines of source code during the first year.
  Japan 1.96
  United States 4.44
- Lines debugged source code delivered per person year of work
  Japan 12,447
  United States 7,290
- $1 in design = $100 fix in the field

Figure 10.1 Software failures.

Lahner, J., 1991. U.S. Software Suppliers Could Face Hard Times. *The Quality Observer* (November): 1, 8–9.

Information Development

- Book plan—may be incomplete
- Documentation standards—standards may not be clear
- Examples—documentation does not match the code
- Books—documentation is late
- Responses to reader comment form—spelling errors

1. The PCjr
2. Top View, the company's first attempt at multitasking software
3. Losing early members of its original PC design team to competitors such as Compaq, Apple, and Dell Computer
4. The second release of the 3270 PC Control program, which consumed so much memory that users could not run applications
5. Early problems with PC AT hard disk drives
6. A design oversight in the XT 286 meant that add-in cards designed for the PC AT were too tall to be inserted in the XT 286
7. The company's failure to introduce the first 80386-based PC, which gave Compaq a competitive edge as a high-technology innovator
8. Ceasing production of the best-selling PC AT without having an effective PS/2 available to replace it
9. Failure to keep abreast of rapid technological and market changes in the laptop/portable markets; case in point: IBM's portable and convertible
10. The failure to competently and unequivocally demonstrate to users the benefits of the Micro Channel Architecture, which led to its slow acceptance in the market
11. Delivery problems with the PS/2 Model 80-111 in early 1989
12. Hard drive and early delivery problems with the 25MHz PS/2 Model 70

Figure 10.2 IBM's 12 biggest PC blunders.

As reported in "IBM's PC Strategies for the 1990s," a report published by the Computer Technology Research Corp, Holtsville, N.Y.

Testers

- Test plan—does not specify the environment
- Test cases—cases not updated to latest release level
- Documentation—test escapes or inadequate test coverage
- Verified code—test and build plan conflict

Developers

- Design material—design built on self-expectations rather than the customer's

- Documentation—incorrect level of design
- Unit tests—build or driver content lists incomplete
- Plans, schedules—escapes from unit tests
- Team assignments—unit test scaffolding incorrect
- Fixes—design or programming tips not documented

Managers

- Evaluations—late evaluations
- Development plans—lengthy transition of trainees and/or new hires
- Education plans—development plans not done; education plans not up to date
- Budgets—budget did not include software purchases
- Status—status information is missing and/or is incorrect

Early Support Program

- Support program—support has not been planned
- Customer selection criteria—the true customer has not been identified
- Requirements documentation—not all requirements have been understood; fixes not delivered to all sites; documentation not kept up to date with fixes

Defect Description

What is the error? Can it be defined? Is it really the problem? Can it be quantified? To answer these questions, a team with a leader must work together for a resolution that everyone will have ownership. To do that an understanding of group dynamics must be in place. For example, similar to any situation of a team environment, a leader will conduct the meeting.

First, the leader must establish the role by physical, verbal, or procedural methods. In each case the leader must communicate that she or he is in charge of the team process, *not the content.* This is very important because a team does not have to prove its expertise. The leader is there to facilitate the process.

Second, the leader must establish the role of the team members again through physical, verbal, or procedural means. In no uncertain terms the leader must communicate to the team members the importance of their contribution as well as make them feel important and that their opinions count (Stamatis 1992). Reestablish the commitment of *no fear* for whatever the opinion is (Deming 1986).

The leader always must ask probing questions and in some cases leading questions to make the team start the thinking process. Some questions may be in the form of the following:

1. *Communications*—What was *not* communicated from whom to whom? Some of the considerations may be
   - Circulate reports on...
   - Provide tools that will...
   - Define common focal points for...
   - Get correct information to the right people at the right time
   - Embedded communication requirements in process for...
   - Communicate process changes to...
2. *Education*—What was *not* understood? Some of the considerations may be
   - Document education requirements that will...
   - Provide back-ups for key jobs that will...
   - Target to job responsibility by...
   - Use forms (standard whenever possible) to share information
   - Make education timely by...
   - Focus on projects, *not* people, titles, and/organizations
3. *Oversight*—What was overlooked or not considered? Some of the considerations may be
   - Improve process by streamlining...
   - Reduce distractions when...

- Add to common error list…
- Help peer reviews that…
- Reduce interruptions when…
- Develop a tool to…
- Create a checklist to…
- Centralize communication for…

4. *Process*—How did the process require or encourage introduction of the error? Some of the considerations may be
   - Make processes flexible by…
   - Recognize the need for continual improvement by…
   - Reduce complexity through…
   - Automate the task of…
   - Communicate changes in… to…
   - Evaluate processes versus schedule when…
   - Improves inputs by…
   - Allocate resources to…
   - Define ownership of processes for…
   - Develop a work item focus by…
5. *Transcription*—What technique or procedure was used? Some of the considerations may be
   - Eliminate need for…
   - Develop tools to ease the task of…
   - Reduce interruptions during…
   - Specify training for…

If, on the other hand, an error has been identified, the leader must ask leading questions for confirmation and understanding of the problem. The leader may probe or guide the discussion in the areas of who, what, where, agreement, disagreement, and possible alternatives to the problem. At all times the leader must be careful not to use the why, address a problem on a personal level, or put people on the defensive.

Another function of the leader is to summarize the events of the meeting, so that benchmarks in the progress of resolution may be established for future reference. All that is going on in the meeting must be recorded by either the leader or a secretary.

The FMEA may contribute the following benefits from a development perspective to the software industry considering the relative effectiveness of the team effort in conjunction with the specific methodology of the FMEA.

Type of action	**Effectiveness** (percent)
Improve or extend testing	0
Improve or introduce inspections	0
Do it better next time	0–30
Improve product documentation	30–60
Improve process documentation	30–60
Add to common errors list	30–60
Education	30–60
Redesign/rewrite code	60–100
Redesign part/subassembly	60–100
Tool (avoid or remove)	60–100
Improve system or production	60–100

To generate specific actions the team must be willing to ask specific questions about the project at hand. For example,

- If the team could change anything at all, what would it change to prevent this error in the future?
- How could the team automatically eliminate this error?
- How could the team remove this error where it exists in other parts of the product?

The questions seem easy and straightforward, but the experience of the author indicates that the answers to these questions are the heart of the team effort for improvement. The answers to these questions will depend on the time allotted for discussion and the willingness of the team to participate. To encourage participation, the leader may want to make sure that each suggested action is

- Specific and clearly understood
- Stated with an active verb
- Expressed as a complete thought
- As effective and understandable as the team can make it
- Practical
- Usable right now
- Based on sound rationale
- Justifiable
- Data driven

One example as to where and how an FMEA may be used is in the data processing system (DPS). Some of the concerns at the starting point follow.

Implementation of the System

- Summary files (open, close, action, archive)
- Control tables for customization
  –Product control tables
  –Verification tables
  –Configuration tables
  –Search synonyms

Security

- Lock files
- System passwords
- Authorizations to specific points

Installation, Customization, and Operation

- Set up disconnected identification
- Set up tool and database disks
- Customize DPS configuration

- Customize product control table
- Customize verification table

For software the following may be addressed.

- Documented development process
- Focus on customer
- Verification and validation
- Early software manufacturing involvement
- Benchmarking
- Dependency management
- In-process measurements
- Defect prevention
- Robust change control
- Tools
- Education
- Reuse
- Linkage to other product
- Productivity and cycle time

The model follows for performing an FMEA on software.

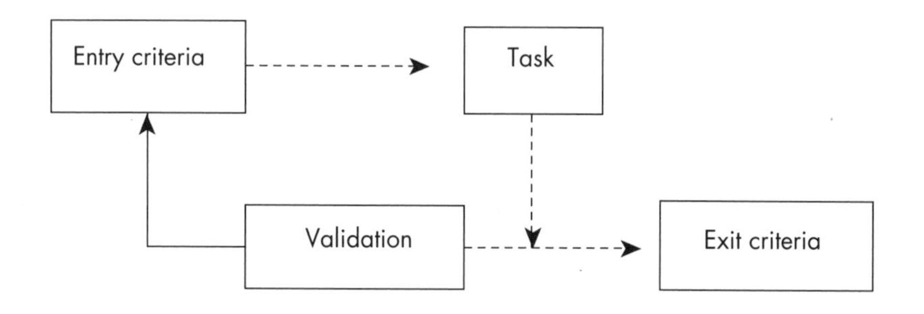

Figure 10.3 shows the overview software structure for an FMEA application. It is interesting to note, that the possibility exists to conduct an FMEA in the development stage, changing control stage, and evaluation and implementation stage.

In each case one can follow up with evaluation to determine if effectiveness has been accomplished. If not the cycle can start over again.

For a detailed example of a software analysis examine the code. Some questions and/or possibilities that the FMEA may address are

- Is the code completed?
- Does the code meet the customer's requirements?
- Is the first draft evaluated?
- Are the appropriate standards applied?
- Is the appropriate library initialized?
- Have the appropriate drivers and macros for the drivers been finalized?
- Has the *clear del* been created?
- Is the code placed in the appropriate *clear del*?
- Have all the test tools been developed?
- Are the tools appropriate?
- Have the project and product databases been updated?
- Have all the technical and publication inspectors been identified?
- Have all the unnecessary calculations been removed?
- Have all path lengths been identified?
- Is the path length appropriate?
- Does the code meet the product's coding conventions?
- Have all the reinspection criteria been followed?
- Have all deviations been accounted for?
- Does the code follow the structure programming?

A checklist of specific issues and/or concerns may be developed based on the above questions. An example of checklist in specific areas are

Logic missing

- Are all constants defined and used?
- Are all defaults checked explicitly (for example, blanks in an input stream)?

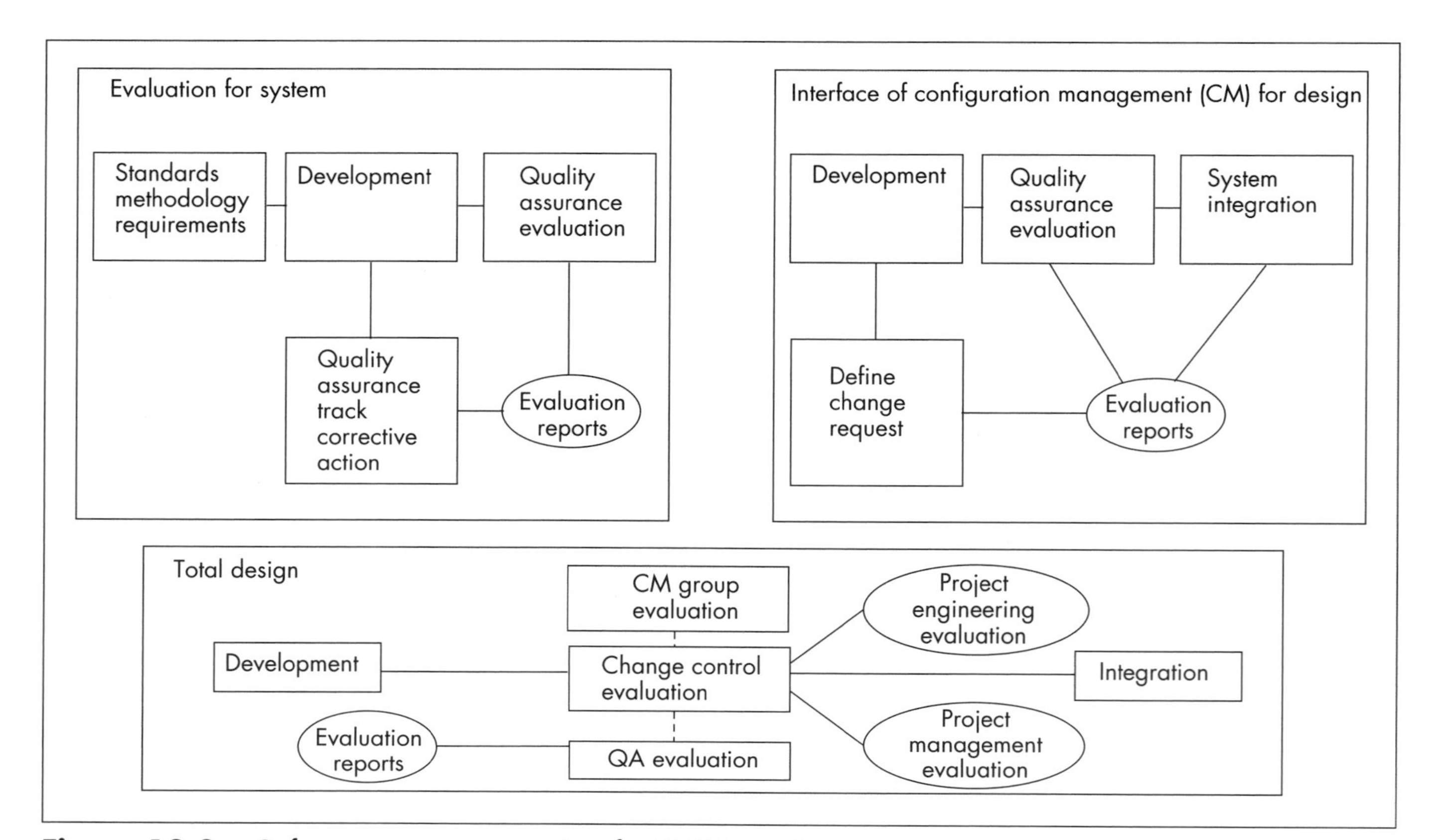

Figure 10.3 Software structure overview for FMEA application.

- If character strings are created, are they complete? Are delimiters used as necessary?
- If a key word has many unique values, are they all checked?
- Are all key words tested in a macro?
- Are all key word related parameters tested in a service routine?
- Are all increment counts properly initialized (0 or 1)?
- After processing a table entry, should any value be decremented/incremented?
- Is provision made for possible processing at logical checkpoints in the program (end-of-file, end-of-volume, and so on).
- If a queue is being manipulated, can the execution be interrupted? If so, is the queue protected by a locking structure? Can the queue be destroyed over an interrupt?
- After queueing/dequeueing, should any value be decremented or incremented?
- Should any registers be saved on entry?
- Should registers be restored on exits?

Logic wrong

- Are literals used where there should be constant data names?
- On comparison of group items, should all fields be compared?
- Are internal variables unique?

Logic extra

- Are all data areas necessary?
- Does this module contain redundant logic (tests for something already screened out)?

Linkage

- Are all correct linkage macros used?
- When a module is an external subroutine?
- When a module is the last module to be called?

Control block definition/usage missing

- Are pointers declared as XX bit pointers?
- Is the bit configuration for input/output parameters defined?
- Is the field properly defined in the control block/data area?
- If the design is dependent on building/creating/deleting various control blocks/data areas, is it provided for in the code?

Common errors in the code stage

- Coded incorrect copyright
- Consider all operating environments when developing code
- Consider all possible error conditions
- Fiche flag all code changes
- Communicate all changes to components with dependencies on the organization
- When changing a macro, make sure all affected modules are paralleled
- Compare each stage of development against previous stage(s) to prevent oversights

Bits, bytes, ptrs, or regnot reset after processing (This is very common.)

- Initialize all variables before usage—never assume zeroes
- Initialize all fields of a control block; do not leave garbage
- *Reserved* fields must be initialized to zero
- Early termination—pointer, values not reset
- First buffer released, but not others

Be concerned with data types and variable lengths

- When defining counters, make sure boundaries are sufficient—try to predict possible future size changes
- Make code data independent whenever possible

- Control block not fullword aligned
- DCL not properly aligned
- Field definition as FIXED (XX) based later on CHAR string (which is not properly aligned, causing bugs)
- Bit versus mask equate used
- FIXED (XX) versus CHAR (X)

Consider all permutations of parameter values

- Parms passed in wrong order
- Update return code on error conditions

Open and close all I/O files properly

- Use a different work area for each I/O file
- When changing I/O file lrecls and blksizes, make sure file definitions reflect these changes

Duplicate labels

- Made up labels as coder went along
- Names misunderstood or confused with others
- Do not assume control block bit meanings

Parenthesis missing in parameter

- Comma missing
- Did not understand implications of in-line macros
- Register destroyed by in-line macro
- Macro assumed space for save area
- Moved code (copied code) is very error prone. Deleted code is very error prone. Check all paths and instructions. (This is very common.)
- Easy code change near complex code change is error prone
- Use positive logic whenever possible

Loop logic errors

- Consider all flags on each iteration
- Consider three loop conditions: first pass, last pass, and middle iteration
- Initialize all flags and counters before entering loop
- Increment counters on each iteration
- Update all pointers on each iteration
- Wrong bit checked

Resetting of bits in wrong place

- Flag set in control block at wrong time

DO WHILE instead of DO UNTIL

- OR instead of AND on IF statement
- Tested OFF instead of ON
- X'YY' should have been X'10'

Assembler 1/2 word usage

- Make sure data will always fit in 2 bytes
- Make sure high-order bytes are cleared
- Registers clobbered (This is very common.)
- Wrong registers used
- No addressability established
- Save areas not bumped; register does not point to save area

How to Get Started

The sequence for performing an FMEA in the computer industry with the intent of (1) identifying the problem, (2) providing for a solution, and (3) providing for follow-up is

- Form a team

- Select a leader
- Collect or anticipate error data
- Have a kickoff meeting(s)
- Do a causal analysis
- Conduct the FMEA
- Utilize the action team
- Gather feedback and other communications
- Analyze results
- Confirm results
- Gain publicity
- Extend application
- Monitor improvements

A System Approach to Implementation

A complete system development methodology outline using the six phases of project management follows (Kerzner 1992). Please note that within each phase there is a tremendous opportunity to develop an FMEA.

Phase 1—Project Initiation Phase

Activity task	Approvals required
• Prepare direction of project	Project management administrator, QA, project manager, project leader
• Project assessment	
• Define the education requirements	ISD training and development

• Education schedule	Project manager, project leader
• Prepare project plan	
• Management objectives	Project manager, project leader
• Assumptions and constraints	Project manager, project leader
• Current system resource requirements	Project manager, project leader
• Proposed system resource requirements	Project manager, project leader, department manager
• Cost benefit analysis	Project manager, project leader
• Design considerations	Project manager, project leader
• Approval mechanism	Project manager, project leader Requisition approvals as noted
• Major milestones	Project manager, project leader
• Planning	Project manager, project leader, department manager
• Authorization to proceed	
• Review project initiation phase	Project management administrator, QA, information services director, Non-ISD director or chair

Phase 2—General Analysis Phase

Activity task	Approvals required
• Prepare general system design proposal	
• Prepare cover sheet, table of contents	Project manager, project leader
• Interview schedule	Project manager, project leader
• Interview the functional areas	Project manager, project leader, interviewee
• Current system/subsystem description	Project manager, project leader
• Project objectives	Project manager, project leader
• Assumptions and constraints	Project manager, project leader
• Proposed system/subsystem description	Project manager, project leader
• Data requirements analysis	Project manager, project leader, data administrator
• Security analysis	Project manager, project leader, security administrator, department managers
• Resource requirements analysis	Project manager, project leader, department managers
• Expected benefits	Project manager, project leader, department managers
• Cost-benefit analysis	Project manager, project leader

• Future considerations	Project manager, project leader
• Alternatives evaluation	Project manager, project leader
• Planning	Project manager, project leader, department managers
• Authorization to proceed	
• Review general analysis phase	Project management administrator, QA, information service director, Non-ISD director or chair

Phase 3—System/Subsystem Design Phase

Activity task	Approvals required
• Prepare system/subsystem design specs	
• Prepare cover sheet, table of contents	Project manager, project leader
• Define the purpose	Project manager, project leader
• Functional comparison	Project manager, project leader
• Detail comparison (external devel)	Project manager, project leader
• Function analysis	Project manager, project leader, interviewee
• Data requirements analysis	Project manager, project leader, data administrator, database administrator

• Data element analysis	Project manager, project leader, data administrator
• Processing analysis	Project manager, project leader
• Control requirements	Project manager, project leader
• Application analysis	Project leader, data administrator, database administrator
• Simulation development	Project manager, project leader, data administrator
• Simulation walk-through	Department managers
• Normalize data	Data administrator
• Define logical file structure design	Data administrator
• Define physical file structure design	Database administrator
• Informal file structure design review	Data administrator, database administrator, project leader, system analyst
• Doc. file structure design assump.	Data administrator, database administrator
• Define file structure install req	Database administrator
• Define file structure security	Data administrator
• Formal file structure review	Data administrator, database administrator, project leader, system analyst
• Integrated application and file structure	Project leader, data administrator, database administrator
• Procedure analysis	Project manager, project leader

• System acceptance criteria	Project manager, project leader, department managers
• Final resource requirements analysis	Project manager, project leader, department managers
• Expected benefits	Project manager, project leader, department managers
• Cost benefit analysis	Project manager, project leader
• Planning	Project manager, project leader, department managers
• Authorization to proceed	
• Review system/subsystem design phase	Project management administrator, QA, information service director, Non-ISD director or chair

Phase 4—Development Phase

Activity task	Approvals required
• Acquire resources for implementation	Project manager, project leader
• Prepare user procedures	Project manager
• Develop training plan	Project manager, project leader
• Prepare system test plan	Project manager, project leader
• Prepare installation plan	Project leader, database administrator

Activity task	Approvals required
• File structure install (test)	
• Define file structure elements	Data administrator
• Define file structure records	Data administrator, database administrator
• Physical file description	Database administrator
• File restructure	Database administrator
• Create new files	Database administrator
• Prepare file backups	Database administrator, department managers
• Programming specifications	Project leader
• Application roundtable	
• Program coding	
• Unit testing	
• Revise specifications	Project leader
• Document operations procedures (see operations documentation req)	
• Planning	Project manager, project leader, department managers
• Authorization to proceed	
• Review system development phase	Project management administrator and QA, information service director, Non-ISD director or chair

Phase 5—System Acceptance and Implementation Phase

Activity task	Approvals required
• Execute system test plan	Project manager, project leader, project management administrator, QA

• Execute training plan	Project management administrator, QA
• Execute conversion	Project management administrator, QA
• Execute parallel	Project management administrator, QA
• Review the documentation	Project administrator, and QA
• Planning	Project manager, project leader, department managers
• Authorization to proceed	
• Review system acceptance and implementation phase	Project management administrator, QA information service director Non-ISD director or chair
• Implementation	
• Notification	
• Install files	
• Install operations documentation	
• Implementation summary report	

Phase 6—Postimplementation Audit Phase

Activity task	Approvals required
• Interview schedule	
• Interview the functional areas	
• Prepare summary report	
• Authorization to close the projectect	
• Review postimplementation audit phase	ISD director, Non-ISD director or chair

The team composition for the hardware design and process FMEA may reflect the cross-functionality and multidisciplines of the appropriate personnel for the design and/or the process. It may follow the general guidelines discussed in the section on team development.

The team composition for the software FMEA should follow the general guidelines of the team composition of cross-functionality and multidisciplines as appropriately defined. In this team, however, it must be emphasized that the team must reflect a makeup of developers who work on the same release or line item; or who go through development stages at approximately the same time. Logically, the person who may be the leader is the chief programmer because he or she is responsible for the ultimate product.

A typical software FMEA team may be include

- Programmer
- System analyst
- Security
- Developer
- Data administrator
- Database administrator

Other appropriate personnel may be added or consulted as needed. For example,

- Code personnel
- Information system personnel
- Projectect manager
- Customer
- Supplier
- Release coordinator

References

Deming, W. E. 1986. *Out of the crisis.* Cambridge, Mass.: Massachusetts Institute of Technology.

Kerzner, H. 1992. *Project management.* 4th ed. New York: Van Nostrand Reinhold.

Lahner, J. 1991. U.S. software suppliers could face hard times. *The Quality Observer* (November): 1, 8–9.

Stamatis, D. H. 1992. *Leadership—Training manual.* Southgate, Mich.: Contemporary Consultants.

CHAPTER 11

FMEA and the Semiconductor Industry

The main focus of the FMEA in semiconductor industry is to determine the cause for device malfunction or parametric degradation. This entails experienced technical personnel pursuing a disciplined analytical approach leading to a root cause of failure. This approach is the FMEA.

Although the methodology of conducting a FMEA is the same as that discussed, there are some distinct differences in the failure mode identification, causes of failure, and control mechanisms in preventing these failure modes.

This chapter addresses some of these differences and presents a summary of possible failure modes testing mechanisms.

Some of the major failure modes in the semiconductor industry are

- Electrostatic discharge (ESD)
- Thermal changes
- Oxide ruptures
- Current heating
- Hot or cold sites on ICs
- Reclaim scrap
- Purity of gold bullion
- Plating uniformity
- Wafer surface problems
- Organic contaminants

- Powder or residue problems
- Solvent or liquid contamination
- Molding compound contamination
- Over/undercuring
- Identification
- Dimensional problems
- Solder bump thickness
- Composition ratios of binary thin films
- Plating thicknesses
- Thicknesses of multilayer backmetal systems
- Trace metals in process solutions and waters
- Concentration of major, minor, and trace elements in
  –Alloys
  –Thin films
  –Solders
  –Residues
- Oxide and junction defects
- Silicon lattice defects
- Grain size
- Oxide slope
- Surface topography
- Bonding defects
- Construction parameters
- Composition
- Intermetallic formation and degree of wire bond deformation
- Surface leakage
- Visual rejects
- Bond voids
- Discoloration
- Flaking
- Dewetting

- Bridging
- Pinhole defects
- Field oxide
  –Patterning/etching defect
- Foreign matter/particulate
  –Interlevel oxide
- Passivation
  –Cracks/crazing
- Defusion
  –N type, doping level
- Scratch
  –Pre-interlevel oxide
  –Mechanical surface damage
- Dielectric breakdown
- Oxide in contact
- Physical damage
- Substrate
  –Dislocations
  –Stacking fault
- Broken leads
- Off bond
- Lifted bond and die
- Lifted bond and post/lead/frame
- Swept wipes
- Broken wire bond
- Heel break and wedge/stitchbond
- Neck break and ball bond
- Improper wire dress
- Scribe grid short
- Wire package short
- Handling damage
- Contamination on external leads

- Flow in mask
- Foreign matter on die
- C-S leakage
- Underetched metal
- Wrong EPI
- Overetched VIA(s)/PREOHMICS
- Passivation pinholes
- Interlayer passivation cracks
- Visual contamination
- Break/reversible leakage
- Mixed product
- EOS
- Metal deformation
- Mechanical surface damage
- Intermetallics
- Retest with specification
- Undetermined
- Equipment malfunction
- Lost units
- Hermeticity rejects
- Metal shorts
- Probe defects
- Corrosion
- Chopped bond
- Silicon defect in collector junction
- Excess photoresist pattern
- C E leakage/short

This list is not exhaustive, but meant as an example of the complex failure modes and/or causes one may encounter in pursuing FMEA in the semiconductor industry. The list should provide the reader with a starting point of investigating problems to seek improvements to existing and/or future designs and/or processes.

As an example of using the list in a prevention mode, consider the problem of ESD. ESD is the process of accumulation of large amounts of charge on a body—resulting in high electric potential and rapid, uncontrollable discharge through another body at lower electric potential with the possibility of damage occurring. There are at least three models developed that describe the methods by which ESD damage can be induced to semiconductor devices (Motorola 1992). They are

1. *The human body model*—It consists of a 100 pF capacitor in series with 1500 ohm resistor and typifies the characteristics of the human body.
2. *The machine model*—It consists of only a 200 pF capacitor with no series resistance.

   Note: These two models are based on the premise that a high potential outside source inflicts an ESD event upon the semiconductor with the possibility of causing damage.
3. *The charged device model*—With this model the device develops voltage potential and upon contact with a lower potential object discharges to cause the ESD event.

After one isolates the problem, the potential for damage is recognized. Based on that knowledge one should plan accordingly for the elimination of the failure either through design changes or process changes. These changes may be incorporated into the company's system of improvement by defining a prevention course for the specific failure or incorporating any one of the tests explained later in this chapter.

First, examine the prevention mode of operation by focusing on the prevention of ESD. The process of prevention for the ESD may be as follows:

- Training of personnel for development of ESD prevention culture
- Special studies for development of ESD resistance structures, materials, and design rules

- Measurement/characterization program using human body and machine models/simulation
- System audit for assuring compliance to ESD policy process

After the skeleton of the policy has been established, the FMEA team may focus on very specific outcomes for prevention. The following specific items may be considered.

- What should the specification documenting minimum ESD prevention procedure cover?
- What specification of approved materials for ESD prevention should be considered? Why? Why not?
- Are specification documenting assessment procedures for compliance verifiable? How?
- Do all areas (wafer fab, assembly, and so on) implement ESD prevention procedures?
- Are individual wafers packed in vacuum-sealed envelopes made of conductive materials?
- Do all working stations have conductive tabletops, properly grounded?
- Are wrist straps for static control used appropriately?
- Are ionization devices used where appropriate for neutralizing static charges?
- Are the floors conductive or antistatic?
- Are shoe straps used by personnel when appropriate? How is one assured that the practice is followed?
- Do antistatic envelopes for storage accompany the product?
- Are antistatic packaging practices followed for transport of the product?
- Are high dielectric materials avoided?
- Are soldering irons grounded properly?

These questions are only a sample of possibilities for one failure in the ESD. One can further the probe with additional reliability questions and testing.

The quest for a superior product in the semiconductor industry is emphasized by a serious focus on quality and reliability. To reach this superior product, superior designs with conservative design rules and process checkpoints must be in place. Even though this superior product is achievable, much planning has to be done in both the design and process FMEA. The reason for this so-called excessive planning is because in the semiconductor devices there is an inherently very low failure rate (Motorola 1992). As a result, the industry uses techniques with accelerating testing to assess the reliability, functionality, and performance of the semiconductors before they reach the customer.

Some of the guidelines to achieve this superior quality with accelerated testing are

- Minimum levels of latch-up protection are required.
- Guidelines are in place to reduce the effects of hot carrier injection.
- All design work is based on simulation.
- Testability must be realistic in new designs.
- There are minimum levels of input protection for ESD.
- Stress relief design rules must be communicated to all appropriate personnel to reduce the effects of packaged induced stress.
- Specific guidelines must be in place for maximum current density allowed in metal lines, contacts, and vias to eliminate electromigration concerns.

Although this text will not discuss in detail each of the available statistical techniques and all the individual testing techniques used today in the industry, it will focus on a summary presentation of such tests for both the design and process FMEA to detect individual failures. This does not suggest that all the tests identified here have to be used in a given FMEA to control failures. Rather, they are presented as brief descriptions to help the engineer plan for controlling the design and/or process. Some of these tests available for design control follow:

Temperature Cycle. This test accelerates the effects of thermal expansion mismatch among the different components within a specific die and packaging system. This test is performed based on MIL-STD 883 or MIL-STD 750.

High Temperature Operating Life. This test accelerates failure mechanisms that are thermally activated through the application of extreme temperatures and the use of biased operating conditions.

Autoclave. This environmental test measures device resistance to moisture penetration and the resultant effects of galvanic corrosion.

Thermal Shock. This test is similar to temperature cycle testing. It emphasizes differences in expansion coefficients for components of the packaging system. This test also is based on MIL-STD 883 and MIL-STD 750.

Temperature Humidity Bias. This test is designed to measure resistance of plastic-encapsulated circuits.

HAST/PTHB (Pressure-Temperature-Humidity-Bias). This test accelerates the effects of moisture penetration with the dominant effect being corrosion.

Cycled Temperature Humidity Bias. This test is used to examine a device's ability to withstand the combined effects of temperature cycling, high humidity, and voltage (test can be run without bias).

Power Temperature Cycling. This test determines the effects of alternate exposures to extremes of high and low temperature with operating voltages periodically applied and removed.

Low Temperature Operating Life. This test is performed to accelerate hot carrier injection (HCI) effects in semiconductor devices by exposing them to room ambient or colder temperatures with the use of biased operating conditions.

Power Cycling. This test is performed at a constant ambient temperature with operating voltage(s) periodically applied and removed, producing a DTJA, typically between 50 degrees and 150 degrees Celsius.

Salt Atmosphere. This test evaluates the corrosive effects of a seacoast-type atmosphere on device and package elements. It is performed based on MIL-STD 883 or MIL-STD 750.

Lead Integrity. This test examines the mechanical properties of a device's leads, welds, and seals. It is performed based on MIL-STD 883 or MIL-STD 750.

Solder Heat. This test examines the device's ability to withstand the temperatures present in soldering over a more extended period as compared to the typical exposure levels in a production process.

Constant Acceleration. This test is based on MIL-STD 883 or MIL-STD 750. It is used to indicate structural or mechanical weaknesses in a device/packaging system by applying a severe mechanical stress.

Variable Frequency Vibration. This test is based on MIL-STD 883 or MIL-STD 750. It is used to examine the ability of the device to withstand deterioration due to mechanical resonance.

Write/Erase Cycling of EEPROMs. This test evaluates the effects of repeated programming and erasing excursions on EEPROM devices without corruption of data.

High Temperature Storage/Data Retention. This test measures the stability of semiconductor devices, including the data-retention characteristics of EPROM and EEPROM devices, during storage at elevated temperatures with no electrical stress applied.

System Soft Error. This test detects errors caused by impact ionization of silicon by high-energy particles.

Mechanical Shock. This test is based on MIL-STD 883 or 750. It is used to examine the ability of the device to withstand a sudden change in mechanical stress, typically due to abrupt changes in motion as seen in handling, transportation, or actual use.

These tests are a good starting point to make sure that the design has built-in mechanisms that control performance, reliability, and function. When one reaches the process, however, one may want to do a failure analysis of an existing (known) problem. If that is the case, one might proceed with some of the following nondestructive tests.

X-ray Inspection. Check for voids and uniformity, component and wire placement.

Acoustic Imaging. Check for package or internal component voiding or delamination.

Hermeticity Testing. Check for hermetic integrity of the package.

Device Bake or Stress. Check for parametric shifts or recovery.

Electrical Retest. Check for failure if it is present or if it has recovered.

Residual Gas Analysis (RGA). Used to analyze the internal atmosphere of a hermetic cavity device.

Wet or Dry Chemical Decapsulation. Used to remove the encapsulant with acids or solvents to expose the internal components or die surface.

Thermal/Mechanical Decapsulation. Used to remove the lids on either metal or ceramic packages by either remelting the lid-attached material or by grinding into the package.

Microcross Sectioning. Used to reveal various features of the assembly.

Internal Inspection. Used to check if the failure mechanism is still present.

Internal Diagnostic Testing

These techniques are readily used for failure identification. All are considered to be nondestructive.

Liquid Crystal Testing. Used to identify localized spots during device operation.

Voltage Contrast. Used to observe voltage level variations on internal interconnects. It also may be used in a dynamic mode.

Electron Beam Induced Current (EBIC). Used to induce current in relation to its location.

Emission Microscopy. Used as a diagnostic instrument to image the light emission of specific device features.

Thermal Imaging. Used to give a graphical representation of the surface temperature of the device/component under test.

Electrical Probing and Isolation. Used to determine further electrical characterization.

E-Beam Testing. Used to induce and measure localized signals to diagnostically evaluate internal circuitry on a semiconductor.

Focused Ion Beam (FIB). Used for localized material removal to allow access to underlying features for subsequent evaluation. This method also may be used to allow for electrical connection and device troubleshooting.

Electron Microscopy. A generic term to denote the types of electrons or x-rays generated using an electron microscope.

Secondary Electrons. Used for imaging of the specimen.

Backscattered Electrons. Dispersive X-ray Spectroscopy. Chemical—Surface Analysis. These tests are used to evaluate the composition of materials in the course of an analysis.

Secondary Ion Spectroscopy (SIMS). Used to depict profiling of trace contamination of surfaces, thin films, thick films, multilayer structures, and interfaces.

Auger Microscopy. Used for characterization of surface containments which may inhibit bondability and solderability, contribute to surface leakage, or constitute visual rejects.

Fourier Transform Infrared Spectroscopy (FTIR). Used for identification of extractable organic components from a device or wafer surface. Identification of organic contaminants, including polymers, on surfaces of an appropriately reflective substrate. Identification of unknown solid organic compounds, powders, or residues. Solvent or liquid organic sample identification.

Electron Spectroscopy for Chemical Analysis (ESCA). X-ray Fluorescence (XRF). Used for qualitative elemental screening of unknown samples often for subsequent characterization by other methods.

Chemical Deprocessing. There are many methods available for removal of various layers and materials for the deprocessing of semiconductor devices; however, the primary technique is the use of wet chemicals such as acids or solvents for selective etching. Plasma etching or dry etching can be used when wet chemicals are not preferred.

Failure Simulations. Used to evaluate failures under control conditions in which the device was perceived to have failed. Information gained can point to a device weakness or even specific application-related stress.

References

Motorola. 1992. *Reliability and quality handbook.* Phoenix: Motorola Semiconductor Products Sector.

CHAPTER 12

FMEA and ISO 9000

This chapter focuses on the liability of products as defined by the ISO 9000 standards and the need of the application of an FMEA to fulfill the specific requirements of ISO 9001, ISO 9002, and ISO 9003. By no means is this an exhaustive discussion on the issue of liability and the European Union (EU) and/or the ISO 9000 standards.

The Product Liability Directive was passed in 1985. Its aim is to provide consumers with a measure of liability protection. Prior to this directive, EU product liability protection did not exist and European consumers had little protection under a few national laws. Generally, when a consumer was injured by a defective product, the old principle of *caveat emptor* (buyer beware) prevailed (Kolka 1992).

The Product Liability Directive changed the system. If someone is injured and can prove that a defective product caused the injury, the manufacturer is strictly liable, regardless of fault.

In 1989, the EU council adopted the Machinery Safety Directive which creates uniform design and safety requirements for machinery. Its purpose is to promote safety and to eliminate barriers to trade that arise from different safety standards between the community sates.

In June 1992, the EU adopted the Product Safety Directive. This directive lays out basic principles of product safety and is meant to complement the Product Liability Directive.

In addition to all these directives, the EU has proposed a Services Liability Directive, for the service industry in Europe. This is considered a critical element for the economic success of Europe. The proposed directive seeks to protect consumers and to resolve legal differences between community states.

The present and proposed directives have important implications for any company that does business with the EU in either regulated or nonregulated products. It is expected that these new liability and safety laws will bring the EU more in line with consumerism and become more closely related to the United States (Harral 1993; Middleton 1993; Stamatis 1992).

The legal issues of the directives raise some very important questions. For example,

- The Product Liability Directive employs the theory of strict liability. It holds a manufacturer liable, regardless of fault or negligence. What is the full scope of this law?
- The Product Liability Directive does not require proof that a product is both defective and unreasonably defective, as in the case of U.S. law. As such, it will be easier to prove a defect under the EU law than under U.S. law. What preventive steps can companies take to reduce their liability exposure?
- The Product Safety Directive requires manufacturers to mark and monitor the safety of their products. What kind of duty is required by this monitoring process?
- How broad is the scope of the law concerning service supplier liability?
- Does the definition of service supplier in the proposed directive include agencies that certify quality assurance systems, certify and endorse products, or create standards? What about the liability of ISO 9000 consultants?

These questions raise more questions and concerns for the European and U.S. companies, and for the international companies at large. The Product Liability Directive has changed the climate in new and profound ways.

Article 1 of the Product Liability Directive states, "The producer shall be liable for damage caused by a defect in his product."

Article 2 of the directive defines a product as, "all movables, with the exception of primary agricultural products and game...product includes electricity." A movable is any product, not a fixture, that is not attached to or part of real property.

In Article 3 of the directive a producer is defined as "The manufacturer of a finished product, the producer of any raw material or the manufacturer of a component part, and any person who, by putting his name, trademark or other distinguishing feature on the product, presents himself as its producer."

Article 6 of the directive defines defective product as

1. A product is defective when it does not provide the safety which a person is entitled to expect, taking all circumstances into account, including
   a. The presentation of the product
   b. The use to which it could reasonably be expected that the product would be put, and
   c. The time when the product was put into circulation

2. A product shall not be considered defective for the sole reason that a better product is subsequently put into circulation.

With this limited overview of the directive and the concept of liability from an ISO 9000 perspective, it is imperative that the domestic and multinational companies change the way they do business.

One way to change is to require specific responses to distinct laws in reference to liability. One such response is the failure mode and effect analysis (FMEA).

Paragraph 19.0 of ISO 9004-1 specifically addresses product safety and liability. It states

> The safety aspects of product or service quality should be identified with the aim of enhancing product safety and minimizing product liability. Steps should be taken both to limit the risk of product liability and to minimize the number of cases by
>
> Identifying relevant safety standards in order to make the formulation of product or service specifications more effective.
>
> Carrying out design evaluation tests and prototype—or model—testing for safety and documenting the test results.

> Analyzing instructions and warnings to the user, maintenance manuals and labeling and promotional material in order to minimize misinterpretation.
>
> Developing a means of traceability to facilitate product recall if features are discovered that compromise safety and to allow a planned investigation of products or services that are suspected of having unsafe features (see ISO 9004-1: 11.2, 14.2, 14.6, and 15.4).

One may argue that the ISO 9004-1 is not a certifiable standard. It is only a guideline and therefore has no application to the company at large.

It is the opinion of the author that since the entire set of standards is a holistic approach to quality, and prevention oriented, paragraph 19 of ISO 9004-1 specifically codifies product liability and describes the procedures necessary to create safe products. If the court believes otherwise, the author suspects that noncompliance would be disastrous both in the product liability domain and compliance of the spirit of ISO 9000.

To offer some further support to the argument, study paragraph 5.2.5 of ISO 9004-1 entitled Operational Procedures.

> The management system should emphasize preventive actions that avoid occurrence of problems, while not sacrificing the ability to respond to and correct failures should they occur.

If that is not enough, look further.

- Can the company document its design function? Has it done an FMEA? How about a Hazard Analysis? How does the company interpret "give due consideration to 'safety' and 'environmental and other regulations'"?
- What does the company do to consider "fitness for purpose" and "safeguards against misuse" as required by 8.2.5? In the same clause, reliability, maintainability, and serviceability (including safe failure and safe disposability) are addressed.
- What can the company do to communicate the results of 8.4, which asks for design review (evaluation of performance, durability, safety, reliability, maintainability under expected storage and operation conditions)? How can it do this?

- How can the company substantiate the quality records on clause 5.3.4? The impact of not having the appropriate substantiation may prove devastating.
- How can the company prove continual improvement through customer feedback in clause 7.3?
- How does the company satisfy the requirements of clause 8.4?
- How will the company demonstrate that it performed the design reviews provided in clause 8.4.2?
- Can the company document its market readiness review as provided in clause 8.7?
- How does the company handle clause 10 of ISO 9004-1?

One can see that the language of ISO 9004-1 provides provisions that may greatly expand liability issues. For example, paragraph 0.4 talks about "Risks, Costs, and Benefits." The exact language is

> Risk, cost, and benefit considerations have great importance for both company and customer (0.4.c....Consideration has to be given to risks related to deficient products or services (0.4.a)....Consideration has to be given to increased profitability and market share.

In the author's opinion, this language talks and addresses a risk-benefit analysis. It must be remembered, however, that the EU Product Liability Directive has specifically rejected a risk-benefit analysis in considering whether product is defective in favor of a user expectation test.

From all the clauses of ISO 9004-1 discussed here it is evident that the EU has made it clear that the principle focus in the product liability area is on product liability *prevention,* rather than on liability per se.

This prevention may be accomplished by audits, tests, and reliability studies. One specific method is the FMEA. The reason for the applicability of the FMEA into the system of ISO 9000 standards is because FMEA is a prevention tool in both design and manufacturing.

There are many clauses that require the intervention of an FMEA in ISO 9001, ISO 9002, and ISO 9003. This text will touch on the most important clauses.

ISO 9001 in clause 4.4.1 states

> The supplier shall establish and maintain procedures to control and verify the design of the product in order to ensure that the specified requirements are met.

Elsewhere, ISO 9001 clause 4.4.2 states

> The supplier shall draw up plans that identify the responsibility for each design and development activity. The plans shall describe or reference these activities and shall be updated as the design evolves... The design and verification activities shall be planned and assigned to qualified staff equipped with adequate resources.

ISO 9001 clause 4.4.3 states

> Organizational and technical interfaces between different groups shall be identified and the necessary information documented, transmitted and regularly reviewed.

Furthermore, ISO 9001 in clause 4.4.4 requires "design requirements...and their selection reviewed...." Clause 4.4.4 requires proper identification for "those characteristics of the design that are crucial...." Clause 4.4.5 (the entire section) defines requirements that the FMEA can handle efficiently. Clause 4.4.6 requires "appropriate review and approval of all changes and modifications."

Clauses 4.9 and 4.14 in ISO 9001 definitely ask for appropriate proof of documentation in both process control and corrective action, respectively.

ISO 9002, clauses 4.9 and 4.14 also ask for appropriate proof of documentation in both process control and corrective action, respectively.

ISO 9003 clause 4.5 contains the strongest language implying an FMEA technique as part of "appropriate records."

The reason why the FMEA applies to all the aforementioned clauses of ISO 9000 is that the FMEA lives the intent and spirit of the prevention mode of the entire standard. One must always remember that the FMEA by definition is a tool that wants to optimize the system, design, process, and/or service by modifying, improving, and/or eliminating any known or potential problems.

References

Harral, W. 1993. ISO 9000: What every supplier must know. *ACTIONLINE* (Automotive Industry Action Group, Southfield, Mich.) (May): 16–18.

ISO 9001. 1994. *Quality systems—Model for quality assurance in design, development, production, installation and servicing.* Geneva, Switzerland: International Organization for Standardization.

ISO 9002. 1994. *Quality systems—Model for quality assurance in production, installation and servicing.* Geneva, Switzerland: International Organization for Standardization.

ISO 9003. 1994. *Quality systems—Model for quality assurance in final inspection and test.* Geneva, Switzerland: International Organization for Standardization.

ISO 9004-1. 1994. *Quality management and quality systems elements—Part 1: Guidelines.* Geneva, Switzerland: International Organization for Standardization.

Kolka, J. W., and G. G. Scott. 1992. *Product liability and product safety directives.* Fairfax, Va.: CEEM Information Services.

Middleton, D. 1993. Implementing ISO 9000 in the automotive industry. In *Symposium on project management in the automotive industry.* Troy, Mich.: Project Management Institute and International Institute for Learning.

Stamatis, D. H. 1992. ISO 9000 standards: Are they for real? *Technology* (Engineering Society of Detroit) (August): 13–17.

CHAPTER 13

FMEA and the Medical Device Industry

The proliferation of the ISO 9000 standards and the related Product Liability Directives have caused acceptance of these standards by both companies and countries. The United States is no different. Even though in 1991 the United States accounted for 40 percent of the overall $18 billion market it must comply with the new EC directives (Kolka 1992).

In the process of complying, however, there are some questions that should be addressed.

- Which standards apply to medical devices and to what extent?
- Will certification be required?
- What kind of testing is required?
- Who is going to perform the testing?
- Are there applicable directives for medical devices? What do they require?
- How are the compliance procedures going to be met? Are there considerations for detail?
- What is the overall plan of EC in the area of medical devices?

Athough these questions are some of the most critical ones, this chapter will address the applicability of several standards to the reliability of *safe* products in the medical device industry. Furthermore, the FMEA is recommended on the basis that it will contribute much toward the safety of the products.

First, one must define what a medical device is. A medical device is an instrument, apparatus, implement, appliance, implant, or other similar or related article, that is intended for use in the treatment of humans, contraception, or in diagnosis (Kolka 1992). (A device achieving its principal intended purpose through chemical action within or on the body is excluded from the definition.)

Second, one must study the appropriate standards relating to medical devices.

- European Norm (EN) 46000 for medical devices
- BS 5750: Part 1 Quality Systems: Specification for design, manufacture, and installation.
- BS 5781: Part 1 Specification for measurement and calibration systems
- BS 6000: Guide to the use of BS 6001, Sampling procedures and tablets for inspection by attributes
- BS 6001: Sampling procedures and tablets for inspection by attributes
- BS 6002: Sampling procedures and charts for inspection by variables for percent defective
- HMSO (Guide to Good Manufacturing Practice—GMP)
- U.S. Current GMP: Part 210-211 Pharmaceuticals
- U.S. Current GMP: Part 820 Medical Devices
- U.S. Controlled Substances Regulations: Part 1301-1304.

The Active Implantable Medical Devices Directive (AIMD) was adapted on June 1990 and became effective January 1, 1993. As of now, there is a two-year transition for compliance.

The application of AIMD is to

> Any active device which is intended to be totally or partially introduced, surgically or medically, into the human body or any medical intervention into a natural orifice and which is intended to remain after the procedure.

It also covers

- Custom-made active implantable medical devices developed for individuals by medical specialists

- Any active implantable medical devices intended for clinical investigation.

The implications of the AIMD to FMEA are in Procedure A (Article 1a). To complete this procedure, a manufacturer must take into account the language and requirements of

- ISO 9001
- Annex 2
- EN 46001
- EN 50103

For the requirements of a FMEA program in ISO 9001 see chapter 12. The requirements of Annex 2 ask that verification and declaration of conformance be present in the design and manufacturing. The requirements of the EN standards request

- Surveillance systems
- System consistency
- Record maintenance
- Safety
- Complaint feedback

The Medical Devices Directive (MDD) was proposed on August 30, 1991. The implementation date is set for July 1, 1994, with a three-year transition period.

As for liability concerns, the MMD raises the same issues as the AIMD and IVD. Specifically, Annex I: Essential Requirements, Section 2 of all three directives states

> The solutions adopted by the manufacturer for the design and construction of the devices must conform to safety principles taking account of the generally acknowledged state of the art.

In addition, the MDD raises the following concerns

- Personnel responsibility for product quality
- Labeling
- Warnings

- Complaints
- Recalls
- Feedback system
- Environmental control and manufacturing conditions
- Maintenance of quality records

One of the most relevant clauses for FMEA application is in Annex 1, paragraph 1, regarding "acceptable risk" which states

> Devices must be designed and manufactured in such a way that... any risk which may be associated with their use constitute acceptable risks when weighed against the benefits to the patient and are compatible with a high level of protection of health and safety.

The In Vitro Diagnostics Directive (IVD) was introduced in August 1992 and is still considered a draft proposal. It is designed for noninvasive use with body fluids or tissues, however, and it is considered to be one of the preventive law programs that will help reduce liability exposure.

The FDA medical device developments essentially are regulations for the manufacturers in pursuing quality standards. These regulations are called Good Manufacturing Practices (GMP) for Medical Devices.

Some of the requirements that GMPs require are

- Equipment service reports
- Process validation
- Design control

The intent of the requirements is to reduce the number of defects and whenever possible improve the design and/or process.

The issue of all the mentioned standards and directives is *product liability prevention.* As such, manufacturers dealing with medical devices can prevent accidents and liability issues by

- Providing safe products with legally adequate warning labels and instruction manuals (appropriate for their intended users).
- Creating safety committees to analyze relevant data and to determine whether or not some action is necessary. The *some* may be changes or modifications in design or process.

- Establishing document retention policies (not only for legalistic reasons) to track improvements, changes, and to document the process from a historical perspective.

Is all this relative to FMEA? The answer is a definite *yes*. Why? Because, as already shown, product liability creates defenses for manufacturers. Generally, the availability of data (especially for improvement) will make it easier to defend against a claim of defective product. An FMEA is precisely the instrument that will define the need for the data and determine how the data should be implemented as part of the design or process improvement.

In addition, an FMEA is part of a prevention mechanism within the organization that includes analysis of standards and laws as they apply to a given product. This application in the medical device industry allows the FMEA to help identify current or potential problems.

Is the FMEA applicable to the medical device industry? Yes. The medical device industry is becoming a global market. As such, the standards that they are going to follow for continual improvement and elimination of problems are the ISO 9000 series. Specifically, ISO 9001, ISO 9002, ISO 9003, and ISO 9004-1 call for some important and critical issues relating to medical devices. Some of these issues include

- Risks
- Problem analysis
- Health and safety
- Complaints
- Problem prevention
- Corrective action
- Incorporation of new technologies
- Unintended use and misuse
- Regulation requirements
- Documentation
- Record keeping
- Reporting

Obviously the FMEA has a very strong role to play in the medical device industry. As for the FDA and the GMPs, the FDA is moving toward harmonizing the new GMPs and the EC medical device directive.

References

Active Implantable Medical Devices Directive (AIMD). June 20, 1990. Brussels: Council Directive.

Amended proposal to MDD. July 28, 1992. Brussels: Council Directive.

In Vitro Diagnostics Working Document. (IVD). October 1988. European Diagnostics Manufacturing Association.

ISO 9001. 1994. *Quality systems—model for quality assurance in design, development, production, installation and servicing.* Geneva, Switzerland: International Organization for Standardization.

Kolka, J. W., D. M. Link, and G. G. Scott. 1992. *Medical device directives: Certification, quality assurance, and liability.* Fairfax, Va.: CEEM Information Services.

Medical Device Directive. August 30, 1991. Brussels: EC Commission to the EC Council.

Food and Drug Administration. April 1990. Part 820. United States Good Manufacturing Practices (GMP) for Medical Devices. Rockville, Md.: Department of Health and Human Services.

Epilogue*

The FMEA can be a legal document. As such, the engineer, the entire organization, and everyone involved with producing or using FMEAs must be familiar with the ramifications of the FMEA content.

It is hoped that by having an FMEA as part of the total records in the organization's system, design, process, and/or service the courts will take a favorable view of the liability or negligence at hand. It is important to note that the liability or negligence of the product or service (either because of deficiencies in design or safety considerations) is not negated in any way, shape, or form—it always stays with the product and the organization.

Conversely, punitive damages may be proved to be one area where the FMEA can contribute infinitely. Punitive damages may be minimized and/or eliminated, if it can be proven that a proper FMEA was conducted and the appropriate risks were identified and acted upon with state-of-the-art tools.

As it was addressed in the section covering liability, the courts recognize that a perfect system, design, process, and/or service is not attainable. Therefore, a business and the engineer must prove that the risks taken for the system, design, process, and/or service are accounted for, analyzed, and the appropriate actions are in place to either minimize or eliminate them.

---

*Portions of this chapter were adapted from the following source with permission: Bass, L. 1993. Cumulative supplement to *Products Liability: Design and Manufacturing Defects.* Colorado Springs, Colo.: Shepard's/McGraw-Hill.

The FMEA does all that plus it contributes to the efficiency, manufacturability, maintainability, and integrity of the product and/organization. In addition, the FMEA can contribute to minimizing liability through other documentation in the organization.

One of the primary supplemental contributions the FMEA can make in minimizing product liability exposure involves marketing and advertising claims. The information must be technically correct. Specifically, sales agreements should be carefully reviewed in order not to expose the company to unnecessary product liability claims. Many product liability loss prevention programs are compromised because the company has accepted unnecessary product liability from its suppliers or distributors. The company should make conscious choices as to whether to give hold-harmless agreements to the suppliers, distributors, or customers.

All sales personnel and distributors of a company's products should be made aware of their role in product liability prevention and risk reduction. The representations by the sales force as they relate to durability, performance, compatibility, safety, and recommended uses carry great weight in a court of law. The FMEA is the perfect tool to contribute to the knowledge base of such activity. Some guidelines for the sales forces follow.

1. Do not make unrealistic statements regarding the performance of products. The capability of a company's products to meet standards and other performance criteria is the result of engineering analysis and testing. These are the groups that know best the performance limitations of the product. The engineering department should be consulted in the event of any questions as to whether products can meet the performance criteria of a particular user.

2. Do not get involved in any unnecessary discussions regarding product failures or defects with people outside the company. Sales personnel should promptly notify the product review board of any information relating to product failures or defects. Without the advice of company management or legal counsel, no further discussions should be held.

3. Do not suggest or approve the use of any product for a specific purpose which is not explained in the product literature. A great deal of time and effort has gone into the development of the prod-

uct literature. This has been with a view toward both the ability of the products to perform successfully and of potential product liability exposure. Recommending a product for a purpose that has not been approved by engineering or the product safety review board may be offering a customer a warranty that the company cannot fulfill. Statements of this nature will increase the product liability exposure of the company.

4. Do not use adjectives and superlatives to describe the performance and use of products unless they accurately reflect the capability of the product. Representatives of product performance and use should be carefully worded to be sure that they are accurate and of the proper degree. With the use of superlatives, a salesperson may unintentionally expose the company to a high product liability risk.

5. Do not inform a customer that a product conforms to the specifications of a given code or standard unless this information is contained in the product literature.

6. Do not get involved in discussions regarding the legal interpretation of warranties or contracts. Discussions relating to warranties or contracts are best left to legal counsel. When in doubt, refer the question back to management for clarification.

7. Do not recommend or suggest the use of replacement parts manufactured by others unless they are equivalent to original manufacturing company's parts.

8. Do not make specific recommendations to customers regarding how a product should be assembled or installed except in accordance with applicable service bulletins and manuals.

9. Promptly report all customer complaints.

10. Report all instances or alleged instances regarding product failure, product defects, property damage, or bodily injury.

11. Make realistic oral and written statements regarding the performance of products.

12. Discard old and/or obsolete advertising or sales literature.

13. Do not assume that labels and warnings on the product are sufficient to prevent liability. They may not be adequate.

Creation and Retention of Documentation

The questions always seem to be "What is appropriate documentation?" and "What is the retention period for such documentation?" All documentation begins with an identification of the types of records that are significant to the design, manufacturing, and distribution of the product. These records fall into the following categories:

1. Research and development records indicating how and why a product design was approved for manufacture. These documents include records of alternative designs which were analyzed, tested, and rejected. In addition they may include analyses and tests that document compliance with industry and/or government standards and other design criteria.
2. Production records documenting the purchase of component parts and raw materials; production steps and processes; and product blueprints defining the materials, surface finishes, and tolerances allowed during manufacturing.

3. Quality control and inspection records describing general quality control procedures, as well as acceptance or rejection criteria for the product.

4. Quality assurance records describing procedures and/or rejection criteria for the product.

5. Sales and marketing records, including brochures, promotional literature, product specifications, product models or samples, and instructional materials which accompanied or proceeded introduction of the product into the marketplaces. Marketing records also include the results of market research relating to the functions and potential market for a new product. Sales records include the names, location, and sales of distributors, and the names or description of purchasers of the product.

6. Product service and performance records, including reports of failures of the product and injuries caused by the product. Service records also include warranty returns, repairs, requests for spare parts, and the service history of the product. Of particular impor-

tance in this category are any documents that might establish that the manufacturer knew or should have known that a defect or problem existed in the design of the product.

Practices to Minimize the Risk of Harmful Documents

Documents are created during the development, production, sale, and use of a product in order to run the company effectively. (The actual length of the documentation will depend on the scope and definition of the project, the requirements of the organization itself, and/or its customers, and/or the government regulations.) The problem of creating damaging documents must be dealt with at all levels of the company. For many products, safety decisions are made by middle and lower management. Most documents are created at that level, or at the engineering, manufacturing, or sales level. The company needs honest, accurate documentation of test and inspection results. This includes failure analysis of products that have not performed satisfactorily in service or are the subject of a consumer complaint. These documents should be prepared in a way that will not prove damaging to the company in the event it is required to defend itself from a product liability lawsuit.

For example, the quality assurance department should not use the legal term *defect.* They should substitute the term *nonconforming,* or *noncompliance* and describe the nonconformance or noncompliance. A company can use such practices to minimize the likelihood of creating damaging documents during the product's life cycle. The tool for such document is the FMEA.

Critical Documents Should Be Reviewed and Maintained by One Responsible Person

Safety-critical and sensitive documents prepared during each stage of the product's life cycle should be maintained under the direction of one designated person. Documents pertaining to that stage of the product's life cycle should be reviewed by this person. A document control instead of copies should be used for especially sensitive documents. Any comments that personnel have regarding the document are made on attachments to the document. Answers or responses to these comments can be prepared and attached to the document package so that a complete history of comments and resolutions is maintained. If necessary, a revision of the FMEA could be considered, if appropriate.

A Clear and Complete Product History File Should Be Maintained

The manufacturer should establish a product history file which documents why certain design alternatives, warnings, or instructions were chosen. The records should also show why other possible design and warning alternatives were rejected. The same type of documentation should be established for the manufacturing, quality control, marketing, sales, use, and disposal phases of the product's life cycle. The perfect document for such documentation is the FMEA.

Unfavorable Reports or Test Results Should Be Evaluated

Unfavorable test results, reports, or complaints regarding the product or service must be evaluated for potential corrective action. The organization cannot ignore information relating to a potential safety problem. Not responding to unfavorable results or comments may provide the basis for both general and punitive damages. Even a negligent response by a concerned manufacturer probably will eliminate the possibility of an award for punitive damages. Again, the FMEA is the perfect tool to help develop a trail or history of the problems and improvements to the product or service.

Appendix A

Formulae

This appendix provides some of the advanced equations used in the electronic industry for failure identification, as well as miscellaneous information about block diagrams, how and when to use the appropriate reliability calculations, and so on. Specifically, the following items are covered.

- The Arrhenius equation and the Eyring Type model
- The Eyring and Reich-Hakim model
- Equations for accelerated factors
- Reliability block diagrams
- Development of block diagrams from system to units
- Equations for the calculation of the MTBF in series
- Equations for the calculation of the MTTF in parallel
- Equations for the reliability and mean life of complex systems with cyclical units
- Conversion factors for failure rate measurement units

The Arrhenius Equation

$$R(T) = Ce^{-\frac{Ea}{KT}}$$

where C is a constant, E_a is activation energy in e^V, T is temperature in °K, K is Boltzman's constant 8.625×10^{-5} e^V/°K

Acceleration equation:

$$\frac{r_1}{r_2} = e^{\frac{E_a}{K}\left(\frac{1}{T_2} - \frac{1}{T_1}\right)}$$

where $\frac{r_1}{r_2}$ is the acceleration factor.

Activation energy equation:

$$E_a = e\frac{K 1n\left(\frac{r_1}{r_2}\right)}{\left(\frac{1}{T_2} - \frac{1}{T_1}\right)}$$

Standard deviation equation:

$$\sigma = 1n\left(\frac{t_{50}}{t_{16}}\right)$$

where t_{50} is the median life or time to 50 percent failure and t_{16} is the time to 16 percent failure.

The Eyring Type Model

$$t_{50} = Ae^{\frac{\phi}{K} \times \frac{1}{T}} \times e^{\frac{B}{RH}} \times E_{CA}^{-1}$$

Where A and B are constants.

ϕ is the activation energy in e^V

T is the temperate in °K

K is the Boltzman constant in e^V/°K

RH is relative humidity in %

E_{CA} is the electric field in the corrosion area.

The Eyring and Reich-Hakim Model

$$t_{50} = A\left(e^{\frac{\phi}{K}} e^{\frac{1}{T}} eBe^{\frac{1}{RH}}\right)E_{CA}^{-1}$$

$$= G\left(e^{\frac{T+RH}{T(RH)}}\right)E_{CA}^{-1}$$

where G is a factor combining all the constants A, $e^{\phi/K}$, e^{B}

Equations for Accelerated Factors

The equations for acceleration factors associated with temperature and voltage accelerated burn-ins use the following.

The Arrhenius equation is:

$$\text{Accel. factor} = \exp\frac{\theta}{K} \times \frac{1}{Td} - \frac{1}{Ts}$$

where:

K = Boltzman's Constant, 8.62E – $5e^{V}/°K$

θ = activation energy, e^{V}

T_s = stress temperature, $°K$

T_d = operating temperature, $°K$

The voltage acceleration equation is:

$$\text{Accel. factor} = \exp\frac{C}{T_{ox}} \times (VS - VD)$$

where:

C = electric field constant

T_{ox} = thickness of gate oxide, $Å$

VS = stress voltage, V

VD = dynamic life operating voltage, V

The purpose of burn-in is to create accelerated temperature and voltage stress conditions to screen out early life failures, especially those related to MOS oxide defects.

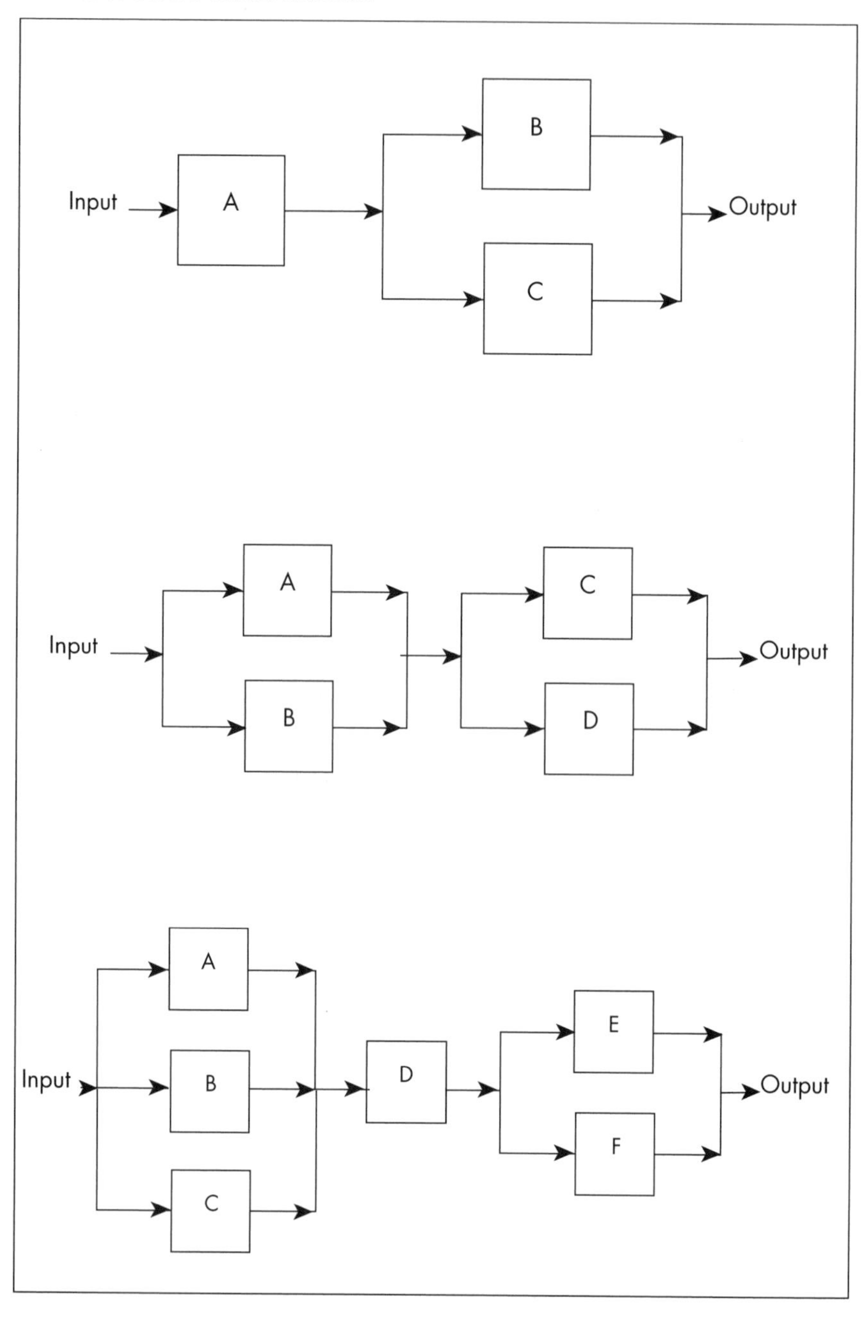

Figure A.1 Reliability block diagrams.

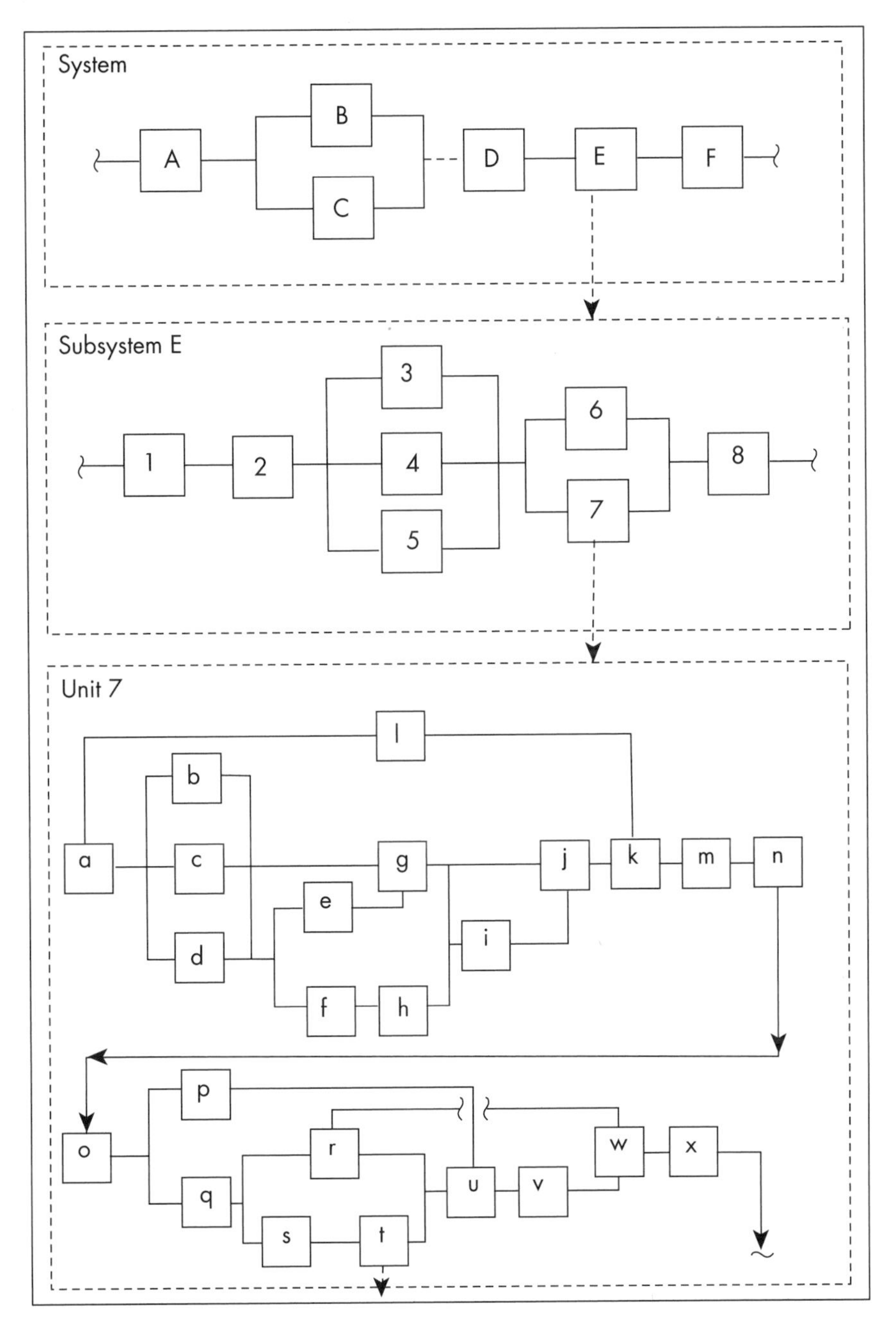

Figure A.2 Development of block diagrams from system to units.

Case number	System structure	MTTF	Comment
1		$\frac{1}{\lambda}$	Single, constant failure rate unit
2	$\lambda(T) = kT$	$\left(\frac{\pi}{2k}\right)^{\frac{1}{2}}$	Single, linearly increasing, failure rate unit. In the Rayleigh pdf $k = \frac{2}{2}$. In the Weibull pdf $\beta = 2$, $k = \frac{2}{\eta^2}$, and $\gamma = 0$.
3	$\lambda(T) = \frac{\beta}{\eta}\left(\frac{T-\gamma}{\eta}\right)^{\beta-1}$	$\gamma = \eta\Gamma\left(\frac{1}{\beta} + 1\right)$ $\Gamma(n) = \int_0^\infty e^{-x} x^{n-1} dx$ is the gamma function.	Single, Weibull failure rate unit.

The calculations for MTBF, MTTF, complex systems, and the conversion table have been adapted from: Kececioglu, D. 1991. *Reliability Engineering Handbook*. Vol. 2. pp. 5–7, 24–25, 195–197. Reprinted by permission of Prentice Hall, Engelwood Cliffs, New Jersey.

Table A.1 Equations for the calculation of the MTBF in series.

Case number	System structure	MTTF	Comment
4	$\lambda_1(T) = \frac{\beta_1}{\eta_1}\left(\frac{T-\gamma_1}{\eta_1}\right)^{\beta_1-1}$ $\lambda_2(T) = \frac{\beta_2}{\eta_2}\left(\frac{T-\gamma_2}{\eta_2}\right)^{\beta_2-1}$ $\gamma_2 < \gamma_1$ →[ ]—[ ]→	$\gamma_2 + \frac{\eta_2}{\beta_2} \; G\frac{1}{\beta_2}\left[\frac{\gamma_1-\gamma_2}{\eta_2}\right] +$ $\int_{\gamma_1}^{\infty} e^{-\left[\left(\frac{T-\gamma_1}{\eta_1}\right)^{\beta_1} + \left(\frac{T-\gamma_2}{\eta_2}\right)^{\beta_2}\right]} dT,$ where $G(n,z) = \int_0 e^{-x} x^{n-1} \, dx$ is the incomplete gamma function. If $\gamma_1 = \gamma_2 = \gamma$ and $\beta_1 = \beta_2 = \beta$, then the MTTF becomes $\gamma + \Gamma\left(\frac{1}{\beta}+1\right) \Big/ \left[\left(\frac{1}{\eta_1}\right)^{\beta} + \left(\frac{1}{\eta_2}\right)^{\beta}\right]^{\frac{1}{\beta}}$ where $\Gamma(n) =$ gamma function.	Two series, Weibull failure rate units.
5	$\lambda_1(T) = \lambda_1, \lambda_2(T) = \lambda_2, \ldots$ $\lambda_n(T) = \lambda_n.$ →[1]—[2]— . . . —[n]→	$\frac{1}{\sum_{i=1}^{n} \lambda_i}$	*n* series, constant failure rate units.

Table A.1 (continued)

Case number	System structure	MTTF	Comment
6	$\lambda_1(T) = \frac{\beta_1}{\eta_1}\left(\frac{T-\gamma_1}{\eta_1}\right)^{\beta-1}$, $\lambda_2(T) = \frac{\beta_2}{\eta_2}\left(\frac{T-\gamma_2}{\eta_2}\right)^{\beta-1}$, ⋮ $\lambda_n(T) = \frac{\beta_n}{\eta_n}\left(\frac{T-\gamma_n}{\eta_n}\right)^{\beta-1}$. [→ 1 — 2 — · · · — n →]	$\gamma + \Gamma\left(\frac{1}{\beta}+1\right) \Big/ \left[\sum_{i=1}^{n}\left(\frac{1}{\eta_i}\right)^{\beta}\right]^{\frac{1}{\beta}}$ where $\Gamma(n)$ = gamma function	n series Weibull failure rate units, all with the same shape parameter β and location parameter γ.
7	$\lambda_1(T) = \lambda_1, \lambda_2(T) = \lambda_2$, . . . , $\lambda_n(T) = \lambda_n$ $\lambda_{n+1}(T) = k_1 T,\ \lambda_{n+2}(T) = k_2 T_2$, . . . , $\lambda_{n+r}(T) = k_r(T)$. [→ 1 — 2 — · · · — n — n+1 — n+2 — · · · — n+r ←]	$\left(\frac{\pi}{k}\right)^{\frac{1}{2}} e^{\frac{\lambda}{k}^{2}} \left\{1-\phi\left[\lambda\left(\frac{2}{k}\right)^{\frac{1}{2}}\right]\right\}$, where $\lambda = \frac{1}{2}\sum_{i=1}^{n}\lambda_i$, and $k = \frac{1}{2}\sum_{i=1}^{r}k_i$, $\phi(z) = \frac{1}{(2\pi)^{\frac{1}{2}}}\int_{-\infty}^{2} e^{-\frac{x^2}{2}}\,dx$.	$n + r$ series units, n with a constannt failure rate and r units with a linearly increasing failure rate.

Table A.1 (continued)

Case number	System structure	MTTF	Comment
1	$\lambda_1(T) = \lambda_1$, $\lambda_2(T) = \lambda_2$,	$\frac{1}{\lambda_1} + \frac{1}{\lambda_2} - \frac{1}{\lambda_1 + \lambda_2}$.	Two parallel, constant failure rate units.
2	$\lambda_1(T) = \frac{\beta_1}{\eta_1}\left(\frac{T-\gamma_1}{\eta_1}\right)^{\beta_1 - 1}$, $\lambda_2(T) = \frac{\beta_2}{\eta_2}\left(\frac{T-\gamma_2}{\eta_2}\right)^{\beta_2 - 1}$, $\gamma_2 < \gamma_1$.	$\gamma_1 + \eta_1 \Gamma\left(\frac{1}{\beta_1} + 1 \quad + \eta_2 \Gamma\left(\frac{1}{\beta_2} + 1\right)\right.$ $- \frac{\eta_2}{\beta_2} G\left[\frac{1}{\beta_2}, \left(\frac{\gamma_1 - \gamma_2}{\eta_2}\right)^{\beta_2}\right]$ $- \int_{\gamma_1}^{\infty} e^{-\left[\left(\frac{T-\gamma_1}{\eta_1}\right)^{\beta_1} + \left(\frac{T-\gamma_2}{\eta_2}\right)^{\beta_2}\right]}$ where $\Gamma(n)$ = gamma function, and $G(n,z) = \int_{\gamma_1}^{\infty} e^{-x} x^{n-1} dx$, is the incomplete gamma function. If $\gamma_1 = \gamma_2 = \gamma$ and $\beta_1 = \beta_2 = \beta$, then the MTTF becomes $\gamma + \Gamma\left(\frac{1}{\beta} + 1\right)\left\{\eta_1 + \eta_2 - \frac{1}{\left[\left(\frac{1}{\eta_1}\right)^{\beta} + \left(\frac{1}{\eta_2}\right)^{\beta}\right]^{\frac{1}{\beta}}}\right\}$	Two parallel, constant failure rate units.

Table A.2 Equations for the calculation of the MTTF in parallel.

Table A.2 (continued)

Case number	System structure	MTTF	Comment
3	$\lambda_i(T) = \lambda_i, \quad i = 1, \ldots, n.$ 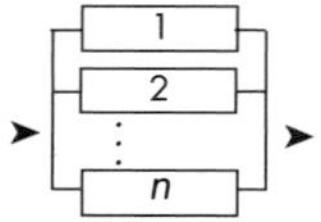	$\left(\frac{1}{\lambda_1}+\frac{1}{\lambda_2}+\ldots+\frac{1}{\lambda_n}\right)-\left(\frac{1}{\lambda_1+\lambda_2}+\frac{1}{\lambda_1+\lambda_3}+\ldots+\frac{1}{\lambda_{n-1}+\lambda_n}\right)$ $+\ldots+(-1)^{n+1}\frac{1}{\sum_{i=1}^{n}\lambda_i},$ If $\lambda_i = \lambda$, $i=1,\ldots,n$, then $\sum_{k=1}^{n}\frac{1}{k\lambda}$	n parallel, constant failure rate units.
4	$\lambda_i(T) = \frac{\beta}{\eta_i}\left(\frac{T-\gamma}{\eta_i}\right)^{\beta-1},$ $i = i, \ldots, n$ 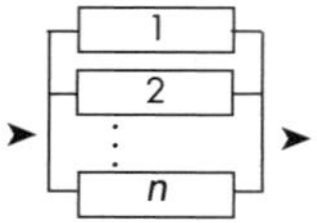	$\gamma+\Gamma\left(\frac{1}{\beta}+1\right)\left\{\sum_{i=1}^{n} n_i - \left[\frac{1}{\left[\left(\frac{1}{\eta_1}\right)^{\beta}+\left(\frac{1}{\eta_2}\right)^{\beta}\right]^{\frac{1}{\beta}}}+\frac{1}{\left[\left(\frac{1}{\eta_1}\right)^{\beta}+\left(\frac{1}{\eta_3}\right)^{\beta}\right]^{\frac{1}{\beta}}}+\ldots+\frac{1}{\left[\left(\frac{1}{\eta_{n-1}}\right)^{\beta}+\left(\frac{1}{\eta_n}\right)^{\beta}\right]^{\frac{1}{\beta}}}\right]+\ldots+(-1)^{n+1}\frac{1}{\left[\sum_{i=1}^{n}\left(\frac{1}{\eta_i}\right)^{\beta}\right]^{\frac{1}{\beta}}}\right\}$ where $\Gamma(n)$ = gamma function,	n parallel, Weibull units having the same shape parameter β and location parameter γ.

Case number	Circuit	Reliability of circuit	Mean life of circuit
1		$r^2 + 2\frac{\lambda_c}{\lambda} rq$	$(1.5 - \frac{\lambda_c}{\lambda})\ m$
2	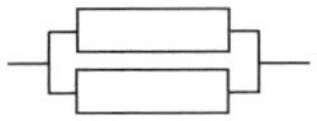	$r^2 + 2\frac{\lambda_o}{\lambda} rq$	$(1.5 - \frac{\lambda_o}{\lambda})\ m$
3	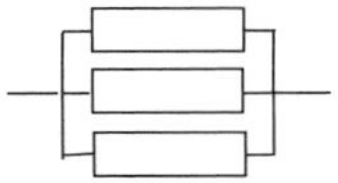	$r^3 + 3\frac{\lambda_o}{\lambda} r^2 q + 3\left(\frac{\lambda_o}{\lambda}\right)^2 rq^2$	$\left[2 + 3\frac{\lambda_o}{\lambda} + 6\left(\frac{\lambda_o}{\lambda}\right)^2\right]\frac{m}{6}$
4	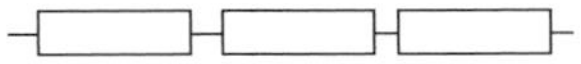	$r^3 + 3\frac{\lambda_c}{\lambda} r^2 q + 3\left(\frac{\lambda_c}{\lambda}\right)^2 rq^2$	$\left[2 + 3\frac{\lambda_c}{\lambda} + 6\left(\frac{\lambda_c}{\lambda}\right)^2\right]\frac{m}{6}$
5	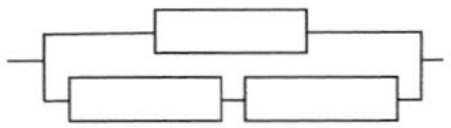	$r^3 + \left(2 + \frac{\lambda_o}{\lambda}\right) r^2 q + \left[4\frac{\lambda_o}{\lambda} - 3\left(\frac{\lambda_o}{\lambda}\right)^2\right] rq^2$	$\left[\frac{2}{3} + \frac{3}{2}\left(\frac{\lambda_o}{\lambda}\right) - \left(\frac{\lambda_o}{\lambda}\right)^2\right] m$
6	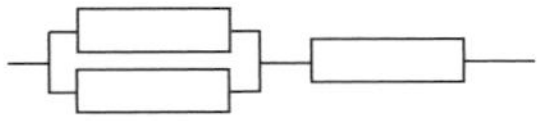	$r^3 + \left(2 + \frac{\lambda_c}{\lambda}\right) r^2 q + \left[4\frac{\lambda_c}{\lambda} - 3\left(\frac{\lambda_c}{\lambda}\right)^2\right] rq^2$	$\left[\frac{2}{3} + \frac{3}{2}\left(\frac{\lambda_c}{\lambda}\right) - \left(\frac{\lambda_c}{\lambda}\right)^2\right] m$

Table A.3 Equations for the reliability and mean life of a complex system with cyclical units.

Case number	Circuit	Reliability of circuit	Mean life of circuit
7		$r^4 + 4\frac{\lambda_o}{\lambda} r^3 q + 6\left(\frac{\lambda_o}{\lambda}\right)^2 r^2q^2 + 4\left(\frac{\lambda_o}{\lambda}\right)^3 rq^3$	$\left[\frac{1}{4} + \frac{1}{3}\left(\frac{\lambda_o}{\lambda}\right) + \frac{1}{2}\left(\frac{\lambda_o}{\lambda}\right)^2 + \left(\frac{\lambda_o}{\lambda}\right)^3\right] m$
8		$r^4 + 4\frac{\lambda_c}{\lambda} r^3 q + 6\left(\frac{\lambda_c}{\lambda}\right)^2 r^2q^2 + 4\left(\frac{\lambda_c}{\lambda}\right)^3 rq^3$	$\left[\frac{1}{4} + \frac{1}{3}\left(\frac{\lambda_c}{\lambda}\right) + \frac{1}{2}\left(\frac{\lambda_c}{\lambda}\right)^2 + \left(\frac{\lambda_c}{\lambda}\right)^3\right] m$
9		$r^4 + 4r^3q + \left[2 + 8\frac{\lambda_o}{\lambda} - 6\left(\frac{\lambda_o}{\lambda}\right)^2\right] r^2q^2 + 4\left[\frac{\lambda_o}{\lambda} - \left(\frac{\lambda_o}{\lambda}\right)^3\right] rq^3$	$\left[\frac{3}{4} + \frac{5}{3}\left(\frac{\lambda_o}{\lambda}\right) - \frac{1}{2}\left(\frac{\lambda_o}{\lambda}\right)^2 - \left(\frac{\lambda_o}{\lambda}\right)^3\right] m$
10		$r^4 + 4r^3q + \left[2 + 8\frac{\lambda_c}{\lambda} - 6\left(\frac{\lambda_c}{\lambda}\right)^2\right] r^2q^2 + 4\left[\frac{\lambda_c}{\lambda} - \left(\frac{\lambda_c}{\lambda}\right)^3\right] rq^3$	$\left[\frac{3}{4} + \frac{5}{3}\left(\frac{\lambda_c}{\lambda}\right) - \frac{1}{2}\left(\frac{\lambda_c}{\lambda}\right)^2 - \left(\frac{\lambda_c}{\lambda}\right)^3\right] m$
11		$r^4 + \left(3 + \frac{\lambda_o}{\lambda}\right) r^3 q + 3\left[1 + \frac{\lambda_o}{\lambda} - \left(\frac{\lambda_o}{\lambda}\right)^2\right] r^2q^2 + \left[6\frac{\lambda_o}{\lambda} - 9\left(\frac{\lambda_o}{\lambda}\right)^2 + 4\left(\frac{\lambda_o}{\lambda}\right)^3\right] rq^3$	$\left[\frac{3}{4} + \frac{11}{6}\left(\frac{\lambda_o}{\lambda}\right) - \frac{5}{2}\left(\frac{\lambda_o}{\lambda}\right)^2 + \left(\frac{\lambda_o}{\lambda}\right)^3\right] m$

Table A.3 (continued)

Case number	Circuit	Reliability of circuit	Mean life of circuit
12	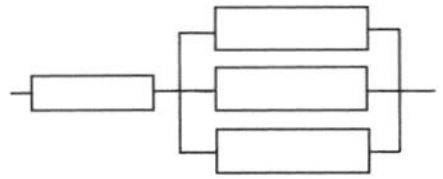	$r^4 + \left(3 + \frac{\lambda_c}{\lambda}\right)r^3q + 3\left[1 + \frac{\lambda_c}{\lambda} - \left(\frac{\lambda_c}{\lambda}\right)^2\right]r^2q^2 + \left[6\frac{\lambda_c}{\lambda} - 9\left(\frac{\lambda_c}{\lambda}\right)^2 + 4\left(\frac{\lambda_c}{\lambda}\right)^3\right]rq^3$	$\left[\frac{3}{4} + \frac{11}{6}\left(\frac{\lambda_c}{\lambda}\right) - \frac{5}{2}\left(\frac{\lambda_c}{\lambda}\right)^2 + \left(\frac{\lambda_c}{\lambda}\right)^3\right]m$
13	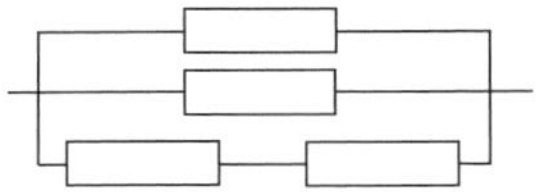	$r^4 + \left(2 + 2\frac{\lambda_o}{\lambda}\right)r^3q + 6\frac{\lambda_o}{\lambda}r^2q^2 + \left[6\left(\frac{\lambda_o}{\lambda}\right)^2 - 4\left(\frac{\lambda_o}{\lambda}\right)^3\right]rq^3$	$\left[\frac{5}{12} + \frac{2}{3}\left(\frac{\lambda_o}{\lambda}\right) + \frac{3}{2}\left(\frac{\lambda_o}{\lambda}\right)^2 - \left(\frac{\lambda_o}{\lambda}\right)^3\right]m$
14	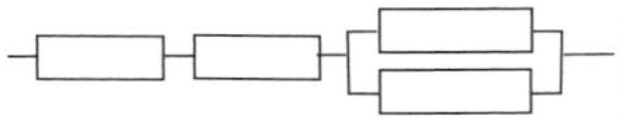	$r^4 + \left(2 + 2\frac{\lambda_c}{\lambda}\right)r^3q + 6\frac{\lambda_c}{\lambda}r^2q^2 + \left[6\left(\frac{\lambda_c}{\lambda}\right)^2 - 4\left(\frac{\lambda_c}{\lambda}\right)^3\right]rq$	$\left[\frac{5}{12} + \frac{2}{3}\left(\frac{\lambda_c}{\lambda}\right) + \frac{3}{2}\left(\frac{\lambda_c}{\lambda}\right)^2 - \left(\frac{\lambda_c}{\lambda}\right)^3\right]m$

r = reliability of each unit,

$m = \int_0^\infty r\,dt = \frac{1}{\lambda}$, mean life of each unit

$\lambda = \lambda_o + \lambda_c$, the total failure rate of each unit

λ_o = failure rate in the failing open mode

λ_c = failure rate in the failing open mode

Table A.3 (continued)

Appendix B

Sample Checklist for Design Review

This appendix provides the reader with a very detailed checklist and miscellaneous information about the FMEA. The intent of the checklist is to provide the reader with a structured tool that facilitates the questions regarding the system, design, process, and/or service. Obviously the checklist is not exhaustive. The miscellaneous information will guide the team with the flow of the FMEA, as well as the interrelationships of the FMEA with other tools in the development process. Specifically, the following information is provided.

- Sample checklists for design review
- System development process
- Considerations for a new product design
- Design FMEA procedure
- Process FMEA interrelationships
- Sequence of FMECA activities and responsibilities
- Design review schedule in relationship to program phases
- Reliability growth in terms of contract milestones
- Critical characteristics

Checklist

Portions of this checklist are adapted from questions and concerns from several Ford Motor Company publications and *Logistics*

Engineering and Management by B. Blanchard (1986) with their permission. These questions will help teams identify missing information and problem areas. Read each question and answer it "Yes" or "No." If necessary, write comments in the space provided below each question. Comments should indicate areas or items that are not complete and need additional information or work.

Engineering Drawings

1. Have all characteristics that affect fit, function, and durability been identified?

   Yes No

   Comments: ______________________________

   ____

2. Are tolerances compatible with accepted manufacturing standards?

   Yes No

   Comments: ______________________________

   ____

3. Are enough control points and datum lines identified to design functional gauges?

   Yes No

   Comments: ______________________________

   ____

4. Are features dimensioned to prevent unnecessary loss of tolerance during normal processing?

   Yes No

   Comments: ______________________________

   ____

5. Have all critical/significant characteristics been identified?

   Yes No

   Comments: ______________________________

   ____

6. Have feasibility meetings been held to establish the feasibility of the design?

   Yes No

   Comments: ______________________________

   ____

7. Have prints been drawn using geometric dimensioning and tolerancing principles with control points and datum lines identified for the design of gauges and test equipment? Will the gauges facilitate gathering variable data?

   Yes No

   Comments: ______________________________

   ____

8. Are there any requirements that must be inspected that cannot be evaluated using the known inspection techniques?

   Yes No

   Comments: ______________________________

   ____

9. Are tolerance stack-ups containable for assembly and function?

   Yes No

   Comments: ______________________________

   ____

10. Are all specified tests and requirements, including heat treat and metallurgical requirements, clearly defined and understood?

    Yes No

    Comments: ______________________________

    ____

11. Are required standards for color, grain, and so on available?

    Yes No

    Comments: ______________________________

    ____

12. Are there any requirements shown that cannot be evaluated using known inspection techniques?

    Yes No

    Comments: ______________________________

    ____

13. Are tolerance stack-ups containable?

    Yes No

    Comments: ______________________________

    ____

Engineering Specifications

14. Is test loading sufficient to provide all conditions (in other words, production validation, ongoing and annual recertification)?

    Yes No

    Comments: ______________________________

    ____

15. Have dimensional or material characteristics that affect ES durability testing results been included in the control plan?

    Yes No

    Comments: ______________________________

    ____

16. Are all specified tests and requirements clearly defined and understood?

    Yes No

    Comments: ______________________________

    ____

Materials Specifications

17. Are the intended material suppliers on the approved source list?

    Yes No

    Comments: ______________________________

    ____

18. Will material suppliers be required to provide certification with each shipment?

    Yes No

    Comments: ______________________________

    ____

19. Are specified materials, heat treat, and surface treatments suitable for the intended environment?

    Yes No

    Comments: ______________________________

    ____

Design FMEA

20. Have operations that affect high-risk failure modes been identified?

    Yes No

    Comments: ______________________________

    ____

21. Have previous manufacturing experiences shown that high-risk operations are not capable?

    Yes No

    Comments: ______________________________

    ____

22. Will new/untried processing techniques be employed that will affect high-risk operations?

    Yes No

    Comments: ______________________________

    ____

23. Have operations for capability studies been identified?

    Yes No

    Comments: ______________________________

    ____

24. Have design FMEAs been conducted? (A design FMEA is required on all parts having critical characteristics and recommended for all new parts.)

    Yes No

    Comments: ______________________________

    ____

25. Will a process FMEA be conducted?

    Yes No

    Comments: ____________________

    ____

Process Flow Diagram

26. Is a process flow diagram available that shows the sequence of production and inspection stations?

    Yes No

    Comments: ____________________

    ____

27. Was the process FMEA used as an aid to develop the process flow?

    Yes No

    Comments: ____________________

    ____

28. Have provisions been made to send repaired material to an inspection station before being used?

    Yes No

    Comments: ____________________

    ____

29. Has a list of possible quality problems been identified for off-line operations such as repair and salvage stations?

    Yes No

    Comments: ____________________

    ____

30. Should a design of experiments analysis be used to improve capability?

    Yes No

    Comments: ______________________________

    ____

31. Are statistical control points identified?

    Yes No

    Comments: ______________________________

    ____

Process FMEA

32. Have all operations affecting fit, function, and durability been identified and listed in order?

    Yes No

    Comments: ______________________________

    ____

33. Have required corrective actions been planned or taken for high-risk operations?

    Yes No

    Comments: ______________________________

    ____

34. Were historical warranty and consuming plant problems used as aids in developing the process FMEA?

    Yes No

    Comments: ______________________________

    ____

35. Have provisions been made to conduct process potential students on high-risk operations where the possibility of occurrence is the major factor?

    Yes No

    Comments: ____________________

    ____

36. On operations where the FMEA shows detection as the major factor, have provisions been made in the quality plan to control the cause before the operation in question?

    Yes No

    Comments: ____________________

    ____

37. Should a cause-and-effect analysis (fishbone diagram) be used to identify additional causes?

    Yes No

    Comments: ____________________

    ____

38. Have high-risk failure modes and operations that affect them been identified?

    Yes No

    Comments: ____________________

    ____

39. Have previous manufacturing experiences shown any high-risk operations that are not capable?

    Yes No

    Comments: ____________________

    ____

40. Will new/untried processing techniques be employed that will affect high-risk operations?

    Yes No

    Comments: ______________________________

    ____

41. Have operations for capability studies been identified?

    Yes No

    Comments: ______________________________

    ____

42. Has a process FMEA been conducted? (A process FMEA is required on all parts that have critical/significant characteristics and is recommended for all processes.)

    Yes No

    Comments: ______________________________

    ____

43. Was a check of historical warranty and consuming plant problems used as an aid in developing the process FMEA?

    Yes No

    Comments: ______________________________

    ____

Manufacturing Floor Plan Considerations

44. Are process and quality control stations large enough, well lighted, and include all necessary equipment and files?

    Yes No

    Comments: ______________________________

    ____

45. Are repair areas logically located to prevent accidental shipment of defective material?

    Yes No

    Comments: ______________________________

    ____

46. Have provisions been made to post visual aids for critical operations?

    Yes No

    Comments: ______________________________

    ____

47. Are controls adequate to prevent movement of rejected incoming material to storage or point of use?

    Yes No

    Comments: ______________________________

    ____

New Equipment List

48. Has the new equipment list been reviewed and, in your best judgment, is the equipment adequate?

    Yes No

    Comments: ______________________________

    ____

49. Has process potential been demonstrated on the new equipment?

    Yes No

    Comments: ______________________________

    ____

50. Have inspection gauges been identified to conduct capability studies?

    Yes No

    Comments: ____

    ____

51. Has adequate test equipment been provided?

    Yes No

    Comments: ____

    ____

52. Have requirements for special gauges been defined?

    Yes No

    Comments: ____

    ____

53. Are test capacities sufficient to provide additional sampling when defectives are found? Is the data recorded?

    Yes No

    Comments: ____

    ____

54. Was machine potential established on the equipment builder's floor before delivery?

    Yes No

    Comments: ____

    ____

Comments and Conditions

55. Have causes of field failure modes been identified?

    Yes No

    Comments: ______________________________

    ____

56. Have actual or possible causes of consuming plant quality problems been identified?

    Yes No

    Comments: ______________________________

    ____

57. Are design changes needed to make characteristics in question more workable?

    Yes No

    Comments: ______________________________

    ____

58. Have process changes been planned or taken to eliminate all quality concerns?

    Yes No

    Comments: ______________________________

    ____

59. Have control charts and capability studies been planned for characteristics and causes in question?

    Yes No

    Comments: ______________________________

    ____

60. Are enough personnel available to cover control plan requirements, layout, ES durability testing, and problem analysis?

    Yes No

    Comments: ______________________________

    ____

61. Have provisions been made to certify and routinely calibrate new gauge and test equipment?

    Yes No

    Comments: ______________________________

    ____

62. Is there a procedure for controlling incoming quality from subsuppliers, that requires documentation of rejects and follow-up?

    Yes No

    Comments: ______________________________

    ____

63. Is there a procedure available for the installation, maintenance, and reaction plan for statistical control charts?

    Yes No

    Comments: ______________________________

    ____

64. Are forms available for inspections/auditors to log/tally inspection results?

    Yes No

    Comments: ______________________________

    ____

65. Are routine warehouse audits used to ensure integrity of ongoing controls?

    Yes No

    Comments: ______________________________

    ____

Sample Size

66. Are sample sizes sufficient to handle multistation equipment?

    Yes No

    Comments: ______________________________

    ____

67. Are sample sizes compatible with preset minimum requirements?

    Yes No

    Comments: ______________________________

    ____

68. Are all operators and inspectors provided with an inspection instruction that is keyed to the control plan? Do they have a complete set of instructions that show how to control the part?

    Yes No

    Comments: ______________________________

    ____

69. On operations where the FMEA shows the chance of detection as insufficient, have provisions been made in the quality plan to control the cause, (in other words, reduce the occurrence) during or before the operation in question?

    Yes No

    Comments: ______________________________

    ____

70. Was a cause-and-effect analysis (fishbone diagram) used to identify additional causes?

    Yes No

    Comments: ______________________________

    ____

Reaction Plan

71. Has a reaction plan been documented?

    Yes No

    Comments: ______________________________

    ____

72. Does the reaction plan include responsibilities for production, process engineering, and quality control?

    Yes No

    Comments: ______________________________

    ____

Special Conditions

73. Have all measuring devices been calibrated?

    Yes No

    Comments: ______________________________

    ____

New Equipment List

74. Can variables data be generated from the gauge?

    Yes No

    Comments: ______________________________

    ____

75. Have provisions been made to certify and routinely calibrate new gauge and test equipment?

    Yes No

    Comments: ______________________________

    ____

Incoming Material

76. Are intended material suppliers on the approved source list?

    Yes No

    Comments: ______________________________

    ____

77. Will material suppliers be required to provide certification data with each shipment? A certification letter is not satisfactory. Data that show statistical evidence of stability and capability must be provided.

    Yes No

    Comments: ______________________

    ____

78. Is there a procedure for controlling incoming quality from subsuppliers?

    Yes No

    Comments: ______________________

    ____

Control Plan

79. Has a control plan been established and approved by SQA?

    Yes No

    Comments: ______________________

    ____

80. Have dimensional performance or material characteristics that affect ES durability testing results been included in the control plan?

    Yes No

    Comments: ______________________

    ____

81. Are routine finished-product audits used to ensure integrity of ongoing controls? Is a feedback system in place?

    Yes No

    Comments: ______________________

    ____

82. Were gauge repeatability and reproducibility (R&R) studies completed?

    Yes No

    Comments: ______________________________

    ____

83. Have unusual occurrences been recorded in a log?

    Yes No

    Comments: ______________________________

    ____

84. Has the goal that the measurement system variation does not consume more than one-tenth of the specification tolerance been met?

    Yes No

    Comments: ______________________________

    ____

Quality Improvement

85. Have necessary DOE analyses been used to improve capability?

    Yes No

    Comments: ______________________________

    ____

86. Are design changes needed to make characteristics in question more workable?

    Yes No

    Comments: ______________________________

    ____

87. Have process changes been planned or taken to eliminate all quality concerns?

    Yes No

    Comments: ______________________________

    ____

Note: This checklist is not exhaustive. It is offered as a starting point of questioning the system, design, and/or process with the intent of improvement.

The following questions are arranged by system and design. The focus is to show the level of complexity that a checklist may take. In no way does this list pretend to be complete. The format and level is based on B. Blanchard's work. It is used here with permission.

System Design

General

1.0 System Operational Requirements

- Has the mission been defined? Mission scenarios?
- Have all basic system performance parameters been defined?
- Has the planned operational deployment been defined (quantity of systems per location)?
- Has the system life cycle been defined?
- Have system utilization requirements been defined? This includes hours of system/equipment operation or quantity of operational cycles per a given time period. Define an operational cycle if used.
- Has the operational environment been defined in terms of temperature extremes, humidity, shock and vibration, storage, transportation, and handling?

2.0 Effectiveness Factors

- Have system availability, dependability, readiness, or equivalent operational effectiveness factors been identified?

- Have quantitative reliability and maintainability factors been specified? This includes MTBF, MTBM, MDT, M, Mct, Mpt, Mmax, MMH/OH, Cost/OH, Cost/MA, and so on.

3.0 System Maintenance Concept

- Have the echelons or levels of maintenance been specified and defined?
- Have basic maintenance functions been identified for each level?
- Have quantitative parameters been established for turnaround time (TAT) at each level and logistics pipeline time between levels?
- Has the logistics pipeline time between levels been minimized to the extent feasible considering cost? The lack of adequate supply responsiveness has a major detrimental effect on total logistic support.
- Have level of repair policies been established? Repair versus discard? Repair at intermediate/depot level?
- Have the criteria for level of repair decisions been adequately defined?
- Has the level of maintenance (organizational, intermediate, depot, or supplier) been defined for each repairable item?
- Have criteria been established for test and support equipment at each level of maintenance? Software?
- Have criteria been established for personnel quantities and/or skills at each level of maintenance?

4.0 Functional Analysis and Allocation

- Have system operational and maintenance functions been defined?
- Have reliability and maintainability factors been allocated to the appropriate system elements (for example, unit, assembly, subassembly, and so on)
- Have cost factors been allocated to the appropriate system elements?
- Have logistic support factors been allocated where appropriate?

5.0 Logistic Support Analysis

- Have trade-off evaluations and analyses been accomplished to support all logistic support requirements?
- Is the response to all questions in the analysis checklist positive? These questions cover lifestyle cost analyses, maintenance analyses, and logistics modeling.
- Does the logistic support analysis data package justify system design for supportability?
- Have trade-off evaluations and analyses been adequately documented?

6.0 Logistic Support Operational Plan

- Has a plan been developed for the design, production, acquisition, deployment, and integration of the prime equipment and logistic support elements in the field? This includes a preliminary logistic support plan and an integrated logistic support plan (ILSP).
- Has a plan been developed for the handling of system modifications in the field?
- Has a plan been developed covering system/equipment phaseout?

Logistical Support Elements

1.0 Test and Support Equipment

- Have the test and support equipment requirements been defined for each level of maintenance?
- Have standard test and support equipment items been selected? Newly designed equipment should not be necessary unless standard equipment is unavailable.
- Are the selected test and support equipment items compatible with the prime equipment? Does the test equipment do the job?
- Are the test and support equipment requirements compatible with logistic support analysis?
- Have test and support equipment requirements (both in terms of variety and quantity) been minimized to the greatest extent possible?

- Are the reliability and maintainability features in the test and support equipment compatible with those equivalent features in the prime equipment? It is not practical to select an item of support equipment that is not as reliable as the item it supports.
- Have logistic support requirements for the selected test and support equipment been defined? This includes maintenance tasks, test equipment, spare/repair parts, personnel and training, data, and facilities.
- Is the test and support equipment selection process based on cost-effectiveness considerations (in other words, life cycle cost)?
- Have test and maintenance software requirements been adequately defined?

2.0 Supply Support (Spare/Repair Parts)

- Are the types and quantity of spare/repair parts compatible with the level of repair analysis?
- Are the types and quantity of spare/repair parts designated for a given location appropriate for the estimated demand at that location? Too many or too few parts can be costly.
- Are spare/repair part provisioning factors consistent with logistic support analysis?
- Are spare/repair part provisioning factors directly traceable to reliability and maintainability predictions?
- Are the specified logistics pipeline times compatible with effective supply support? Long pipeline times place a tremendous burden on logistic support.
- Have spare/repair parts been identified and provisioned for preoperational support activities (for example, interim supplier support, test programs, and so on)?
- Have spare/repair part requirements been minimized to the maximum extent possible?
- Have test and acceptance procedures been developed for spare/repair parts? These should be processed, produced, and accepted on a similar basis with their equivalent components in the prime equipment.

- Have the consequences (risks) of stock-out been defined in terms of effect on mission requirements and cost?
- Has an inventory safety stock level been defined?
- Has a provisioning or procurement cycle been defined (procurement or order frequency)?
- Has a supply availability requirement been established (the probability of having a spare available when required)?

3.0 Personnel and Training

- Have operational and maintenance personnel requirements (quantity and skill levels) been defined?
- Are operational and maintenance personnel requirements minimized to the greatest extent possible?
- Are operational and maintenance personnel requirements compatible with logistic support analysis and with human factors data?
- Are the planned personnel skills levels at each location compatible with the complexity of the operational and maintenance tasks specified?
- Has maximum consideration been given to the use of existing personnel skills for new equipment?
- Have personnel attrition rates been established?
- Have personnel effectiveness factors been determined (actual time that work is accomplished per the total time allowed for work accomplishment)?
- Have operational and maintenance training requirements been specified? This includes consideration of both initial training and replenishment training throughout the life cycle.
- Have specific training programs been planned? The type of training, frequency of training, duration of training, and student entry requirements should be identified.
- Are the planned training programs compatible with the personnel skill level requirements specified for the performance of operational and maintenance tasks?
- Have training equipment requirements been defined? Acquisitioned?

- Have maintenance provisions for training equipment been planned?
- Have training data requirements been defined?
- Are the planned operating and maintenance procedures (designated for support of the system throughout its life cycle) utilized to the maximum extent possible in the training program?

4.0 Technical Data (Operating and Maintenance Procedures)

- Have operating and maintenance procedure requirements been defined? Have the necessary procedures been prepared?
- Are operating and maintenance procedures compatible with logistic support analysis data? This pertains particularly to the logic troubleshooting flow diagrams, task sequences, and support requirements defined in the maintenance analysis.
- Are operating and maintenance procedures as brief as possible without sacrificing necessary information?
- Are operating and maintenance procedures adequate from the standpoint of presenting simple step-by-step instructions; including appropriate use of illustrations and tables for presenting data?
- Are operating and maintenance procedures compatible with the level of activity performed at the location where the procedures are used? Depot maintenance instructions should not be included in manuals which are used at the intermediate level of maintenance. The maintenance procedures should be compatible with the level of repair analysis and the maintenance concept.
- Are operating and maintenance procedures written at the skill level of the individual accomplishing the functions covered by the procedures? Procedures should be written in a simple, clear, and concise manner for low-skilled personnel.
- Do the operating and maintenance procedures specify the correct test and support equipment, spare/repair parts, transportation and handling equipment, and facilities?
- Do the procedures include special warning notices in areas where safety is a concern?

- Are the designated operating and maintenance procedures used in system/equipment test programs?

5.0 Facilities and Storage

- Have facility requirements (space, volume, capital equipment, utilities, and so on) necessary for system operation been defined?
- Have facility requirements (space, volume, capital equipment, utilities, and so on) necessary for system maintenance at each level been defined?
- Have operational and maintenance facility requirements been minimized to the greatest extent possible?
- Have environmental system requirements (for example, temperature, humidity, and dust control) associated with operational and maintenance facilities been identified?
- Have storage or shelf-space requirements for spare/repair parts been defined?
- Have storage environments been defined?
- Are the designated facility and storage requirements compatible with the logistic support analysis and human factors data?

6.0 Transportation and Handling

- Are transportation and handling requirements for both operational and maintenance functions defined? This includes transportation of prime equipment, test and support equipment, spares, personnel, and data. National and international requirements should be identified.
- Are transportation and handling environments (temperature, shock and vibration, exposure to dust and salt spray, storage, and so on) defined?
- Are the modes (air, ground vehicle, rail, sea, or a combination) of transportation known? A profile or scenario, similar to that accomplished for mission definition, should be developed showing the various transportation and handling requirements.
- Are the requirements for reusable containers known? Design information should be developed on reusable containers.

• Are the requirements for packing known? This includes labor, material, preservation, storage limitations, and the processing of an item for shipment.

Design Features

1.0 Selection of Parts

• Have appropriate standards been consulted for the selection of components?

• Have all component parts and materials selected for the design been adequately evaluated prior to their procurement and application? Evaluation should consider performance parameters, reliability, maintainability, and human factors.

• Have supplier sources for component part procurement been established?

• Are the established supplier sources reliable in terms of quality level, ability to deliver on time, and willingness to accept part warranty provisions?

• Have the reliability, maintainability, and human factors engineers been consulted in the selection and application of parts? Reliability is concerned with part failure rates, stresses, tolerances, allowable temperature extremes, signal ratings, and so on. Maintainability and human factors are concerned with the part effects on maintenance times, mounting provisions, human interfaces, and so on.

2.0 Standardization

• Are standard equipment items and parts incorporated in the design to the maximum extent possible (except for items not compatible with effectiveness factors)? Maximum standardization is desirable.

• Are the same items and/or parts used in similar applications?

• Are the number of different part types used throughout the design minimized? In the interest of developing an efficient supply support capability, the number of different item spares should be held to a minimum.

- Are identifying equipment labels and nomenclature assignments standardized to the maximum extent possible?
- Are equipment control panel positions and layouts (from panel to panel) the same or similar when a number of panels are incorporated and provide comparable functions?

3.0 Test Provisions

- Have self-test provisions been incorporated where appropriate?
- Is the extent or depth of self-testing compatible with the level or repair analysis?
- Are self-test provisions automatic?
- Have direct fault indicators been provided (either a fault light, an audio signal, or a means of determining that a malfunction positively exists)? Are continuous performance monitoring provisions incorporated where appropriate?
- Are test points provided to enable checkout and fault isolation beyond the level of self-test? Test point for fault isolation within an assembly should not be incorporated if the assembly is to be discarded at failure. Test point provisions must be compatible with the level of repair analysis.
- Are test points accessible? Accessibility should be compatible with the extent of maintenance performed. Test points on the operator's front panel are not required for a depot maintenance action.
- Are test points functionally and conveniently grouped to allow for sequential testing (following a signal flow), testing of similar functions, or frequency of use when access is limited?
- Are test points adequately provided for a direct test of all replaceable items?
- Are test points adequately labeled? Each test point should be identified with a unique number, and the proper signal or expected measured output should be specified on a label located adjacent to the test point.
- Are test points adequately illuminated to allow the technician to see the test point number and labeled signal value?

- Can every equipment malfunction (degradation beyond specification tolerance limits) which could possibly occur in the equipment be detected through a no-go indication at the system level? This is a measure of test thoroughness.
- Will the prescribed maintenance software provide adequate diagnostic information?

4.0 Packaging and Mounting

- Is functional packaging incorporated to the maximum extent possible? Interaction effects between modular packages should be minimized: It should be possible to limit maintenance to the removal of one module (the one containing the failed part) when a failure occurs and not require the removal of two, three, or four modules.
- Is the packaging design compatible with level of repair analysis decisions? Repairable items are designed to include maintenance provisions such as test points, accessibility, plug-in components, and so on. Items classified as discard at failure should be encapsulated and relatively low in cost. Maintenance provisions within the disposable module are not required.
- Are disposable modules incorporated to the maximum extent practical? It is highly desirable to reduce overall support through a no-maintenance design concept as long as the items being discarded are relatively high in reliability and low in cost.
- Are plug-in modules and components utilized to the maximum extent possible (unless the use of plug-in components significantly degrades the equipment reliability)?
- Are accesses between modules adequate to allow for hand grasping? Are modules and components mounted such that the removal of any single item for maintenance will not require the removal of other items? Component stacking should be avoided where possible.
- In areas where module stacking is necessary because of limited space, are the modules mounted in such a way that access priority has been assigned in accordance with the predicted removal and replacement frequency? Items requiring frequent maintenance should be more accessible.

- Are modules and components, not of the plug-in variety, mounted with four fasteners or less? Modules should be securely mounted, but the number of fasteners should be held to a minimum.
- Are shock-mounting provisions incorporated where shock and vibration requirements are excessive?
- Are provisions incorporated to preclude installation of the wrong module?
- Are plug-in modules and components removable without the use of tools? If tools are required, they should be of the standard variety.
- Are guides (slides or pins) provided to facilitate module installation?
- Are modules and components labeled?
- Are modules and component labels located on top or immediately adjacent to the item and in plain sight?
- Are the labels permanently affixed and unlikely to come off during a maintenance action or as a result of environment? Is the information on the label adequate? Disposable modules should be so labeled.
- In equipment racks, are the heavier items mounted at the bottom of the rack? Unit weight should decrease with the increase in installation height.
- Are operator panels optimally positioned? For personnel in the standing position, panels should be located between 40 and 70 inches above the floor. Critical or precise control should be between 48 and 64 inches above the floor. For personnel in the sitting position, panels should be located 30 inches above the floor. Refer to the latest reference on anthropometric data.

5.0 Interchangeability

- Are modules and components having similar functions electrically, functionally, and physically interchangeable?
- Are components with the same part number but provided by different suppliers completely interchangeable?

6.0 Accessibility

- Are access doors provided where appropriate? Are hinged doors utilized?
- Are access openings adequate in size and optimally located for the access required?
- Are access doors and openings labeled in terms of items that are accessible from within?
- Can access doors that are hinged be supported in the open position?
- Are access door fasteners minimized?
- Are access door fasteners of the quick-release variety?
- Can access be attained without the use of tools?
- If tools are required to gain access, are the number of tools held to a minimum? Are the tools the standard variety?
- Are accesses between modules and components adequate?
- Are access requirements compatible with the frequency of maintenance? Accessibility for items requiring frequent maintenance should be greater than that for items requiring it infrequently.

7.0 Handling

- For heavy items, are hoist lugs (lifting eyes) or base-lifting provisions for forklift-truck application incorporated? Hoist lugs should be provided on all items weighing more than 150 pounds.
- Are hoist and base-lifting points identified relative to lifting capacity? Are weight labels provided?
- Are packages, units, components, or other items weighing over 10 pounds provided with handles? Are the proper size handles used, and are they located in the right position? Are the handles optimally located from the weight-distribution standpoint? (Handles should be located over the center of gravity.)
- Are packages, units, or other items weighing more than 40 pounds provided with two handles (for two-person carrying capability)?

- Are containers, cases, or covers provided to protect equipment vulnerable areas from damage during handling?

8.0 Fasteners

- Are quick-release fasteners used on doors and access panels?
- Are the total number of fasteners minimized?
- Are the number of different types of fasteners held to a minimum? This relates to standardization.
- Have fasteners been selected based on the requirement for standard tools in lieu of special tools?

9.0 Panel Displays and Controls

- Are controls standardized?
- Are controls sequentially positioned?
- Is control spacing adequate?
- Is control labeling adequate?
- Have the proper control/display relationships been incorporated?
- Are the proper type of switches used?
- Is the control panel lighting adequate?
- Are the controls placed according to frequency of use?
- Has a human factor engineer been consulted relative to controls and panel design?

10.0 Adjustments and Alignments

- Are adjustment requirements and frequencies known?
- Have adjustment requirements been minimized?
- Are adjustment points accessible?
- Are adjustment-point locations compatible with the maintenance level at which the adjustment is made?
- Are adjustment interactions effects eliminated?
- Are factory adjustments specified?
- Are adjustment points adequately labeled?

11.0 Cables and Connectors

- Are cables fabricated in removable sections?
- Are cables routed to avoid sharp bends?
- Are cables routed to avoid pinching?
- Is cable labeling adequate?
- Is cable clamping adequate?
- Are connectors of the quick-disconnect variety?
- Are connectors that are mounted on surfaces far enough apart so that they can be firmly grasped for connecting and disconnecting?
- Are connectors and receptacles labeled?
- Are connectors and receptacles keyed?
- Are connectors standardized?
- Do the connectors incorporate provisions for moisture prevention?

12.0 Servicing and Lubrication

- Have servicing requirements been held to a minimum?
- When servicing is indicated, are the specific requirements identified? This includes frequency of servicing and the materials needed?
- Are procurement sources for servicing materials known?
- Are servicing points accessible?
- Have personnel and equipment requirements for servicing been identified? This includes handling equipment, vehicles, carts, and so on.
- Does the design include servicing indicators?

13.0 Calibration

- Have calibration requirements been held to minimum?
- Are calibration requirements known?
- Are calibration frequencies known?
- Are calibration tolerances known?

- Are standards available for calibration?
- Are calibration procedures prepared?
- Is traceability to the National Bureau of Standards possible?
- Have the facilities for calibration been identified?
- Are the calibration requirements compatible with the logistic support analysis and the maintenance concept?

14.0 Environment

- Has the equipment design considered the following: temperature, shock, vibration, humidity, pressure, wind, salt spray, sand and dust, rain, fungus, and radiation? Have the ranges and extreme conditions been specified and properly addressed in design?
- Have provisions been made to specify and control noise, illumination, humidity, and temperature in areas where personnel are required to perform operating and maintenance functions?

15.0 Storage

- Can the equipment and spare parts be stored for extended periods of time without excessive degradation (beyond specification limits)?
- Have scheduled maintenance requirements for stored equipment been defined?
- Have scheduled maintenance requirements for stored equipment been eliminated or minimized?
- Have the required maintenance resources necessary to service stored equipment been identified?
- Have storage environments been defined?
- Has the need for specialized environmentally controlled facilities been eliminated where possible?

16.0 Transportability

- Have transportation and handling requirements been defined?
- Have transportation requirements been considered in the equipment design? This includes consideration of temperature

ranges, vibration and shock, humidity, and so on. Has the possibility of equipment degradation been minimized if transported by air, ground vehicle, ship, or rail?

- Can the equipment be easily disassembled, packed, transported from one location to another, reassembled, and operated with a minimum of performance and reliability degradation?
- Have container requirements been defined?
- Have the requirements for ground-handling equipment been defined?
- Was the selection of handling equipment based on cost-effectiveness considerations?

17.0 Producibility

- Has the design been stabilized (minimum change)?
- Has the design been verified through prototype and qualification testing?
- Is the design such that many models of the same item can be produced with identical results?
- Are the production databases, drawings, and material lists adequate?
- Are common materials used (in lieu of special materials)?
- Can standard tooling and existing facilities be used for fabrication, assembly, and test operations?
- Is the design such that rework requirements are minimized? Are spoilage factors held to a minimum?
- Are standard fabrication, assembly, test, and inspection procedures applicable?
- Is the design such that automated manufacturing processes (for example, robotics or numerical control techniques) can be applied for repetitive functions?
- Is the design definition such that two or more suppliers can produce the equipment from a set of specifications and drawings with identical results?

18.0 Safety

- Have fail-safe provisions been incorporated in the design?
- Have protruding devices been eliminated or are they suitably protected?
- Have provisions been incorporated for protection against high voltages? Are all external metal parts adequately grounded?
- Are sharp metal edges, access openings, and corners protected with rubber, fillets, fiber, or plastic coating?
- Are electrical circuit interlocks employed?
- Are standoffs or handles provided to protect equipment from damage during the performance of bench maintenance?
- Are tools that are used near high-voltage areas adequately insulated at the handle or at other parts of the tool which the maintenance person is likely to touch?
- Are the environments protected so that personnel safety is ensured? Are noise levels within a safe range? Is illumination adequate? Is the air relatively clean? Are the temperatures at a proper level?
- Has the proper protective clothing been identified for areas where the environment could be detrimental to human safety? Radiation, intense cold or heat, gas, and loud noise are examples.
- Are safety equipment requirements identified in areas where ordinance devices and the like are activated?
- Has a system hazard analysis been completed where required?

19.0 Reliability

- Has the system/equipment wear-out period been defined?
- Have failure modes and effects been identified?
- Are item failure rates known?
- Have parts with excessive failure rates been identified?
- Has mean life been determined?
- Have adequate derating factors been established and adhered to where appropriate?

- Has equipment design complexity been minimized?
- Is protection against secondary failures (resulting from primary failures) incorporated where possible?
- Has the use of adjustable components been minimized?
- Has the use of friction or pressure contacts in mechanical equipment been avoided?
- Have all critical, useful-life items been eliminated from the equipment design?
- Have cooling provisions been incorporated in design hot spot areas? Is cooling directed toward the most critical items?
- Have all reliability program requirements been met?

20.0 Software

- Have all system software requirements for maintenance activities been met?
- Is the maintenance software complete in terms of scope and depth of coverage?
- Is the software compatible relative to the equipment with which it interfaces? Is the maintenance software compatible with the operating software? With other elements of the system?
- Is the maintenance software language compatible with system language requirements in general?
- Has the software been adequately tested and verified for accuracy and reliability?

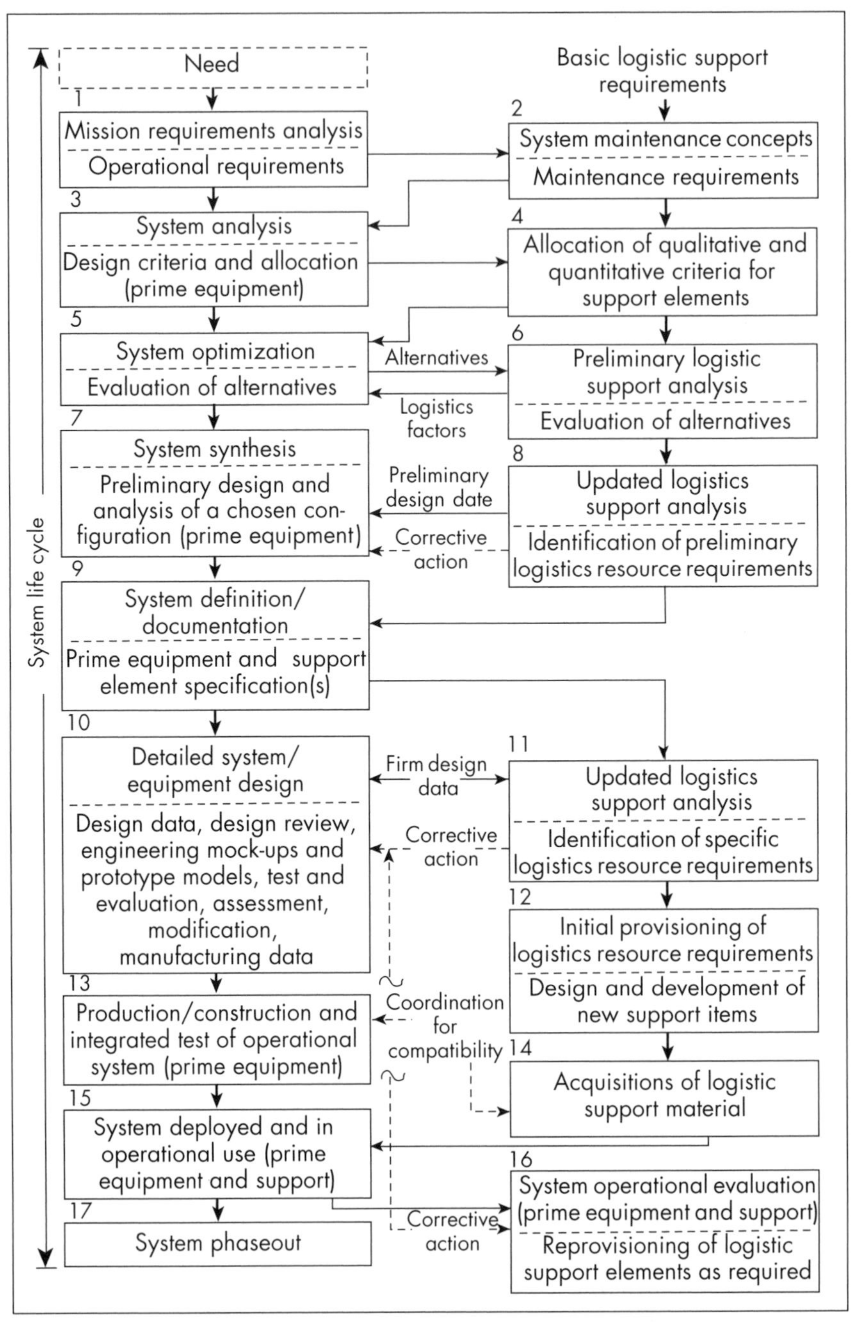

Adopted from Blanchard, B. 1986. *Logistics Engineering and Management.* p. 7. Reprinted by permission of Prentice Hall, Englewood Cliffs, New Jersey.

Figure B.1 Typical process flow diagram of system development process.

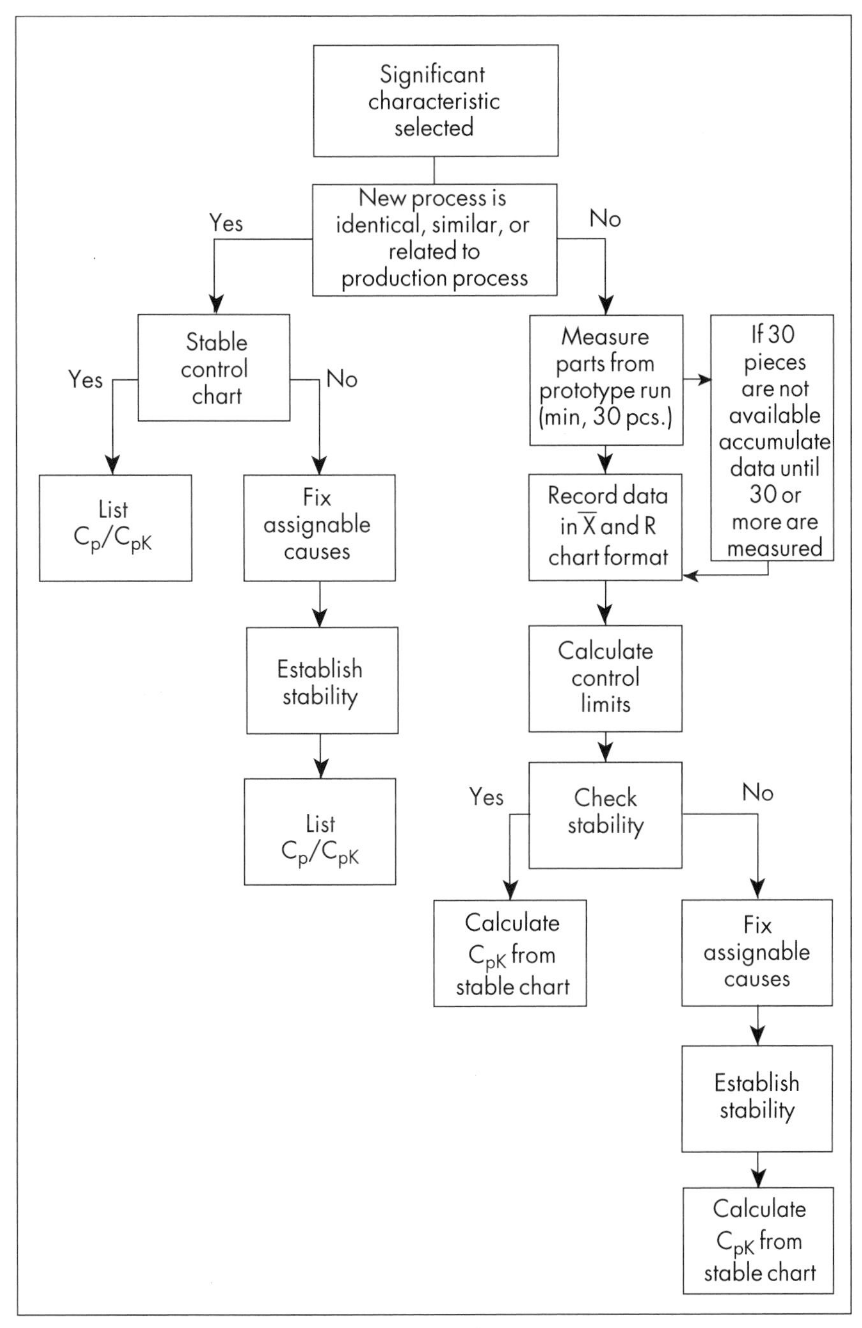

Figure B.2 Process flow diagram of typical considerations of a new product to be produced.

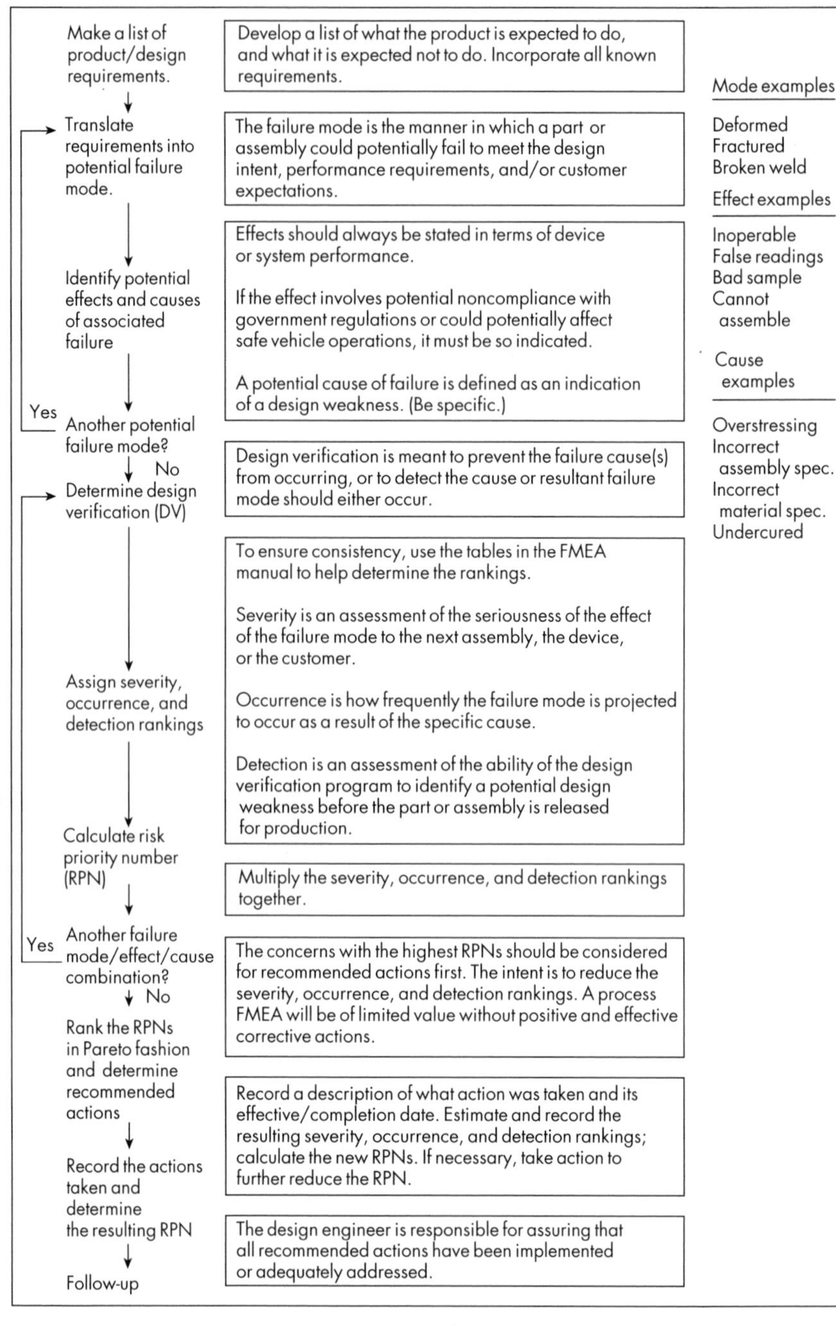

Figure B.3 Design FMEA procedure.

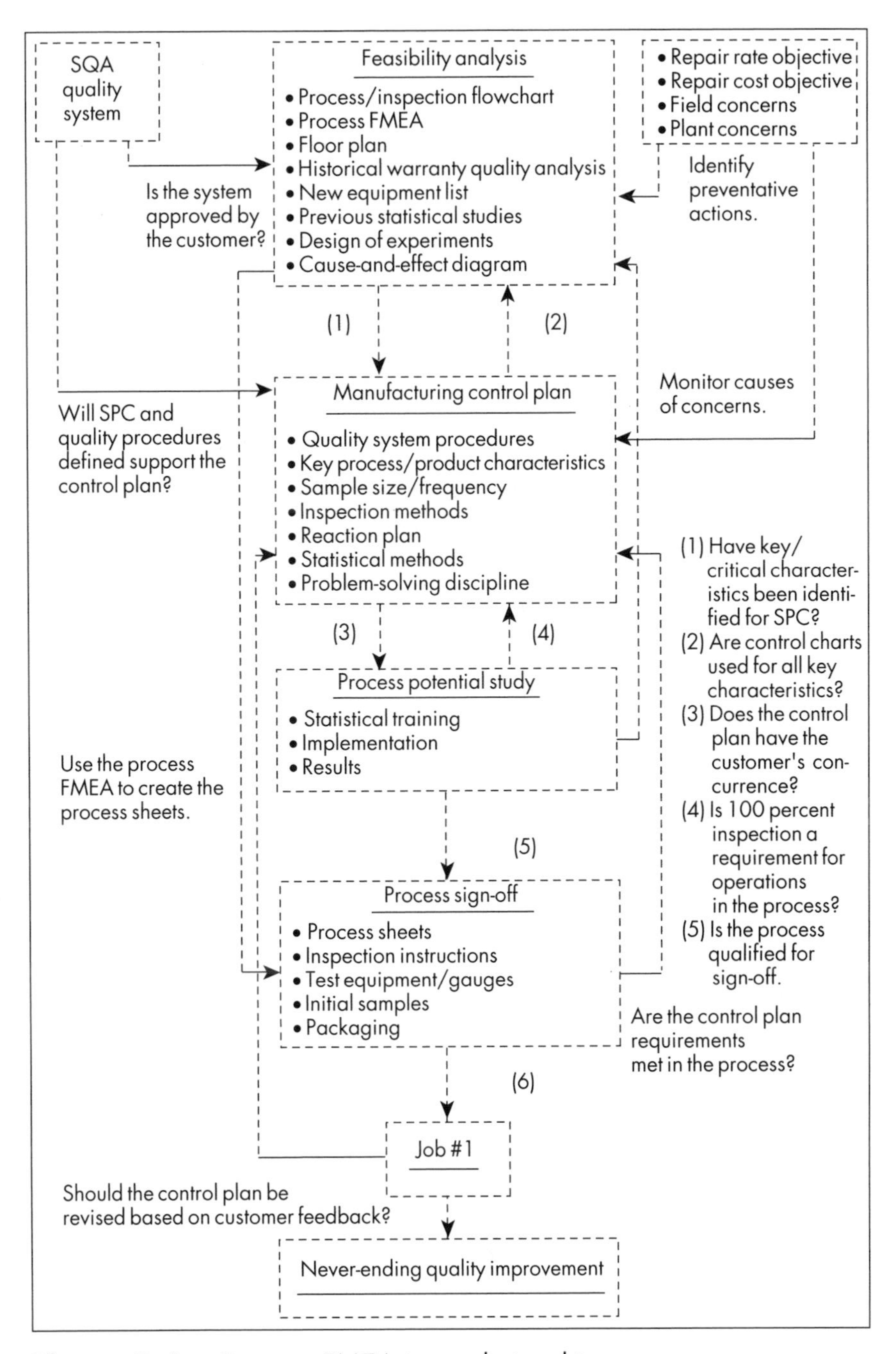

Figure B.4 Process FMEA interrelationships.

Component design engineer	System design engineer	Project reliability engineer
Prepare analyses of all component failure modes and associated detection means. Submit analyses to system design engineer.	Determine effects of each components failure mode on subsystem. Identify those component failure modes that would result in subsystem failure.	Prepare failure mode analysis control log for components and subsystems. Distribute component failure modes analysis forms and subsytems failure modes analysis forms to responsible design groups.
		Conduct criticality analysis. Prepare order list of critical components. Prepare recommendations for criticality reduction. Submit critical components list and recommendations to system design engineer.
	Review critical items list and recommendations. Wherever feasible, incorporate design changes that will produce or reduce component criticality. Record action taken for every critical component. Prepare recommendations for those parts that remain critical. Submit action taken to reduce component criticality and recommendations for component design changes to project reliability engineer.	Revise critical components list in accordance with reduction in parts criticality through subsystem redesign. Delete those components that are no longer critical. Prepare additional recommendations for those components list and recommendations to component designers.
Wherever feasible, incorporate design changes that will reduce component criticality through use of part redundancy, part derating, redesign to fail-safe, etc. Submit action taken to reduce criticality of components to project reliablity engineer.		Prepare final critical components list to identify those components that are still critical. Submit final critical component list to quality control for implementation of special control of critical components. Distribute copies of critical components list to responsible design groups. As design changes are made, the entire process is reiterated to insure that the critical components list is compatible with the latest design.

Adapted from Kececioglu, D. 1991. *Reliability Engineering Handbook.* Vol. 2, p. 475. Reprinted by permission of Prentice Hall, Englewood Cliffs, New Jersey.

Table B.1 Sequence of FMECA activities and responsibilities.

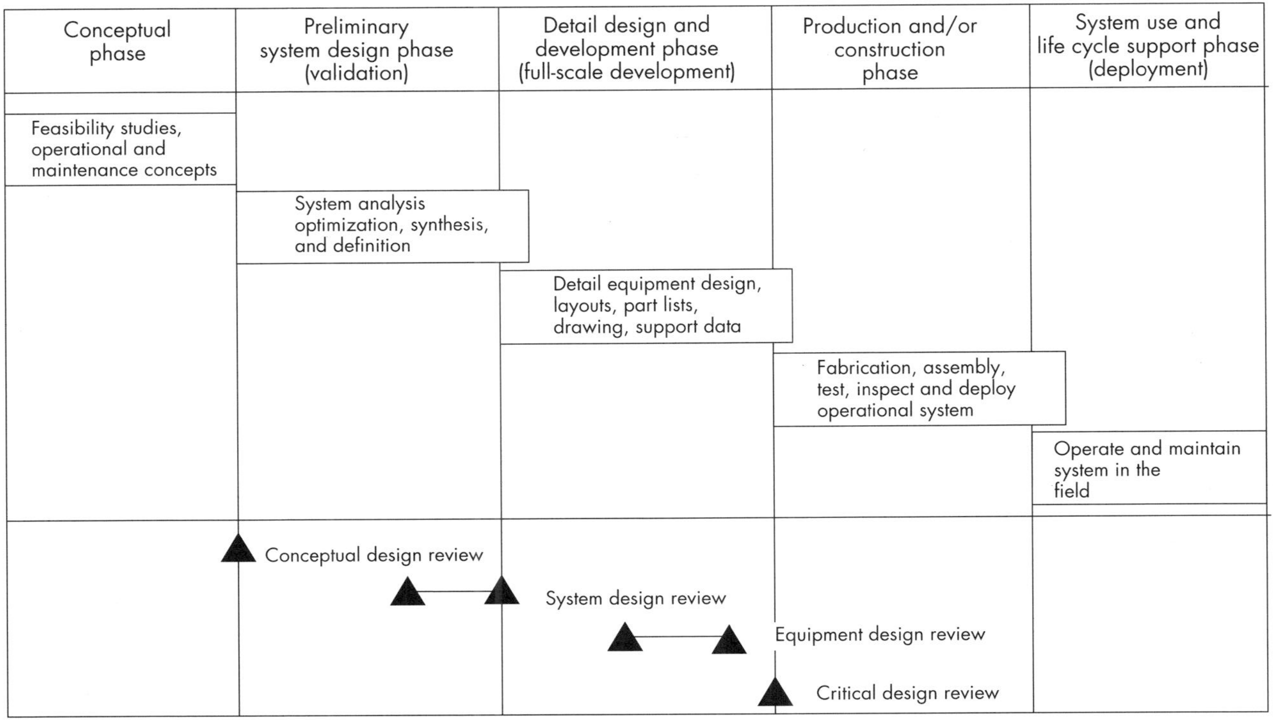

Conceptual phase	Preliminary system design phase (validation)	Detail design and development phase (full-scale development)	Production and/or construction phase	System use and life cycle support phase (deployment)
Feasibility studies, operational and maintenance concepts				
	System analysis optimization, synthesis, and definition			
		Detail equipment design, layouts, part lists, drawing, support data		
			Fabrication, assembly, test, inspect and deploy operational system	
				Operate and maintain system in the field
	Conceptual design review			
	System design review	System design review		
		Equipment design review		
			Critical design review	

Adopted from Kececioglu, D. 1991. *Reliability Engineering Handbook.* Vol. 2, p. 405. Reprinted by permission of Prentice Hall, Englewood Cliffs, New Jersey.

Table B.2 A typical design review schedule in relationship to process phases.

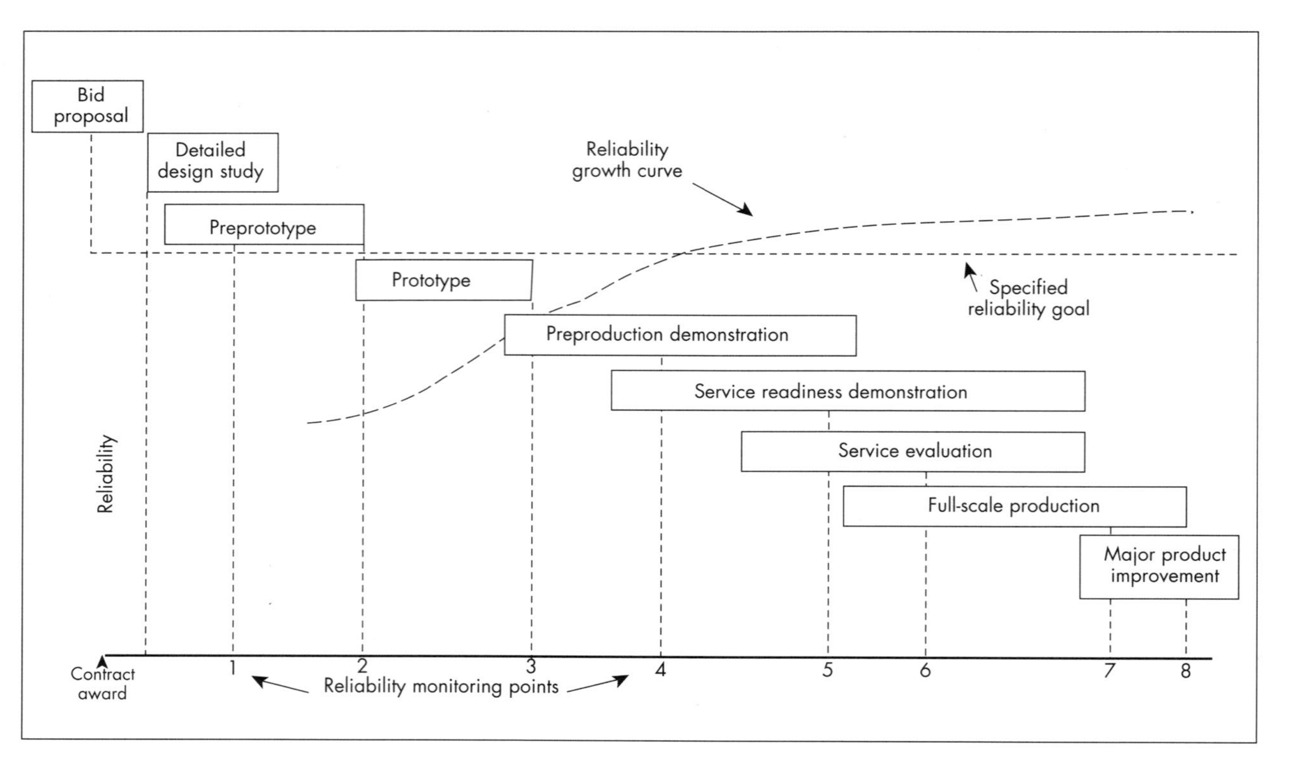

Adopted from Kececioglu, D. 1991. *Reliability Engineering Handbook*. Vol. 2, p. 402. Reprinted by permission of Prentice Hall, Englewood Cliffs, New Jersey.

Table B.3 Reliability growth in terms of contract milestones.

Critical characteristics

All safety items
Key measurements (for example, dimensions, temperature, pressure, and so on)

Significant characteristics

All items associated with the process and defined as important by the customer and/or the design or process engineer (such as dimensions, speed, temperature, pressure, and so on)

Leading quality indicators

Results of
- First-run capability
- Process throughput
- Internal audits
- Statistical process control
- Process reviews
- Process testing
- Product validation testing
- Engineering specification testing
- Design verification testing
- Inspection records

Key leading indicators

Intermediate indicators

Result of
- Long-term durability testing
- Audits
- Review and analysis of process yield points
- Customer surveys
- Production validation tests

Lagging indicators

Result of
- Inspection studies
- Warranty data analysis
- Supplier review analysis
- Customer complain analysis

Table B.4 Critical characteristics.

APPENDIX C

Active Verbs and Nouns Used for Function

This appendix provides the reader with an example of verbs, nouns, and functions used in the construction of the FMEA. For obvious reasons, this is not an exhaustive list, but a sample of how the reader may go about starting the thinking process for the construction of an FMEA.

Table C.1 Verbs and nouns for system/design FMEA.

A partial list of verbs and nouns used in the construction of a system FMEA is provided.

Verbs		Nouns	
actuate	insulate	appearance	light
amplify	interrupt	circuit	liquid
apply	limit	contacts	noise
change	locate	contamination	oxidation
close	maintain	convenience	paint
collect	module	current	panel
conduct	mount	damage	piston
contain	move	density	protection
control	prevent	dust	radiation
create	protect	effect	repair
decrease	rectify	energy	rust
emit	reduce	features	style
establish	repel	flow	switch
fasten	rotate	fluid	symmetry
filter	secure	force	torque
hold	shield	form	vibration
ignite	shorten	friction	voltage
impede	space	heat	volume
improve	support	insulation	weight
increase	time (verb)		
induce	transmit		

Table C.2 Verbs and nouns for process/service FMEA.

A partial list of verbs and nouns used in the construction of a process FMEA is provided.

Verbs		Nouns	
allow	minimize	corrosion	light
apply	modify	current	material
bake	move	decor	motion
band	produce	effort	power
compress	receive	electricity	shape
convey	reduce	energy	supplies
decrease	remove	environment	tools
discard	resist	equipment	torque
drive	restrict	fixtures	voltage
dry	shape	force	waste
eliminate	sort		
friction	stake		
finish	store		
fire	support		
form	transmit		
generate	transport		
improve	weigh		
lift	wrap		
load			

Table C.3 Typical functions used in FMEA.

Typical functions used in the construction of an FMEA.	
accept	reinforce
attach	remain instact
bearing surface	retain
conduct	return to normal position
connect	seal in
contain	seal out
damp	secure
indicate	sense
insulate	shield
isolate	store
locate	support
lubricate	transfer
position	transmit
protect	transport
provide pivot axis	vent
provide signal	

Appendix D

FMEA Samples

This appendix provides samples as opposed to examples of FMEAs. The reason for this is because some of the FMEAs are quite lengthy and will detract from the purpose of providing the reader with a variety of examples in different stages.

System FMEA

- Example 1 Sample of a Generic System FMEA
- Example 2 Fidd Quad LSD

Design FMEAs

- Example 3 Throttle Body Machine (Print, Flow Diagram, and Design FMEA)
- Example 4 Package/Layout
- Example 5 Armature

Product Design and Development FMEA

- Example 6 Cooling Fan Assembly

Process FMEAs

- Example 7 Nitride Etch
- Example 8 Slit Base Laminate
- Example 9 GDS Assembly

Service FMEA

- Example 10 Complaint Diagnoses

FTA Development

- Example 11 FTA Development of an Air Pumping System

System: Sample				Prepared by:			Date:	
Subsystem:				Approved by:			Revision:	
Subsystem element:							Page 1 OF 1	
				Failure effect on				
Item Identification	Function	Failure mode	Failure cause	Component or functional assembly	Next higher assembly	System	Failure detection method	Remarks
Switch	Initiates motor power function	Fails to open	Release spring failure Contacts fused	None	Maintains energy to circuit relay	Maintains energy to power circuit through relay	Motor continues to runs Smoke-visual when power circuit wire overheats	
Battery #2 (relay circuit)	Provides relay voltage	Fails to provide adequate power	Depleted battery Plates shorted	None Battery gets hot and deplets	Fails to operate relay circuit	System fails to operate	Motor not running	
Relay (relay coil)	Closes relay contacts when energized	Coil fails to produce EMF	Coil shorted or open	Does not close relay contacts	Does not energize power circuit	System fails to operate	Motor not running	
Relay contacts	Energizes and de-energizes power circuit	Fails to open	Contacts fused	None	Maintains energy to motor	Overheated power circuit wire if motor is shorted and circuit breaker fails to open	Motor continues to run Smoke-visual	
Motor	Provides desired mechanical event	Fails to operate	Motor shorted	Motor overheats	High current in power circuit	Overheated power circuit wire if motor is shorted and circuit breaker fails to open and switch or relay fails	Smoke-visual	
Circuit breaker	Provides power circuit fusing	Fails to open	Contacts fused Spring failure	None	Maintains power in motor if relay contacts are closed	Maintains energy to motor	Motor continues to run Smoke-visual	
Battery #1 (power circuit)	Provides motor voltage	Fails to provide adequate power	Depleted battery Plates shorted	None Battery gets hot and depletes	None	System fails to operate	Motor not running	

Example 1 Sample of a generic system FMEA.

Part name and number Part function	Potential failure mode	Potential effect(s) of failure	Sev	∇	Potential cause(s) of failure	Occur	Design verification	Detec	R.P.N.	Recommended action(s)
	Load dump to 60V	Device self-protects and protects load	2		Alternator load dump	3	Load dump test at to 60V (final test)	2	12	Statistical testing
	**************** ******NOTES****** ****************	IC is DC protected to 60V, output turns off at ~35V			(No note present)		(No note present)			
	Load dump to >60V (protection zener failure)	Transient SOA stress on high V. PNP's	8		Alternator load dump and zener failure	2	Characterization test of samples to detect	2	32	None (outside spec)
	**************** ******NOTES****** ****************	What is probability of this double failure mode?			(No note present)		(No note present)			
	S/C to GND (outputs) (pins 1, 2, 14, 15)	Output shorted to ground	1		Shorted load to ground	3	None	2	6	None
	**************** ******NOTES****** ****************	Shows up as off-state open CCT fault			(No note present)		(No note present)			
	S/C to GND (inputs) (Pins 3, 4, 12, 13, 5, 11)	Inputs shorted to ground	1		Shorted lead to ground	3	None	2	6	None
	**************** ******NOTES****** ****************	Device permanently off, status shows OK-resolved by status flag change			(No notes present)		(No notes present)			

Example 2 Fidd Quad LSD.

Part name and number Part function	Potential failure mode	Potential effect(s) of failure	Sev	∇	Potential cause(s) of failure	Occur	Design verification	Detec	R.P.N.	Recommended action(s)
	S/C to GND (select) (pin 6)	PW select shorted to GND	1		Shorted lead to ground	3	None	1	3	None
	**************** ******NOTES****** ****************	HLOS mode not available			(No note present)		(No note present)			
	S/C to GND (VCC) (pin 7) [also S/C to VCC (GND)]	VCC shorted to GND	1		Spanner across battery pin 7 and 8 shorted	4	None	2	8	None
	**************** ******NOTES****** ****************	Let's hope a fuse blows!			(No note present)		(No note present)			
	S/C to GND (GND) (pin 8) [also S/C to VCC (VCC)]	GND shorted to GND	1		None	3	None	2	6	None
	**************** ******NOTES****** ****************	N/A			(No note present)		(No note present)			
	S/C to GND (test pin) (pin 9)	Test pin shorted to GND	1		Pin 8 and 9 shorted	2	None	3	6	None
	**************** ******NOTES****** ****************	Recommended pin configuration			(No notes present)		(No notes present)			

Example 2 (continued).

Part name and number Part function	Potential failure mode	Potential effect(s) of failure	Sev	∇	Potential cause(s) of failure	Occur	Design verification	Detec	R.P.N.	Recommended action(s)
	S/C to VCC (outputs) (pins 1, 2, 14, 15)	Nonfunctioning load	1		Shorted solenoid, incorrect wiring	3	Final test for S/C operation	2	6	Spec testing
	**************** ******NOTES****** ****************	S/C operation applies (I limit then shutdown cycle)			(No note present)		(No note present)			
	S/C to VCC (IP's select, test pin) (pins 3, 4, 12, 13, 5, 11, 6, 9)	IC input CCT destruction	8		Incorrect wiring	3	Final test for ESD operation	2	48	Spec testing
	**************** ******NOTES****** ****************	Part specifically designed to not withstand this condition			(No note present)		(No note present)			
	S/C to 5V rail (output) (pins 1, 2, 14, 15)	Semifunctioning load	1		Incorrect wiring	2	Final test for S/C operation	2	4	Spec testing
	**************** ******NOTES****** ****************	S/C operation applies (I think then shutdown cycle)			(No note present)		(No note present)			

Example 2 (continued).

Part name and number Part function	Potential failure mode	Potential effect(s) of failure	Sev	∇	Potential cause(s) of failure	Occur	Design verification	Detec	R.P.N.	Recommended action(s)
	S/C to 5V rail (inputs) (pins 3, 4, 12, 13, 5, 11)	Inputs on permanently	1		Shorted load to 5V rail	3	None	3	9	None
	**************** ******NOTES****** ****************	Device permanently on, status OK-resolved by status flag change			(No note present)		(No note present)			
	S/C to 5V rail (select) (pin 6)	Operation only in PW mode	1		Shorted lead to 5V rail	3	None	2	6	None
	**************** ******NOTES****** ****************	Normal mode not available			(No note present)		(No note present)			
	S/C to 5V rail (VCC)	System logic functionality	1		Shorted lead to 5V rail	3	None	3	9	None
	**************** ******NOTES****** ****************	Essentially no effect on FIDD IC			(No note present)		(No note present)			
	S/C to 5V rail (GND)	No 5V rail (grounded)	1		Shorted lead to 5V rail	3	None	2	6	None
	**************** ******NOTES****** ****************	Essentially no effect on FIDD IC			(No note present)		(No note present)			

Example 2 (continued).

Part name and number Part function	Potential failure mode	Potential effect(s) of failure	Sev	∇	Potential cause(s) of failure	Occur	Design verification	Detec	R.P.N.	Recommended action(s)
	S/C to 5V rail (test pin) (pin 9)	Test pin shorted to GND	2		Shorted load to 5V rail	3	Characterization out of sample	2	12	None, outside spec
	**************** ******NOTES****** ****************	Designed for O/C or S/C to GND, not to 5V-not recommended			(No note present)		(No note present)			
	O/C (pins 1, 2, 14, 15) (outputs)	O/C load	1		Open circuit/unconnected load	3	Final test for O/C operation	2	6	Spec testing
	**************** ******NOTES****** ****************	O/C load - fault signaled via status line			(No note present)		(No note present)			
	O/C (pins 3, 4, 12, 13, 5, 11) inputs	Nonreporting loads	1		Open circuit unnconnected I/P	3	Modify for "float to zero"	2	6	Modify IC design
	**************** ******NOTES****** ****************	Incorporate a "fare to zero" to hold demo off in O/C mode			(No note present)		(No note present)			
	O/C (pin 6) (select)	Nonresponding loads	1		Open circuit unconnected select	3	Modify for "float to zero"	2	6	Modify IC design
	**************** ******NOTES****** ****************	Incorporate "default to normal" on select			(No note present)		(No note present)			

Example 2 (continued).

Part name and number Part function	Potential failure mode	Potential effect(s) of failure	Sev	∇	Potential cause(s) of failure	Occur	Design verification	Detec	R.P.N.	Recommended action(s)
	O/C (pin 7) (VCC) "loss of supply"	Nonfunctional loads	1		O/C VCC connection	3	None	2	6	None
	**************** ******NOTES****** ****************	If loads connected outputs open CCT (no gate voltage)			(No note present)		(No note present)			
	O/C (pin 8) (GND) "loss of GND"	Nonfunctional loads	6		Unconneccted ground to IC	3	Modify to protect	2	36	Modify IC design
	**************** ******NOTES****** ****************	Incorporate poly res's in input and output lines, modified ESD			(No note present)		(No note present)			
	O/C (pin 9) (test pin)	Test pin open-CCT	1		None	2	None	2	4	None
	**************** ******NOTES****** ****************	Normal operational condition			(No note present)		(No note present)			
	Intermittent load (pins 1, 2, 14, 15)	Intermittent load failure	1		Loose connection to lead	2	None	2	4	None
	**************** ******NOTES****** ****************	Fault detected during operation			(No note present)		(No note present)			

Example 2 (continued).

Part name and number Part function	Potential failure mode	Potential effect(s) of failure	s e v	∇	Potential cause(s) of failure	O c c u r	Design verification	D e t e c	R. P. N.	Recommended action(s)
	Partial short to VCC (all four loads)	Overheating chip	1		Nonapproved loads	1	System design dependent	2	2	Ford FMEA check
	**************** ******NOTES****** ****************	Not a problem if properly heatsinked (I-just under I-limit point)			(No note present)		(No note present)			
	Intermittent switching of load VCC to GND	Nonworking system	1		Loose load connection	1	None	1	1	None
	**************** ******NOTES****** ****************	Indicator discharges through output (SOA)			(No note present)		(No note present)			
	Transients >supply - outputs (pins 1, 2, 14, 15)	Over V spike on inputs	1		ESD, and other transient conditions	3	Final test/ESD	2	6	Include in spec testing
	**************** ******NOTES****** ****************	Less severe than on - off transient			(No note present)		(No note present)			
	Transients >supply - inputs etc (pins 3, 4, 5, 6, 7, 8, 9, 10, 11, 12, 13)	Over V spike on inputs	1		ESD, other transient conditions	3	ESD	2	6	Include in spec testing
	**************** ******NOTES****** ****************	Doesn't induce practice			(No note present)		(No note present)			

Example 2 (continued).

Part name and number Part function	Potential failure mode	Potential effect(s) of failure	Sev	∇	Potential cause(s) of failure	Occur	Design verification	Detec	R.P.N.	Recommended action(s)
	**************** ******NOTES****** ****************	*Serious only if zener V becomes <supply V	8		(No note present)	3	(No note present)	2	48	
	Device overheating	Output I reduction	8		Nonheatsinked device	3	Characterization	2	48	Spec testing
	**************** ******NOTES****** ****************	Add thermal shutdown!			(No note present)		(No note present)			
	DMOS VT increase	Output I reduction	8		Lifetime drift	1	Life test	1	8	Life test
	**************** ******NOTES****** ****************	*Depends on new turn-on value-affect low V first			(No note present)		(No note present)			

Example 2 (continued).

Part name and number Part function	Potential failure mode	Potential effect(s) of failure	Sev	∇	Potential cause(s) of failure	Occur	Design verification	Detec	R.P.N.	Recommended action(s)
	**************** ******NOTES****** ****************	Nonspecified drive could give marginal performance	3		(No note present)	4	(No note present)	1	12	
	Time vs spec drift - input impedance reduced	Capability to overdrive I/Ps	1		Use of nonapproved drive devices	4	System design dependent	1	4	None
	**************** ******NOTES****** ****************	Here nonspecified driver should not impede performance			(No note present)		(No note present)			
	Time vs spec drift - supply >30V	Over V liable to trip	1		Use in 24V systems	3	System design dependent	1	3	Inclusion in Ford system FMEA
	**************** ******NOTES****** ****************	Could also be problems in S/C mode (with no thermal trip)			(No note present)		(No note present)			
	Time vs spec drift - supply <5.5V	Outputs drive limited	1		Dead battery and failed alternator	4	None	2	8	None
	**************** ******NOTES****** ****************	Outside designed operating range			(No note present)		(No note present)			

Example 2 (continued).

Part name and number Part function	Potential failure mode	Potential effect(s) of failure	Sev	∇	Potential cause(s) of failure	Occur	Design verification	Detec	R.P.N,	Recommended action(s)
	Intermittent input (pins 3, 4, 12, 13, 51, 11, 6)	Intermittent load failure	1		Loose connection to load	2	None	2	4	None
	**************** ******NOTES****** ****************	During "fault" condition device is off			(No note present)		(No note present)			
	Time vs spec drift - load increased impedance	Nonworking system	1		Use of nonapproved load	4	System design dependent	1	4	Include in Ford system FMEAs
	**************** ******NOTES****** ****************	Use of nonspecified load often causes unforeseen problems			(No note present)		(No note present)			
	Time vs spec drift - load reduced impedance	Nonworking system	1		Use of nonapproved load	4	System design dependent	1	4	Inclusion of FMEA check
	**************** ******NOTES****** ****************	Nonspecified load of reduced impedance could cause thermal stress			(No note present)		(No note present)			
	Time vs spec drift - input impedance increased	Nonworking system	1		Use of nonapproved drive devices	3	System design dependent	1	3	Inclusion of FMEA check

Example 2 (continued).

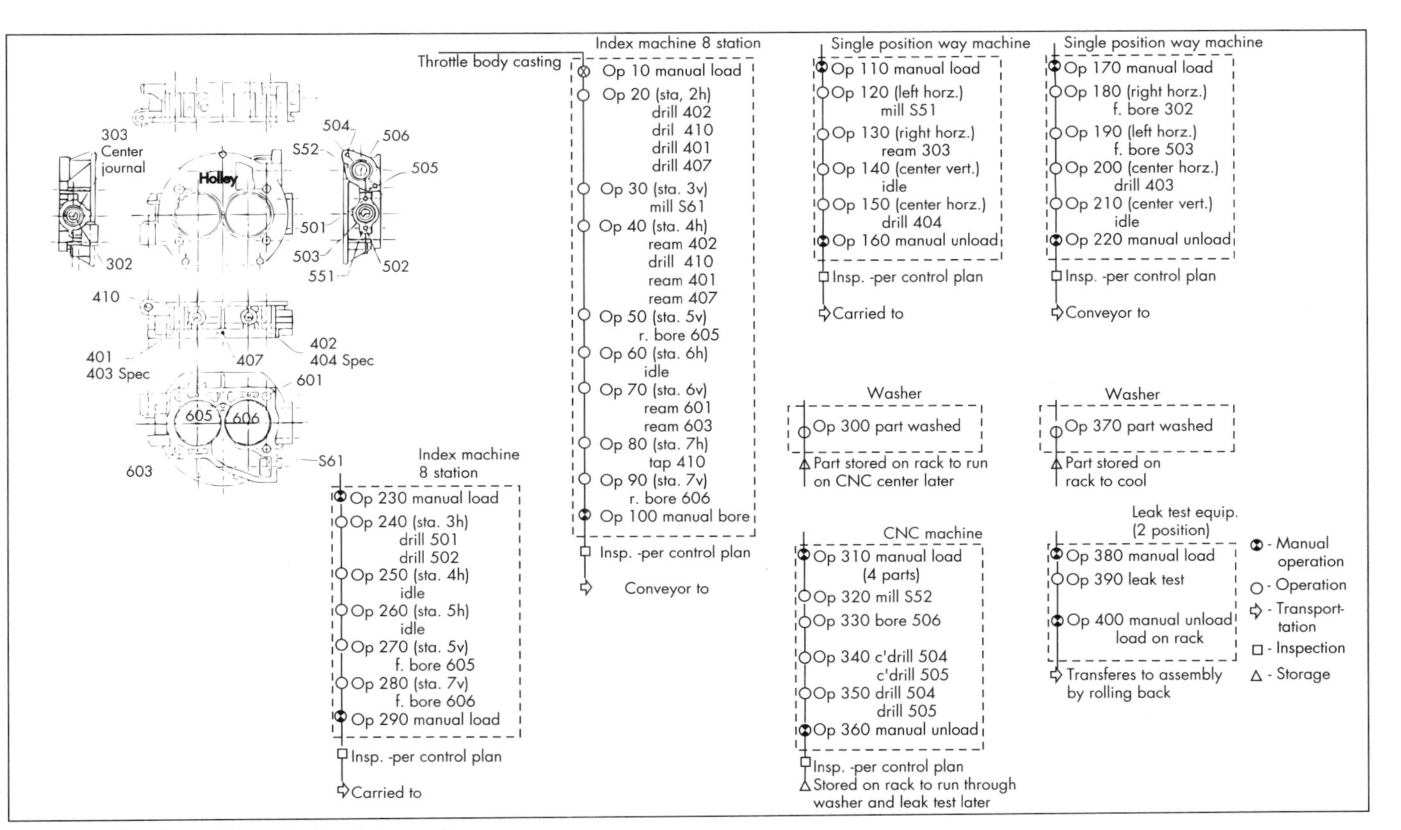

Example 3 Throttle body machine.

P = Probability (chance) of occurrence
S = Seriousness of failure to vehicle
D = Likelihood defect will reach customer
R = Risk priority measure (PxSxD)
P.F.M.E.A.. ______ Date ______
Revised ______
Created ______

1 = very low or none 2 = low or minor 3 = moderate or significant 4 = high 5 = very high

No.	Process	Failure mode	Effect of failure mode	Cause of failure	Current controls	P	S	D	R	Recommended corrective action
1	Op 10 Load	Machined incorrectly:	Scrap	Operator loaded part incorrectly	Fixed tooling	1	5	1	5	None
2	Op 20 Drill 401 402 410 407	Machined incorrectly: oversize, out of position, missing	Scrap Break other tools	Broken or worn tools Gauging error	Tool break detectors SPC chart	1	5	1	5	None
3	Op 30 Mill 561	Machined incorrectly: bad surface finish flatness	Scrap	Broken or worn inserts Chips on fixtures Gauging error	Visual inspection Flush lines SPC chart	2	4	2	16	None
4	Op 40 Ream Drill 401 410 402 407	Machined incorrectly: oversize, out of position, missing	Scrap Break other tools Assembly problems	Broken or worn tools Gauging error	Tool break detectors SPC charts	1	5	3	15	None
5	Op 50 Rough Bore 605	Machined incorrectly: oversize, out of position	Break finish tool	Incorrectly built roughing tool	Tool layout	2	2	1	4	None
6	Op 60 Idle									
7	Op 70 Ream 601 603	Machined incorrectly: oversize, out of position, missing	Scrap Primary locator position problems	Broken or worn tools Gauging error	Tool inspection SPC charts	1	4	4	16	None

Example 3 (continued).

No.	Process	Failure mode	Effect of failure mode	Cause of failure	Current Controls	P	S	D	R	Recommended corrective action
8	On 80 Tap 410	Machined incorrectly: not tapped, shallow tap	Scrap Customer failure	Broken or worn tools Gauging error	Load monitor Tool detector SPC charts	1	5	1	5	None
9	On 90 Rough Bore 606	Machined incorrectly: oversize, out of position	Break finish tool	Incorrectly built roughing tool	Tool layout	2	2	1	4	None
10	Op 110 Load	Machined incorrectly:	Scrap	Operator loaded part incorrectly	Fixed tooling	1	5	1	5	None
11	Op 120 Mill S51	Machined incorrectly: bad surface finish flatness	Scrap Asm problems w/TPS	Broken or worn inserts Chips on fixtures Gauging error	Visual inspection Flush lines SPC chart Throttle efforts	1	5	2	10	None
12	Op 130 Ream 303	Machined incorrectly: oversize, out of position, burrs	Scrap Asm problems w/shaft	Broken or worn tool Fixture alignment Gauging error	SPC charts	3	3	2	18	None
13	Op 140 Idle									
14	Op 150 Drill 404	Machined incorrectly: out of position, missing	Scrap Purge failure	Broken or worn tool Incorrect setup Gauging error	Tool break detector Part buildup SPC charts	2	4	2	16	None
15	Op 170 Load	Machined incorrectly:	Scrap	Operator loaded part incorrectly	Fixed tooling	1	5	1	5	None

Example 3 (continued).

No.	Process	Failure mode	Effect of failure mode	Cause of failure	Current controls	P	S	D	R		Recommended corrective action
16	Op 180 Bore 302	Machined incorrectly: oversize, out of position, undersized	Scrap Asm problems w/shaft Purge failure	Broken or worn tool Fixture alignment Gauging error	SPC charts Tool inspection	1	5	3	15	*INV	None
17	Op 190 Bore 503	Machined incorrectly: oversize, out of position, undersized	Scrap Asm problems w/shaft Purge failure	Broken or worn tool Fixture alignment Gauging error	SPC charts Tool inspection	1	5	3	15	*INV	None
18	200 Drill 403	Machined incorrectly: out of position, missing	Scrap Purge failure	Broken or worn tool Incorrect setup Gauging error	Tool break detector Part buildup SPC charts	2	2	3	12		None
19	Op 210 Idle										
20	Op 230 Load	Machined incorrectly:	Scrap	Operator loaded part incorrectly	Fixed tooling	1	5	1	5		None
21	Op 240 Drill 501 502	Machined incorrectly: missing holes oversize	Scrap Asm problems w/screws	Broken or worn inserts Chips on fixtures Gauging error	Visual inspection Flush lines SPC chart	1	2	1	2		None
22	Op 250 Idle										
23	Op 260 Idle										
24	Op 270 Finish bore 605	Machined incorrectly: oversize, out of position, incorrect depth, bad finish	Scrap Customer rejects	Broken or worn tool Setup error Gauging error	CNC depth control SPC charts Functional test	2	4	2	16	*INV	None

Example 3 (continued).

No.	Process	Failure mode	Effect of failure mode	Cause of failure	Current controls	P	S	D	R	Recommended corrective action
25	Op 280 Finish bore 606	Machined incorrectly: oversize, out of position, incorrect depth, bad finish	Scrap Customer rejects	Broken or worn tool Setup error Gauging error	CNC depth control SPC charts Functional test	2	4	2	16 *INV	None
26	Op 300 Washer	Parts not clean: chips, residue	Customer rejects	Incorrect concentration levels Water design	Visual inspection Monitor levels	2	2	1	4	None
27	Op 310 Manual load (4 parts)	Machined incorrectly	Scrap	Operator loaded part incorrectly	Fixed tooling	1	5	1	5	None
28	Op 320 Mill 552	Machined incorrectly: bad surface finish flatness	Scrap Asm problems w/AIS	Broken or worn inserts Chips on fixtures Gauging error	Visual inspection Flush lines SPC chart Throttle efforts	2	3	2	12	None
29	Op 330 Ream 506	Machined incorrectly: oversize, out of position, incorrect depth	Scrap Asm problems w/AIS	Broken or worn tool Setup error Gauging error	CNC depth control SPC charts Tool inspection	1	4	3	12	None
30	Op 340 C'Drill 504 505	Machined incorrectly: missing holes	Scrap Drill off location	Broken or worn tool Gauging error	Visual inspection SPC chart	1	2	1	2	None

Example 3 (continued).

No.	Process	Failure mode	Effect of failure mode	Cause of failure	Current controls	P	S	D	R	Recommended corrective action
31	Op 350 Drill 504 505	Machined incorrectly: missing holes oversize	Scrap Asm problems w/screws	Broken or worn tool Chips on fixtures Gauging error	Visual inspection Flush lines SPC chart	1	2	1	2	None
32	Op 370 Washer	Parts not clean: chips, residue	Customer rejects	Incorrect concentration levels Washer design	Visual inspection Monitor levels	2	3	3	18	None
33	Op 390 Leak test	Fail test	Scrap	Part not cooled	Allow cooling time	1	3	1	3	None

Example 3 (continued).

Failure mode and effects analysis
(design FMEA)

Page ____ Rows ____ through ____

Susbsystem/name ____ Suppliers and plants affected ____ Prepared by ____
Design responsibility ____ Model year/vehicle(s) ____
Other areas involved ____ Engineering release date ____ FMEA date (orig.) ____ (Rev.) ____

Part name and number Part function	Potential failure mode	Potential effect(s) of failure	Sev	∇	Potential cause(s) of failure	Occur	Design verification	Detec	R.P.N.	Recommended action(s)	Area/individual responsible & compl. date	Action results: Action taken	Sev	Occ	Det	R.P.N.
	Field plating inadequate	Increased leakage/ premature breakdown	8		Excess packing requirements	2	Check DV/manual	2	32	Standard checks	Sept 1990	None				
	**************** ******NOTES****** ****************	Well-understood problem			(No note present)		(No note present)									
	Voltage - drop (routing - excess	Inaccurate current sources	5		Metal width too narrow	2	Check DV/manual	2	20	Standard checks	Sept 1990	None				
	**************** ******NOTES****** ****************	Well-understood problem			(No note present)		(No note present)									
	Current density analysis - excess	Excess density O/P stages	5		Excessive packing requirements	2	DV, manual check life test	1	10	Standard checks	Sept 1990 Jan 1991	None				
	**************** ******NOTES****** ****************	Well-understood problem			(No note present)		(No note present)									
	Resistor tolerances >20% positive	Low internal current source	5		Faulty processing	4	Final test (PCS)	3	60	Standard checks	Dec 1990	Install process check	5	4	2	40
	**************** ******NOTES****** ****************	Beyond process spec			(No note present)		(No note present)									

Example 4 Package/layout.

Potential
failure mode and effects analysis
(design FMEA)

Suppliers and plants affected ______
Model year/vehicle(s) ______
Engineering release date 90 08 30

Part name and number	Part function	Potential failure mode	Potential effect(s) of failure	Sev	∇	Potential cause(s) of failure	Occur	Design verification	Detec	R. P. N.	Recommended action(s)	Area/individual responsible & Compl. date	Action results				
													Action taken	Sev	Occ	Det	R. P. N.
		Resistor tolerances > 20% negative	High internal current source	1		Faulty processing	1	Final test (PCS)	1	1	Standard check	Dec 1990	None				
		**************** ******NOTES****** ****************	Beyond process spec			(No note present)		(No note present)									
		Thermal mismatch	Resistance mismatch due to thermal effects	5		Poor layout technique	7	Manual layout inspect	3	105	Standard check	Sept 1990	Install process check	5	7	1	35
		**************** ******NOTES****** ****************	Well-understood problem			(No note present)		(No note present)									
		Internal interference (supply V rail)	Intercell interference	5		Poor design/ layout	3	Suppression design	1	15	Design - in	June 1990	None				
		**************** ******NOTES****** ****************	Incorporated 2 vint lines			(No note present)		(No note present)									
		Spice model failure	Inaccurate spice models	5		Lack of extreme models	4	Work with worst case models	2	40	Obtain models	Aug 1990	None				
		**************** ******NOTES****** ****************	Design check with new models			(No note present)		(No note present)									

Example 4 (continued).

Potential
failure mode and effects analysis
(design FMEA)

Suppliers and plants affected ____________
Model year/vehicle(s) ____________
Engineering release date ___90 08 30___

Part name and number	Part function	Potential failure mode	Potential effect(s) of failure	Sev	∇	Potential cause(s) of failure	Occur	Design verification	Detec	R.P.N.	Recommended action(s)	Area/individual responsible & Compl. date	Action results					
													Action taken	Sev	Occ	Det	R.P.N.
		Inadequate guard ring	Leakage/transient failure	5		Excess packing/ poor layout	2	Manual layout inspect	1	10	Visual inspect	Sept 1990	None				
		**************** ******NOTES****** ****************	Well-understood problem			(No note present)		(No note present)									
		Thermal mismatch - transistors	Transistor mismatch due to thermal effects	5		Poor layout techniques	6	Manual layout inspect	3	90	Standard check	Sept 1990	Install process check	5	6	1	30
		**************** ******NOTES****** ****************	Well-understood problem			(No note present)		(No note present)									
		Matching resistors	Well-understood problem	5		Poor layout techniques	8	Manual layout check	3	120	Standard check	Sept 1990	Install process check	5	8	1	40
		**************** ******NOTES****** ****************	Resistors mismatched due to layout effects			(No note present)		(No note present)									
		Matching transistors	Transistors mismatched due to layout	5		Poor layout technique	8	Manual layout check	3	120	Visual inspect	Sept 1990	Install inspection check-point	5	8	2	80
		**************** ******NOTES****** ****************	Well-understood problem			(No note present)		(No note present)									

Example 4 (continued).

Potential
failure mode and effects analysis
(design FMEA)

Suppliers and plants affected ____________

Model year/vehicle(s) ____________

Engineering release date 90 08 30

Part name and number	Part function	Potential failure mode	Potential effect(s) of failure	Sev	∇	Potential cause(s) of failure	Occur	Design verification	Detec	R.P.N.	Recommended action(s)	Area/individual responsible & Compl. date	Action results: Action taken	Sev	Occ	Det	R.P.N.
		Package: solder voids	Voids in solder behind chip	8		Out of spec soldering	2	Characterization evaluation	2	32	Characterization	Jan 1991	None				
		**************** ******NOTES****** ****************	Incorporate thermal trip/theta JC testing			(No note present)		(No note present)									
		Package/system: shorted bonds 1–2, 3–, 12–13, 14–15	Outputs 1–2 etc. shorted	8		Bonding/holding problems	1	Final test	1	8	Final test check	Jan 1991	None				
		**************** ******NOTES****** ****************	2 outputs shorted allowing device to over heat			(No note present)		(No note present)									
		Package/system: shorted bonds 2–3, 13–14	Input and output 2, 3 shorted	8		Bonding/holding problems	1	Final test	1	8	Final test check	Jan 1991	None				
		**************** ******NOTES****** ****************	Nasty!			(No note present)		(No note present)									
		Package/system: shorted bonds 11–12, 4–5	In & PW shorted	1		Bonding/holding problems	1	Final test	1	1	Final test check	Jan 1991	None				
		**************** ******NOTES****** ****************	Could cause system problems			(No note present)		(No note present)									

Example 4 (continued).

Potential
failure mode and effects analysis
(design FMEA)

Suppliers and plants affected ____________
Model year/vehicle(s) ____________
Engineering release date 90 08 30

Part name and number	Part function	Potential failure mode	Potential effect(s) of failure	Sev	∇	Potential cause(s) of failure	Occur	Design verification	Detec	R.P.N.	Recommended action(s)	Area/individual responsible & Compl. date	Action results: Action taken	Sev	Occ	Det	R.P.N.
		Package/system: shorted bonds 10–11	Forced into PW2 mode	5		Bonding/holding problems	1	Final test	1	5	Final test check	1991	None				
		**************** ******NOTES****** ****************	System dependent fault			(No note present)		(No note present)									
		Package/system: shorted bonds 5–6	PW1/Select shorted	5		Bonding/holding problems	1	Final test	1	5	Final test check	Jan 1991	None				
		**************** ******NOTES****** ****************	System dependent fault			(No note present)		(No note present)									
		Package/system: shorted bonds 6–7	VDO/select shorted	8		Bonding/holding problems	1	Final test	1	8	Final test check	Jan 1991	None				
		**************** ******NOTES****** ****************	Blown bond VDO/ select - if select breaks device may still operate			(No note present)		(No note present)									
		Package/system: shorted bonds 7–8	Shorted VCC to GND	8		Bonding/holding problem	1	Final test	1	8	Final test check	Jan 1991	None				
		**************** ******NOTES****** ****************	Bond explodes			(No note present)		(No note present)									

Example 4 (continued).

Suppliers and plants affected ____________

Model year/vehicle(s) ____________

Engineering release date 90 08 30

Part name and number	Part function	Potential failure mode	Potential effect(s) of failure	Sev	∇	Potential cause(s) of failure	Occur	Design verification	Detec	R.P.N.	Recommended action(s)	Area/individual responsible & Compl. date	Action results				
													Action taken	Sev	Occ	Det	R.P.N.
		Package/system: shorted bonds 8–9	GND shorted to test out	1		Bonding/holding problems	1	Final test	1	1	Final test check	1991	None				
		**************** ******NOTES****** ****************	Failure at test (apparent non-functional OSC)			(No note present)		(No note present)									
		Package/system: shorted bonds 9–10	Status and test out shorted	3		Bonding/holding problems	1	Final test	1	3	Final test check	Jan 1991	None				
		**************** ******NOTES****** ****************	False status fault flag			(No note present)		(No note present)									
		EPI tank bias	Increased package/manufacturing cells	8		Misconnected tank on layout/schematic	2	DV/SV check and manual schematic check	1	16	Standard checks	Sept 1990	None				
		**************** ******NOTES****** ****************	Well-understood problem			(No note present)		(No note present)									
		Tunnel (tank) bias	Unexpected biasing at input/output	8		Ill-considered tunnel bias	2	Manual check	1	16	Standard checks	Sept 1990	None				
		**************** ******NOTES****** ****************	Also as EPI tank bias			(No note present)		(No note present)									

Example 4 (continued).

P = Probability (chance) of occurrence S = Seriousness of failure to vehicle D = Likelihood defect will reach customer R = risk Priority measure (PxSxD)

1 = very low or none 2 = low or minor 3 = moderate or significant 4 = high 5 = very high

# Part name	Function	Failure mode	Effect of failure	Cause of failure	Current controls	P	S	D	R	Correct action	Action done
1 Armature	Valves the flow of fluid in response to magnetic field	Friction	Slow or no ride switching. Inferior ride	Nicks/scratches in armature O.D. or flange I.D.	Inspection	1	2	2	4	None	None
				Contaminants in the grooves		1	2	2	4	None	None
				Inadequate surface finish	Print spec.	1	2	2	4	None	None
				Inadequate plating	Print spec.	1	2	2	4	None	None
				Inadequate cylindricity	Print spec.	1	2	2	4	None	None
				Bent armature spring	On/off times	1	2	2	4	None	None
				Bent or broken air gap spacer	On/off times	2	2	3	12	None	None
				Small armature to flange assembly clearance	Select fit armature and flange assembly	2	2	3	12	None	None
				Contaminated oil	Contamination testing	1	2	1	2	None	None
				Armature length too short		1	2	1	2	None	None
				Thermal expansion of armature and flange assembly	Thermal chamber	2	2	1	4	None	None

Example 5 Armature.

# Part name	Function	Failure mode	Effect of failure	Cause of failure	Current controls	P	S	D	R	Correct action	Action done
1 Armature	Valves the flow of fluid in response to magnetic field	Friction	Slow or no ride switching. Inferior ride	Burr generated by impact with stop	Durability	1	2	2	4	None	None
		Armature sticks in open position	Vehicle sticks in soft ridge state. Difficulty handling	Air gap spacer too thin, armature magnetical locks to it	Print spec.	1	3	1	3	None	None
				Armature or air gap spacer mating surface too large, adhesion occurs	Print spec.	1	3	1	3	None	None
				Armature and stop mating surfaces battered	Durability testing	2	3	2	12	None	None
		High leakage	Does not achieve full firm ride. Inferior ride quality	Large armature to flange assembly clearance	Select fit armature and flange assembly	2	3	2	12	None	None
				Armature and sealing post mating surfaces battered	Durability testing	2	3	2	12	None	None
				Sachs portion leaks	Master solenoids tested	2	3	2	12	None	None
	Provides sealing surface against sealing post	Does not seal against sealing post	Does not achieve full firm ride. Inferior ride quality	Nicks/scratches in armature O.D. or flange I.D.	Off time	2	3	2	12	None	None
				Sachs components misaligned or damaged	Master solenoids tested	2	3	2	12	None	None
				Surface finish too rough	Print spec.	1	3	1	3	None	None

Example 5 (continued).

# Part name	Function	Failure mode	Effect of failure	Cause of failure	Current controls	P	S	D	R	Correct action	Action done
1 Armature	Flux core for coil wire	Insufficient force generated	Vehicle has difficulty achieving soft ride. Inferior ride quality	Material flux saturated	On time	1	2	1	2	None	None
1 Protective cap	Hold armature, armature spring, and air gap spacer together during shipment	Cap comes loose	Armature, armature spring, and/or air gap spacer separate from encapsulated housing	Cap improperly installed		2	1	2	4	None	None
				Cap I.D. too large	Print spec.	1	1	1	1	None	None
Housing Encapsulation	Contains and secures in place flange assembly, bobbin assembly, and cable connection	Poor surface finish quality	Visual identification	Poor encapsulation operation	Section batch part	1	1	3	3	None	None
				Worn mold	Encapsulation setup	2	1	3	6	None	None
		Cracks in encapsulation	Visual identification. Jeopardize integrity of connection between cable and bobbin coil	Solenoid exposed to cold temperature		1	2	2	4	None	None
				Poor encapsulation operation	Encapsulation setup	1	2	3	6	None	None
				Worn mold	Encapsulation setup	2	2	3	12	None	None

Example 5 (continued).

# Part name	Function	Failure mode	Effect of failure	Cause of failure	Current controls	P	S	D	R	Correct action	Action done
Housing encapsu-lation	Contains and secures in place flange assembly, bob-bin assembly, and cable connection	Poor cable retention	Cable pulls free of housing. Jeopardize integrity of connection between cable and bobbin coil	Improper encapsulation fill	Encapsulation setup	2	2	3	12	None	None
				No chemical bond formed between cable and terminal molding	Material choice	1	2	2	4	None	None
				No chemical bond formed between terminal molding and cable	Material choice	1	2	2	4	None	None
				Insufficient retention in groove design	Groove design inadequate	1	2	2	4	None	None
				Insufficient cable land to form proper bond between cable and terminal molding	Insufficient cable bond area in design	1	2	2	4	None	None
	Protects components from environ-mental factors	Coil integrity jeopardized by encapsulation	Locked in firm ride	Coil damaged or broken by encapsulation	Near-level wound wound bobbins used	2	2	3	12	None	None
			Erratic ride switching	Short to housing	Ground check. Resistance	1	2	1	2	None	None
		Encapsulation seeps between bobbin terminal and cable connection, reducing metal contact areas	Erratic or no ride response	Encapsulation pressure is too high	Encapsulation setup	2	2	3	12	None	None
				Terminal design not tight enough fit	Print spec.	1	2	1	2	None	None

Example 5 (continued).

# Part name	Function	Failure mode	Effect of failure	Cause of failure	Current controls	P	S	D	R	Correct action	Action done
Housing encapsulation	Protects components from environmental factors	Improper encapsulation fill	Housing or bobbin shows through encapsulation	Worn mold	Section batch part	2	3	2	12	None	None
				Improper insertion into mold	Burst test	2	3	2	12	None	None
				Bobbin terminals not centered in housing		1	3	3	9	None	None
				Improper slot design	Print spec.	1	3	2	6	None	None
			Encapsulation cracks when hit with high pressure. Flange assembly bows	Encapsulant not packed well enough to endure pressure	Encapsulation setup	1	3	2	6	None	None
Housing assembly	Hold bobbin, flange, and housing together	Flange, bobbin, and housing misaligned	Erratic or no ride switching	Improper press fit of flange and housing	Print spec.	1	2	2	4	None	None
				Corrosion on flange assembly	Flange assembly oiled	2	2	3	12	None	None
1 Housing	Provides flux path around coil	Insufficient force generated	Vehicle has difficulty achieving soft ride	Material flux saturated	On time	1	2	2	4	None	None
	Houses bobbin and coil assembly	Bobbin and coil assembly does not fit properly in housing	Dysfunctional solenoid	Bobbin cocked	On/off time	1	3	2	6	None	None
				Coil wire wrapped beyond	On/off time. Ground check	1	3	2	6	None	None
				Improper sizing of bobbin and housing	On/off time	1	3	1	3	None	None

Example 5 (continued).

# Part name	Function	Failure mode	Effect of failure	Cause of failure	Current controls	P	S	D	R	Correct action	Action done
1 Stop	Provides flux path from tube to armature	Insufficient force generated	Vehicle has difficulty achieving soft ride	Improper installation into flange assembly	On time	1	2	2	4	None	None
				Material saturated	On time	1	2	1	2	None	None
	Provides the solid base for air gap spacer	Burr development	Difficulty achieving full soft ride. Eventual functional problems	Wear between armature and stop mating surfaces produces burr	Durability	2	2	3	12	None	None
Armature spring	Provides return force to armature	Armature does not seal against sealing post	Does not achieve full firm ride	No spring installed	On/off times	2	3	3	18	None	None
				Spring rate too low	Spring rate measured	1	3	3	9	None	None
				Spring wear	Durability	1	3	3	9	None	None
				Misalignment on air gap spacer	Air gap spacer's retention design	2	3	3	18	None	None
	Sets return time response characteristics	Spring side loads armature	Achieves firm ride slowly	Bent spring	On/off time	2	3	3	18	None	None
		Spring breaks	Erratic ride control	Wear	Durability	2	3	3	18	None	None
Air gap spacer	Prevents magnetic and mechanical surface lock between armature and stop from occurring when solenoid is energized	Latching when energized	Achieves firm ride slowly or erratically	Air gap spacer not installed	On/off times	1	3	3	9	None	None
				Leg broken on air gap spacer	On time	2	3	3	18	None	None
				Air gap spacer too thin	On/off times	1	3	3	9	None	None
		Armature movement restricted	Achieves soft ride erratically, slowly, or not at all	Air gap spacer too thick	Pressure response for on/off times	1	2	3	6	None	None
				Leg broken or bent on air gap spacer	On time	2	2	3	12	None	None

Example 5 (continued).

# Part name	Function	Failure mode	Effect of failure	Cause of failure	Current controls	P	S	D	R	Correct action	Action done
Air gap spacer	Centers and holds armature spring	Spring biases armature position	Achieves firm ride slowly or erratically	Spring not properly seated	Off time	2	3	3	18	None	None
			Achieves soft ride slowly or erractically	Leg bent on air gap spacer	On time	2	2	3	12	None	None
1 Tube	Provides flux path	Insufficient force generated	Vehicle has difficulty switching to soft ride	Material flux saturated	On time	1	2	1	2	None	None
	Holds stop to disc	Inadequate attachment between disc and stop	Vehicle cannot hold firm ride	Improper braze	Burst	2	3	2	12	None	None
				Improper fits	Print spec.	1	3	2	6	None	None
1 Disc	Provides flux path for coil	Insufficient force generated	Vehicle has difficulty achieving soft ride	Improper installation into flange assembly	On time	1	2	2	4	None	None
				Material flux saturated	On time	1	2	1	2	None	None
				Component corrosion	On time	2	2	3	12	None	None
1 Molded cable assembly	Accommodates electrical and physical attachment of cable to bobbin coil assembly	Poor electrical connection	Erratic or no ride response	Improper terminal attachment	Resistance check	2	3	2	12	None	None
				Terminals bent too severely	Print spec.	1	3	3	9	None	None
		Water penetrates solenoid	Solenoid becomes inactive after time	Poor chemical bond between cable and terminal molding or between terminal molding and encapsulant	Material choice or overmolding design	2	3	3	18	None	None

Example 5 (continued).

# Part name	Function	Failure mode	Effect of failure	Cause of failure	Current controls	P	S	D	R	Correct action	Action done
1 Molded cable assembly	Accommodates electrical and physical attachment of solenoid to vehicle	Poor electrical connection	Erratic or no ride control	Crack in wire connector	Resistance check	1	3	3	9	None	None
				Improper wire connector attachment to cable	Resistance check	1	3	3	9	None	None
				Improper connection to vehicle		2	3	3	18	None	None
				Bent or damaged pin terminals	Resistance check	1	3	2	6	None	None
				Poor dry crimp of pin terminal to wire	Resistance check	1	3	3	9	None	None
				Connector clip missing or cracked	Resistance check	2	3	3	18	None	None
		Poor physical attachment to vehicle	Cable grommet does not line up correctly with vehicle connection	Grommet positioned improperly	Print spec. for grommet position	1	1	2	2	None	None
		Insufficient cable retention	Erratic or n solenoid response after bobbin terminal to cable connection breaks	Cable retention groove design	Pull-out test	1	2	1	2	None	None
	Carries current from vehicle to solenoid	Poor electrical connection	Erratic or no ride response	Cable wires have been nicked or twisted to fracture	Resistance check	2	2	3	12	None	None
		Electrical short	Electrical burning damage to vehicle components	Cable wire exposed and contacting through insulation	Resistance check	1	4	3	12	None	None

Example 5 (continued).

# Part name	Function	Failure Mode	Effect of Failure	Cause of Failure	Current Controls	P	S	D	R	Correct action	Action done
Flange assembly pre-machined	Provide flux path	Insufficient force generated	Vehicle has difficulty achieving soft ride	Corrosion of flange assembly	Oil flange assembly	2	2	3	12	None	None
				Components damaged during brazing	Burst test	1	2	2	4	None	None
				Material flux saturated	Print spec.	1	2	1	2	None	None
		Flange assembly leak	Vehicle cannot hold firm ride	Poor braze	Burst test	1	3	2	6	None	None
				Corrosion of flange assembly	Flange assembly oiled	2	3	3	18	None	None
				Insufficient material strength	Print spec.	1	3	1	3	None	None
				Insufficient encapsulation packing	Section batch part	1	3	2	6	None	None
1 Flange assembly machined	Seats air gap spacer	Air gap spacer damaged	Difficulty achieving soft ride	Improper groove dimension	On/off tests	1	2	1	2	None	None
				Air gap spacer broken or bent	On/off tests	2	2	3	12	None	None
	Armature guide	Friction between armature and flange assembly	Slow ride responses	Poor surface finish		1	2	3	6	None	None
				Contaminants in oil		2	2	3	12	None	None
				Improper fit between flange and armature		1	2	2	4	None	None
				Poor flange roundness and cylindricity		1	2	3	6	None	None

Example 5 (continued).

# Part name	Function	Failure Mode	Effect of Failure	Cause of Failure	Current Controls	P	S	D	R	Correct action	Action done
2 Bobbin terminal	Connects coil wire and cable wire	Poor electrical connection	Erratic or no ride response	Terminal did not scrape insulation away from coil wire to allow proper contact	Resistance check	2	2	2	8	None	None
				Twisted terminal	Resistance check	1	2	3	6	None	None
		High resistance	Slow ride response	Terminal twisted or damaged	Resistance check	1	2	3	6	None	None
1 Bobbin	Holds coil wire	Nonlevel winding	Improper solenoid operation	Flash on bobbin		2	2	3	12	None	None
				Improper winding setup		1	2	3	6	None	None

Example 5 (continued).

Part name/ part no.	Product function	Potential failure mmode	Potential effect(s) of failure	Control critical item	Potentail cause(s) of failure	Existing conditions				
						Current controls	Occureence	Severity	Detection	Risk priority no. (RPN)
		Fan vibration from imbalance and axial T.I.R.	Audible noise, vibration; increased motor wear		Fan center of gravity off axis of rotation; axial T.I.R. causes 2-plane imbalance	Design lightweight fan with min. band mass; part thick-ness to favor uniform mold flow. DV tests on vehicles to assess sensitivity to vibration inputs	5	5	4	100
Motor	Provide mechanical power to fans; position fans within shroud	Motor burnout, bearing or brush failure.	Loss of cooling and A/C function		Overheating, lack of air circuilation	Vent holes in motor case; fins in fan hub pull air through ES, durability tests.	2	5	5	50
		Misassemble to shroud, off-center or crooked.	Loss of cooling function.		Fan contanct shroud, noise or motor burn-out	Design for easy assembly, accurate poistioning in shroud.	2	7	3	42
		Assemble @ ±120° off-nominal angle, motor wire in wrong location.	No-build condition in assy. plant		Symmetrical spacing of screw holes; nonunique mounting interfaces	Power motion motor has unique mount-ing configura-tion. Visual inspection during assembly	6	6	3	108
			Motor wire interferes with engine and shorts; wire is too tight and opens circuit			Power motion motor has unique mount-ing configura-tion. Visual inspection during assembly	6	6	5	180
		Fan retainer compression too high.	Retainer loose, lost, loose fan and lost cool-ing function		"e" clip too close to shaft and slot	Maintain dim-ensional cap-ability within limits of tolerence stack-up	3	6	5	90

Example 6 Cooling fan assembly.

Part name/ part no.	Product function	Potential failure mmode	Potentail effect(s) of failure	Control critical item	Potentail cause(s) of failure	Existing conditions				
						Current controls	Occureence	Severity	Detection	Risk priority no. (RPN)
Motor	Provide mechanical power to fans; position fans within shroud	Fan retainer compression too low or nonexistent	Retainer loose, excess play between slot and "e" clip; breakage; lost cooling		"e" clip too far from shaft and slot	Maintain dimensional capability within limits of tolerence stack-up	3	6	5	90
		Backplate not swaged securely	Motor & fan loose; fan touches shroud, stalls; fan damages coil; loss of cooling, coolant		Designed interference of swaged tangs not sufficient; swaging process not capable	Swage method revised; pull out tests; DV testing; ES tests	2	6	7	84
Screws-motor mount	Attach motor to shroud.	Loosen after extended service	Loose motor allows fan contact with shroud, stalling motor		Plastic creep relieves screw tension, allows back-out	Maintain dimensional capability within limits of tolerence stack-up	2	7	5	70
		Missapplication	Loose motor allows fan contact with shroud, stalling motor		Drive in crooked, miss hole or not fully tight	Counterbore in screw-hole, torque-to-fail much higher than prevailing	2	7	3	42
		Plastic threads strip out	Loose motor, fan contact with shroud		Shroud mount boss splits	Counterbore, optimize boss diameter and height	2	7	4	56
Fan retainer	Attach fan and torque plate to motor.	Come loose after installation	Loose fan, contact w/ coil, loss of cooling		Incomplete installation, not fully snapped on	Design motor and fan for easy clip installation w/tactile snap on lock	3	5	4	60
			T.I.R. increased; vibration or noise; fan dismounts, loss of cooling		Retainer not keyed with respect to flats on motor shaft	ES and DV testing	2	7	7	98

Example 6 (continued).

Part name/ part no.	Product function	Potential failure mmode	Potentail effect(s) of failure	Control critical item	Potentail cause(s) of failure	Existing conditions				
						Current controls	Occureence	Severity	Detection	Risk priority no. (RPN)
Torque plate	Transmit torque from motor to fan	Motor shaft deforms flats in hole	Fan does not reach full RPM, fan bore wears. Loss of cooling, vibration from loose fan		Torque plate hole over-sized; steel not proper thickness or hardness	Maintain dimensional capability within limits of tolerence stack-up, ES tests	3	6	7	126
		Torque plate not fully seated	Engagement of flats is reduced torque plate hoe enloarged from stress		Close toler-ances of fan pockets and legs of plate	Make assy. retainer on unseated plate difficult	3	5	7	105

Example 6 (continued).

Process: P.O. nitride etch

Process name	Process function	Potential failure mode	Potential effects of failures	Potential causes of failure	Existing conditions (1–10)					Recommended actions	Area/ person responsible
					Current controls	OCC	SEV	DET	RPN		Completion date
P.O. nitride etch	P.O. nitride etch	Poor selectivity	Overetch Nitride voids	Chamber leak High O2 flow Low CF4 flow High temperature	Daily and weekly monitors Subsequent wafer inspections SPC	3 2 2 2	6 6 6 6	3 4 4 3	54 48 48 36	Replace A-24-D reactors	Open Open Open Open
		Poor uniformity	Overetch Underetch Nitride voids Dark bond pads	Chamber leak Wrong gas flow Wrong pressure Wrong power	Daily and weekly monitors Subsequent wafer inspections SPC	3 2 2 2	5 5 5 5	3 4 4 4	45 40 40 40	Replace A-24-D reactors	D.S. 3/6/94 3/6/94 3/6/94
		Overetch	Nitride voids Dark bond pads	Etch time too long High O2 flow Low CF4 flow High temperature High RF power	Daily and weekly monitors Subsequent wafer inspections SPC	3 2 2 2 2	7 7 7 7 7	3 3 3 3 3	63 42 42 42 42	Replace A-24-D reactors	Open Open Open Open Open
		Underetch	Poor bondability	Etch time too short High O2 flow Low RF power	Daily and weekly monitors Subsequent wafer inspections SPC	3 2 2	6 6 6	3 3 3	54 36 36	Replace A-24-D reactors	D.S. 3/6/94 3/6/94 3/6/94
		Scratches	Nitride voids Metal shorts	Wafer loading and unloading Subsequent wafer inspection	Daily and weekly monitors Subsequent wafer inspections SPC	7 5	5 5	4 4	140 100	Replace A-24-D reactors Implement wafer-handling system	C.S. Open T.S. Open

Example 7 Nitride etch.

Process name	Process function	Potential failure mode	Potential effects of failures	Potential causes of failure	Existing conditions (1–10) Current controls	OCC	SEV	DET	RPN	Recommended actions	Area/ person respon. Comp date
		Dark bond pads	Poor bondability	Overetch Not rinsed properly after processing	Daily and weekly monitors Subsequent wafer inspections SPC	3 2	7 7	3 3	63 42	Replace A-24-D reactors	D.S. 3/6/94 3/6/94

Device:
Process: Backgrind

Process name	Process function	Potential failure mode	Potential effects of failures	Potential causes of failure	Current controls	OCC	SEV	DET	RPN	Recommended actions	Area/ person respon. Comp date
Back-grind	Back-grind	Too thin	Poor bondability	Improper machine setup	Subsequent thickness measurements	3	4	3	36	Supply computer program to assist operator	D.S. Open
				Grinding wheel dirty	SPC	4	4	3	48	Establish periodic cleaning	D.S. Open
				Poor uniformity within wafer		4	4	2	32	Rebuild slide/ ball screw	D.S. Open
				Poor uniformity wafer to wafer		5	4	4	80	Rebuild slide/ ball screw	D.S. 5/6/94
		Too thick	Poor bondability	Improper machine setup	Subsequent thickness measurements	3	4	4	48	Supply computer program to assist operator	C.S. 5/6/94
				Grinding wheel dirty	SPC	4	4	4	64	Establish periodic cleaning	C.S. Open
				Poor uniformity within wafer		4	4	2	32	Rebuild slide/ ball screw	C.S. 5/2/94
				Poor uniformity wafer to wafer		5	4	5	100	Rebuild slide/ ball screw	C.S. 4/30/94

Example 7 (continued).

Part name/ part number	Process function	Potential failure mode	Potential effect(s) of failures		Potential cause(s) of failure	Existing conditions					Recommended action(s) and status	Action(s) taken	* 6	* 7	* 8	* 9
						Current controls	* 6	* 7	* 8	* 9						
Ford automotive circuits	Slit base laminate/ coverlay	Incorrect width	Images will not fit web or web will not fit tooling		Incorrect setup. Incorrect documentation	Setup monitored. Inspected at proceed-ing operations.	2	3	1	6	Standard web widths used and specified on routing	Completed	1	3	1	3
		Incorrect material	Unreliable part		Incorrect setup	Compare material part number to routing	1	5	4	20	BOM cross-check to routing sheet at all operations	Completed	1	5	3	15
					Incorrect documentation	Engineering maintains route sheets										
					Mislabeled material	Verified at laminations operations										
		Damaged material (dents, wrinkled, rough edges)	Scrap		Dull blades	Preventative maintenance	3	3	1	9	Feedback from next operation	Shutdown procedure implemented	2	3	1	6
					Foreign material Cast off	Clean equipment Reject/scrap material										
					Poor handling	Operator training of mechanized handling equipment										

Example 8 Slit base laminate.

Part name/ part number	Process function	Potential failure mode	Potential effect(s) of failures	Potential cause(s) of failure	Existing conditions					Recommended action(s) and status	Action(s) taken	* 6	* 7	* 8	* 9
					Current controls	* 6	* 7	* 8	* 9						
Ford automotive circuits	Pierce and index material web (coverlay only)	Incorrect material orientation	Scrap material due to mirror imaged registration	Incorrect documentation. Operator training	Orientation specified on routings Compare material part number to routing	1	5	2	10	None	None				
		Cutline quality –Slivers –Slugs –Incomplete cut	Slugs/slivers trapped between layers. Scrap material	Machine setup up and visual tooling wear	Die adjustment and visual inspection	3	4	5	60	Electrical test for opens due to slugs left in pad area. New web cleaner planned for indexing.	1st unit implemented	1	4	3	12

Example 8 (continued).

Part name/ Part number	Process function	Potential failure mode	Potential effect(s) of failures		Potential cause(s) of failure	Existing conditions					Recommended action(s) and status	Action(s) taken	* 6	* 7	* 8	* 9
						Current controls	* 6	* 7	* 8	* 9						
		LED upside down	No light	▼	–Operator error –Bent wrong		1	10	1	10	None	None				
		LED twisted	Won't fit in backer board		–Bent wrong –Handling –Pin twisted in fixture		1	2	1	2	None	None				
	Header assembly	Alignment of	–Circuit and board misaligned –Components misaligned	▼	–Board drilled wrong –Operator error		4	10	3	120	–A.I. NC drill	Installed 4/5/93	2	10	1	20
		Circuit not bonded to board	Customer return	▼	–Didn't roll enough –Bad PSA		3	10	2	60	Inspection and DOE to define the precise material	Done 5/6/94	1	10	1	10

Example 8 (continued).

Part name/ Part number	Process function	Potential failure mode	Potential effect(s) of failures		Potential cause(s) of failure	Existing conditions (1-10)					Recommended action(s) and status	Action(s) taken				
						Current controls	* 6	* 7	* 8	* 9			* 6	* 7	* 8	* 9
		Put header upside down	Won't fit in TI printer	▼	Operator oriented wrong		1	10	2	20	None	None				
		Wrong header	Won't fit in TI printer	▼	Wrong part		1	10	1	10	None	None				
	Dome assembly	Misaligned dome	Field failure	▼	Static fly-out	Nothing	2	10	10	200	100% inspect	Done 2/4/94	2	10	3	60
		Wrong shim	Lump in overlay	▼	Wrong material	Incoming inspection	2	10	7	140	Incoming SPC	Done 5/5/94	2	10	2	40
		No shim	Cosmetic		Operator error	Inspection	2	7	8	112	Keep good parts for comparison	Done 2/4/94	2	7	3	42
		Misregis-tered retainer	Domes slip	▼	Operator error	Inspection	2	10	5	100	Redesign part for fool proof design	Done 3/4/94	1	1	1	1

Example 8 (continued).

Part name/ Part number	Process function	Potential failure mode	Potential effect(s) of failures		Potential cause(s) of failure	Existing conditions (1-10)					Recommended action(s) and status	Action(s) taken	* 6	* 7	* 8	* 9
						Current controls	* 6	* 7	* 8	* 9						
		Shield misaligned	Overlay alignment off	▼	Operator error		2	10	2	40	None	None				
		Shim/ circuit not peeled	Overlay could come off		–Tom release paper –Operator error		1	7	5	35	None	None				
		Double shim	Cosmetic	▼	–2 shims stick together –Put 2 domes		2	10	2	40	None	None				
		Double domes	Force to fire out of spec		–Domes stick together –Put 2 domes		2	5	2	20	None	None				
		Missing domes	Won't test in house	▼	–Operator error –Static fly-out		1	10	1	10	None	None				
		Missing retainer	Domes fall out	▼	Operator error		1	10	1	10	None	None				

Example 8 (continued).

Part name/ Part number	Process function	Potential failure mode	Potential effect(s) of failures		Potential cause(s) of failure	Existing conditions (1-10)					Recommended action(s) and status	Action(s) taken	* 6	* 7	* 8	* 9
						Current controls	* 6	* 7	* 8	* 9						
	Overlay assembly/ ET	Misaligned overlay to circuit	Customer return	▼	Operator error	Inspection	5	10	7	350	Redesign part for foolproof design	Done 5/10/94	1	1	1	1
		Overlay loose	Customer return	▼	–Void in PSA –Release paper on	Inspection	3	10	7	210	Redesign part for fool proof design	Done 5/10/94	1	1	1	1
		Missing overlay	Customer return	▼	Operator error	Inspection	3	10	7	210	Redesign part for fool proof design	Done 5/10/94	1	1	1	1
		LED bent/ fail bent at wrapping	Electrical failure	▼	Poor handling	Inspection	2	10	5	100	Redesign part for fool proof design	Done 5/10/94	1	1	1	1
		Missing keys at testing			Operator error	Inspection	1	5	10	50	Redesign part for fool proof design	Done 5/10/94	1	1	1	1
		Missing/ wrong date code	Cosmetic		Operator error	Inspection	1	5	7	35	Redesign part for fool proof design	Done 5/10/94	1	1	1	1
		Missing/ wrong part number	Customer complaint		Operator error	Inspection	1	5	7	35	Redesign part for fool proof design	Done 5/10/94	1	1	1	1

Example 8 (continued).

Part name/ Part number	Process function	Potential failure mode	Potential effect(s) of failures		Potential cause(s) of failure	Existing conditions					Recommended action(s) and status	Action(s) taken	* 6	* 7	* 8	* 9
						Current controls	* 6	* 7	* 8	* 9						
	LED assembly	Wrong color LEDs	Customer reject	▼	Operator error	Inspection	9	10	8	720	–Color code fixture –Electrical tester modification for LEDs –Add color code in circuit –Picture page with color indicator at work station	Done 3/5/94	2	10	2	40
		Cold solder joints	LED intermittent	▼	–Operator error –Iron temp. low –Bad solder –Contaminated plating in circuit	Inspection	5	10	9	450	–Solder training –Temp control monitor –Samples of soldered pictures	Done 3/5/94	2	10	1	20
		Not enough solder	LED intermittent	▼	–Operator tech –Bad solder –Iron temp. low	Inspection	5	10	9	450	–Solder training –Temp control monitor	Done 3/5/94	2	10	1	20

Example 9 GDS assembly.

Part name/ Part number	Process function	Potential failure mode	Potential effect(s) of failures		Potential cause(s) of failure	Existing conditions					Recommended action(s) and status	Action(s) taken	* 6	* 7	* 8	* 9
						Current controls	* 6	* 7	* 8	* 9						
		Wrong orientation	Won't light	▼	Operator error –Made wrong		10	10	3	300	Redesign for foolproof design	Done 5/10/94	1	1	1	1
		Too much solder	Lump in overlay		–Operator tech –Iron temp too high	Inspection	5	7	4	140	Spec operator training		5	7	1	35
		Cracked LEDs	Failure overtime intermittent	▼	–Bending fixture –Handling	Nothing	1	10	10	100	Redesign	Done 5/10 94	1	1	1	1
		Too much heat	Circuit delamination (reliability)	▼	–Iron not calibrated –Thicker solder –Operator tech	Inspection	1	10	9	90	SPC	Done 5/10/94	1	10	3	30
		Bad LEDs	Won't light	▼	Supplier problem	Inspection	1	10	3	30	Incoming inspection Supplier certification	Done 5/10/94	1	10	2	20

Example 9 (continued).

Part name/ Part number	Process function	Potential failure mode	Potential effect(s) of failures		Potential cause(s) of failure	Existing conditions					Recommended action(s) and status	Action(s) taken				
						Current controls	* 6	* 7	* 8	* 9			* 6	* 7	* 8	* 9
Ford automotive circuits	Copper clean	Poorly cleaned	Poor resist adhesion		Chemical bath concentration	Bath solutions monitored	1	4	3	12	None	None				
					Incorrect web speed	Operator controls web speed. Based on cleaning quality.					None	None				
		Damaged material	Scrap		Cast off	Reject/scrp material	1	3	1	3	None	None				
					Poor handling	Operator training of mechanized handling equipment					None	None				

Example 9 (continued).

Part name/ Part number	Process function	Potential failure mode	Potential effect(s) of failures		Potential cause(s) of failure	Existing conditions: Current controls	* 6	* 7	* 8	* 9	Recommended action(s) and status	Action(s) taken	* 6	* 7	* 8	* 9
Ford automotive circuits	Screen resist	Poor image quality	Conductor criteria violated		Dried in ink in screen	Thorough vision inspection every 25 cycles and constant observation	4	4	5	80	100% electrical test	Electrical testers designed and in house	3	4	3	36
					Foreign material						Web cleaner planned for screening					
					Smears											
					Incorrect setup											
					Tooling wear											
		Incorrect image cure	Incorrect ink adhesion		Oven temperature and web speed	Pre-set electronic temperature control and visual inspection for correct ink color	2	3	2	12	None	None				
			Loss of resistance to etchant chemical								None	None				

Example 9 (continued).

Part name/ Part number	Process function	Potential failure mode	Potential effect(s) of failures		Potential cause(s) of failure	Existing conditions					Recommended action(s) and status	Action(s) taken	* 6	* 7	* 8	* 9
						Current controls	* 6	* 7	* 8	* 9						
Ford automotive circuits		Incorrect registration	Generates rework and added setup time		Improper setup	Image comparison to film gauge and constant visual inspection	1	4	5	20	None	None				
					Incorrect web width						None	None				

Example 9 (continued).

Part name/ Part number	Process function	Potential failure mode	Potential effect(s) of failures		Potential cause(s) of failure	Existing conditions					Recommended action(s) and status	Action(s) taken	* 6	* 7	* 8	* 9
						Current controls	* 6	* 7	* 8	* 9						
Ford automotive circuits	Etch	Over- or under-etched	Violation of conductor width criteria (opens and shorts).		Incorrect web width	SPC—X bar and R charts.	2	5	5	50	Quarterly CpK study computed	Operators received further SPC training to improve data recording and record maintenance.	2	5	1	10
					High etchant concentration	Etchant concentrations monitored and maintained routinely					Standard etching coupon implemented to monitor operator					
					Poor etchant resist.											

Example 9 (continued).

Complaint	Effect	Diagnosis
Chest pain	• Decreased ventilation • Increased carbon dioxide retention and respiratory acidosis • Discomfort • Pain	• Impaired gas exchange • Ineffective breathing pattern • Fear of chest pain • Alteration in comfort
Cough	Chronic and short term (less than one month) • Hazardous elevation in intrahoracic pressure • Intracranial pressure and blood pressure • Cough syncope • Fractured ribs • Musculoskeletal pain	• Alteration in carbon dioxide level • Alteration in comfort
	Chronic and long term (longer than one month) • Fatigue • Weight loss • Anorexia	• Alteration in nutrition
	Forced cough • Collapsed airways • Rupture of thin-walled alveoli • Second degree irritation of tracheobronchical tree • Hemoptysis	• Impaired gas exchange • Fear of seeing blood

Quite often this format is also used for corrective actions in lieu of diagnosis and sometimes numerical values are assigned so that a RPN is calculated.

Example 10 Complaint diagnosis.

Complaint	Effect	Diagnosis
Dyspnea	Acute • Diaphoresis • Restlessness	• Alteration in comfort
	Chronic • Barrel chest • Accessory muscle change	• Ineffective breathing pattern
	Acute and chronic • Emotional distress • Fatigue • Exhaustion • Hypoventilation/hyperventilation	• Fear of breathlessness • Impaired gas exchange • Impaired physical mobility
Increased and abnormal secretions	Hemoptysis • Obstruction with blood • Blood-streaked sputum	• Ineffective airway clearance • Impaired gas exchange • Alteration in tissue perfusion • Fear of seen blood
	Increased sputum • Mucous plugs • Increased secretions and/or abnormal fluids retained in lung	• Ineffective airway clearance • Impaired gas exchange

Example 10 (continued).

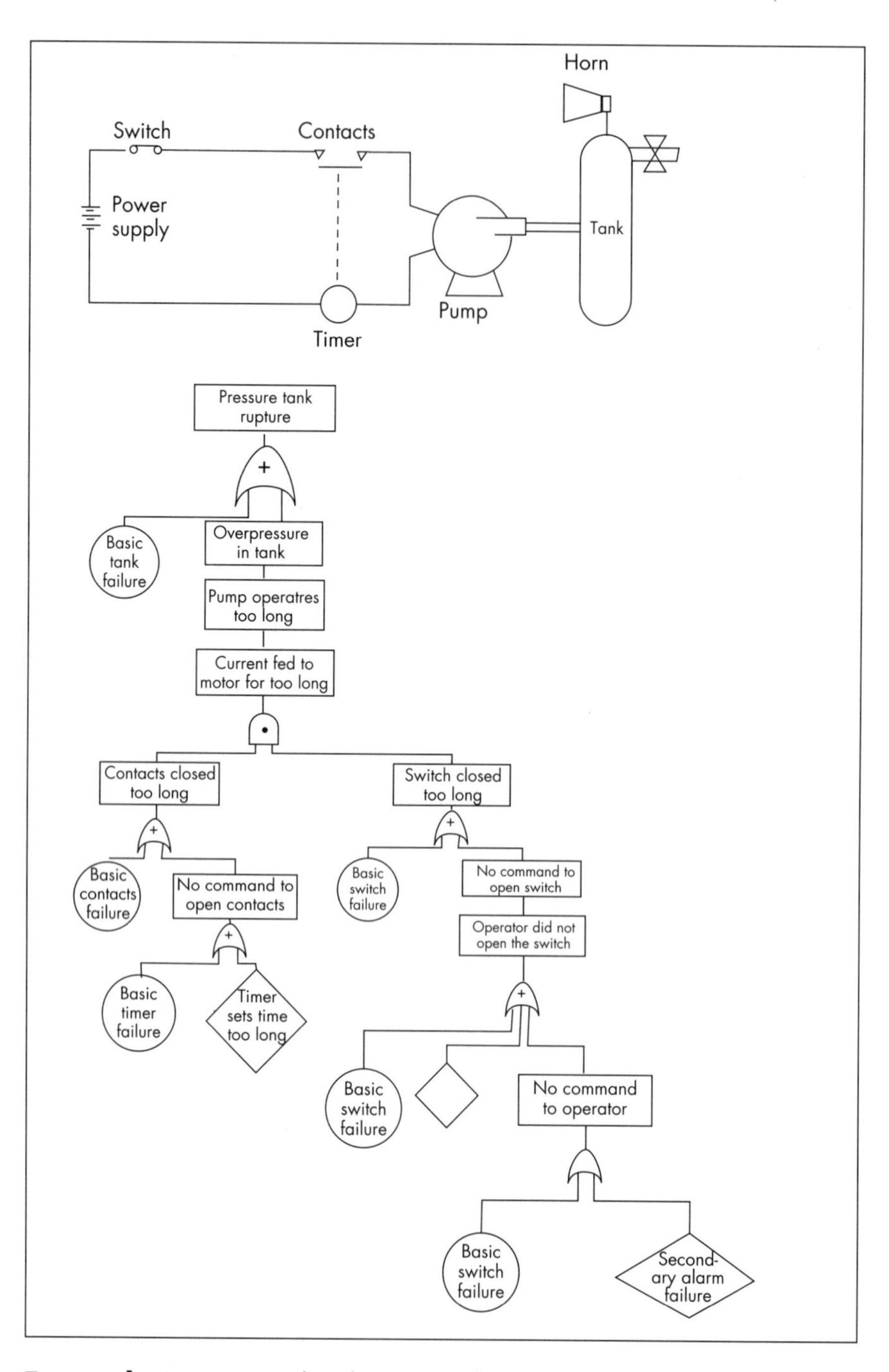

Example 11 FTA development of an air pumping system. (Top) A typical air pumping system. (Bottom) FTA for the air pumping system.

Appendix E
FMEA Forms

This appendix provides a variety of FMEA forms. None of them is a standard for all industries. The intent of this appendix is to give the reader an idea of how to construct a FMEA form with all the essential information for the optimum results. Every one of the FMEA forms may be modified to reflect the specific objective of the organization.

Type of FMEA ______________ FMEA date ______________

Prepared by ______________ Page ______ of ______ pages ______

System/ design/ process/ service function	Potential failure mode	Potential effect(s) of failure	▽	Potential cause(s) of failure	Detection method	OCC	SEV	DET	RPN	Recommended action	Responsibility & completion date	Action results				
												Action taken	SEV	OCC	DET	RPN
						Team										

Figure E.1 A generic FMEA form.

Name ________ Prepared by ________ Part ________
FMEA ID ________ Resp. eng. ________ FMEA date ________
Date ________ Release date ________ FMEA rev. date ________
Page ____ of ____ pages ____

System/ design/ process/ service function	Potential failure mode	Potential effect(s) of failure	▽	Potential cause(s) of failure	Detection method	OCC	SEV	DET	RPN	Recommended action	Responsibility and completion date
					Team						

Figure E.2 A generic FMEA form.

Type of FMEA ____________ FMEA date ____________

Prepared by ____________ Page ______ of ______ pages ______

System function	Potential failure mode	Potential effect(s) of failure	▽	Potential cause(s) of failure	Detection method	OCC	SEV	DET	RPN	Recommended action	Responsibility and completion date	Action results				
												Action taken	SEV	OCC	DET	RPN
					Team											

Figure E.3 A generic FMEA form.

Potential failure mode and effects analysis (design FMEA)																		
Part number Part name Part function	Potential failure mode	Potential effect(s) of failure			Potential cause(s) of failure		Design verification			Recommended action(s)	Responsibility and completion date	Action results						
			Severity	∇		Occurrence		Detection	RPN			Actions taken	Severity	Occurrence	Detection	RPN		

Subassembly no./name ____________
Final assembly no./name ____________
Other areas involved ____________
Suppliers affected ____________

Prepared by ____________
FMEA date (original) ____________
Revision ____________

Figure E.4 A design FMEA form.

Name ________ System ________ Date ________

Part ________ Design engineer ________ Page ____ of ____ pages ____

Design function	Failure mode	Failure effects			Causes	Validation	OCC	SEV	DET	RPN	Recommended action	Action taken	Responsibility
		System/assembly	Product	User									

Figure E.5 A design FMEA form.

Name ______________
System ______________
Date ______________

Part ______________
Design engineer ______________
Page ______ of ______ pages ______

Process function	Failure mode	Failure effects			Causes	Validation	OCC	SEV	DET	RPN	Recommend-ations	Action taken	Responsibility
		System/ assembly	Product	User									

Figure E.6 A process FMEA form.

DESIGN FMEA

Name ____________ System ____________ Date ____________

Page ______ of ______
Part assy no. ____________
Design engineer ____________

Process function	Failure mode	Failure effects			Class					Cause(s)	Design rational/ validation certification	Responsibility	Status/ target date
		System/ assembly	Vehicle	User	S	C	U	L	E				

Figure E.7 A design FMEA form.

PROCESS FMEA

Name ______________ System ______________ Date ______________

Page ______ of ______ Part assy no. ______________ Manufacturing engineer ______________

Process function	Failure mode	Failure effects		Class					Cause(s)	Validation certification	Responsibility	Status/ target date
		Local/ process	System/ assembly	S	C	U	L	E				

Figure E.8 A process FMEA form.

Potential failure mode and effects analysis (process FMEA)															
Part number Part name Part function	Potential failure mode	Potential effect(s) of failure	Severity	∇	Potential cause(s) of failure	Occurrence	Design verification	Detection	RPN	Recommended action(s)	Responsibility and completion date	Action results: Actions taken	Severity	Occurrence	Detection	RPN

Subassembly no./name ________	Prepared by ________
Final assembly no./name ________	FMEA date (original) ________
Other areas involved ________	Revision ________
Suppliers affected ________	

Figure E.9 A process FMEA form.

_____ System
_____ Subsystem
_____ Component
Model year ____________
Core team ____________

Design responsibility ____________
Key date ____________

FMEA number ____________
Page ________ of ______
Prepared by ____________
FMEA date (Orig.) ______ Rev. ____

Item/ function	Potential failure mode	Potential effect(s) of failure	SEV	CRIT	Potential cause(s) mechanism(s) of failure	OCCUR	Current design controls	DETECT	RPN	Recommended action(s)	Responsibility and target completion date	Action results				
												Action taken	SEV	OCC	DET	RPN

Figure E.10 The recommended standard design form for the automotive industry.

Process responsibility ______ FMEA number ______

Item Key date ______ Page ______ of ______

Model year ______ Prepared by ______

Core team ______ FMEA date (Orig.) ______ Rev. ______

Purpose/ function / Requirements	Potential failure mode	Potential effect(s) of failure	SEV	CRIT	Potential cause(s) mechanism(s) of failure	OCCUR	Current process controls	DETECT	RPN	Recommended action(s)	Responsibility and target completion date	Action results				
												Action taken	SEV	OCC	DET	RPN

Figure E.11 The recommended standard process form for the automotive industry.

Part number (1) ____________

Assembly number (2) ____________

Responsible engineer (3) ____________

Production release date (4) ____________

Page(5) ___ of _____ pages

Date (6) ____________

Line number (7)	Cross reference number (8)	Circuit location (9)	Enter the part/component number/name (10)	Function(s) & specification(s) (11)	Potential failure mode(s) (12)	System effect (0=unsafe condition) (13)	UNSAFE (14)	Cause(s) of failure (15)	Internal or external countermeasures (controls) (16)	SEVERITY (17)	Base failure rate λB (18)	Failure mode ratio (19)	Effectiveness (20)	Risk priority number (RPN) (21)

(1) Part number. Enter the part number under consideration.
(2) Assembly number. Enter the number on the part of drawing or part list.
(3) Responsible engineer. Enter the name of the responsible engineer.
(4) Production release date. Enter the date the product is to be released for production.
(5) Page. Enter the FMCA page number.
(6) Date. Enter the date the page was worked on. Or, enter the revision date, if it is a revised FMCA.
(7) Line number. Identify the part for which the FMCA is to be conducted.
(8) Cross reference number. Enter the number if there is a cross reference with other parts or assemblies.
(9) Circuit location. Describe the location of the part on the circuit.
(10) Enter the part/component number/name. Enter the appropriate name.
(11) Function(s) and specification(s). Describe the function the part is to perform and the specification it is to meet. Make the description as clear and concise as possible. Be sure you include all functions. Include pertinent information about the product specification, such as operating current range, operating voltage range, operating environment and everything else that is applicable.

(12) Potential failure mode(s). A failure mode is a design flaw or change in the product that prevents it from functioning properly. The typical failure modes are a short circuit, open circuit, leak loosening. The failure mode is expressed in physical tems of what the customer will experience.
(13) System effect. The system effect is what a system or module might experience as a result of a failure mode. List all conceivable effects, including unsafe conditions or violations of government regulations. A typical system effect is a system shut-down or a failure of a section of the product.
(14) Unsafe. Enter 0 for unsafe end product condition.
(15) Cause of failure. The root cause (not the symptom) is the real cause. Examples: Insufficient/inacccurate voltage, firmware errors, missing instructions on drawings.
(16) Internal or external countermeasures (controls). Identify the controls and or measures established to prevent or detect the cause of the failure mode. Examples: Perform a derating analysis, perform transient testing, perform specific testing, identify specific inspection and manufacturing specifications

Figure E.12 A design FMECA form.

Part number (1) ____________________

Assembly number (2) ____________________

Responsible engineer (3) ____________________

Production release date (4) ____________________

Page (5) __ of ____ pages

Date (6) ____________________

Line number (7)	Cross-reference number (8)	Circuit location (9)	Enter the part/component number/name (10)	Function(s) and specification(s) (11)	Potential failure mode(s) (12)	System effect (0 = unsafe condition) (13)	UNSAFE (14)	Cause(s) of failure (15)	Internal or external countermeasures (controls) (16)	SEVERITY (17)	Base failure rate λB (18)	Failure mode ratio (19)	Effectiveness (20)	Risk priority number (RPN) (21)

(17) Severity. An estimate of how severe the subsystem and/or the end product will behave as a result of a given failure mode. Severity levels are being scaled from 1 to 10. Number 10 is to be used for a definite unsafe condition. Number 0 is to be used for a negligible severity (nuisance). Usually this rating, at this stage, is a very subjective rating.

(18) Base failure rate (λB). A subjective estimate of failure rate (probability of failure in a billion hours). This is also called inherent failure rate.

(19) Failure ratio. A subjective estimate of failure rate (probability of failure in a billion hours). A subjective likelihood in comparison to the other failure modes. The sum of all failure rates for a part/component should be equal to 10 percent.

(20) Effectiveness. A subjective estimate of how effectively the prevention or detection measure eliminates potential failure models. A typical ranking is the following:
- 1 = The prevention or detection measure is foolproof.
- 2–3 = Probability of failure occurrence is low.
- 4–6 = Probability of occurrence is high.
- 7–9 = Probability of occurrence is high.
- 10 = Very high probability. The prevention/detection is ineffective.

(21) Risk priority number (RPN). The product of severity, base failure rate, failure mode ratio, and effectiveness.

Figure E.12 (continued).

Operation name (1) ____________ Subassembly number (4) Production release date (7) ________

Workstation (2) ____________ Supplier (5) Page(8) _____ of _____ pages

Responsible engineer (3) ________ Original date (6) Date (9) ____________

Line number (10)	Cross-reference number (11)	Circuit location (12)	Enter the part/component number/name (13)	Operation steps (14)	Potential failure mode(s) (15)	Cause(s) of failure (16)	Internal or external countermeasures (controls) (17)	SEVERITY (18)	PPM (19)	Effectiveness (20)	Risk priority number (RPN) (21)

(1) Operation name. Enter the name of the operation.
(2) Workstation. Enter the name or number of the workstation.
(3) Responsible engineer. Enter the name of the responsible engineer.
(4) Subassembly number. Enter the subassembly name or number.
(5) Supplier. Indicate where the process is performed.
(6) Original date. Enter the date that the FMCA is due and/or completed.
(7) Production release date. Enter the date the product is to be released for production.
(8) Page. Enter the FMCA page number.
(9) Revise date. Enter the date of the revision.
(10) Line number. Identify the part for which the FMCA is to be conducted.
(11) Cross-reference number. Enter the number if there is a cross-reference with other parts or assemblies.
(12) Circuit location. Describe the location of the part on the circuit.
(13) Enter the part/component number/name. Enter the appropriate name.
(14) List all steps of operation in the process. A good tool to use for this is the process flow diagram.

(15) Potential failure mode(s). A process-related failure mode is a deviation from specification caused by a change in the variables influencing the process. Examples: Damaged board, misaligned, discolored, missing, bent, and so on.
(16) Cause of failure. The root cause (not the symptom) is the real cause. Examples: Transient, human error, machine out of tolerance, ESD equipment failure.
(17) Internal or external countermeasures (controls). Identify the controls and/or measures established to prevent or detect the cause of the failure mode. Examples: Verify tooling to its specification, effective incoming inspection, testing, and so on.
(18) Severity. A subjective estimate of how severe the subsystem and/or the end product will behave as a result of a given failure mode. Severity levels are being scaled from 1 to 10. Number 10 is to be used for a definite unsafe condition. Number 0 is to be used for a negligible severity (nuisance).

Figure E.13 A process FMECA form.

Operation name (1) ______________ Subassembly number (4) Production release date (7) __________

Workstation (2) ______________ Supplier (5) Page(8) _____ of _____ pages

Responsible engineer (3) __________ Original date (6) Date (9) ______________

Line number (10)	Cross-reference number (11)	Circuit location (12)	Enter the part/component number/name (13)	Operation steps (14)	Potential failure mode(s) (15)	Cause(s) of failure (16)	Internal or external countermeasures (controls) (17)	SEVERITY (18)	PPM (19)	Effectiveness (20)	Risk priority number (RPN) (21)

(19) PPM. Is the percent failure per 1 million parts.
(20) Effectiveness. A subjective estimate of how effectively the prevention or detection measure eliminates potential failure models. A typical ranking is the following:

1 = The prevention or detection is foolproof.
2–3 = Probability of failure occurrence is low.
4–6 = Probability of occurrence is moderate.
7–9 = Probability of occurrence is high.
10 = Very high probability. The prevention/detection measure is ineffective.

(21) Risk priority number (RPN). The product of severity, PPM, and effectiveness.

Figure E.13 (continued).

Type of FMEA ____________________ FMEA date ____________

Prepared BY ____________________ Page ____ of ____ pages

Case number	Defect definition	Cause category	Cause definition	Stage created	OCC	SEV	DET	RPN	Recommended action

Figure E.14 An FMEA and causal analysis form.

Type of FMEA ____________________

Prepared by ____________________

FMEA date ____________________

Page ______ of ______ pages

Case number	Defect definition	Cause category	Cause definition	Stage created	Effect of failure	Unit cost of failure	OCC	SEV	DET	RPN	Total dollars for failure*	Recommended action

*Total dollars for failure = Unit cost of failure × occurrence

Figure E.15 An FMEA and value engineering analysis form.

Appendix F

Guidelines for RPN Calculations and Different Scales

This appendix provides some guidelines for RPN calculations based on different scales. The scales may be modified depending on the industry and the application.

Rank*	Mechanical or electromechanical industry	Electronics or semiconductor industry	Medical devices	Automotive industry	General guidelines for severity
1 = very low	<or = 1 in 10,000	< or = 1 in 1 million	< or = 1 in 100,000	< or = 1 in 10,000	None
2 = low or minor	2–10 in 10,000	2 to 10 in 1 million	2 to 10 in 100,000	<or = 1 in 2000	Minor
3 = moderate or significant	11–25 in 10,000	11 to 25 in 1 million	11 to 25 in 100,000	< or = 1 in 500	Significant
4 = high	26–50 in 10,000	26 to 50 in 1 million	26 to 50 in 100,000	<or = 1 in 50	High
5 = very high	>50 in 10,000	>50 in 1 million	>50 in 100,000	>or = 1 in 10	Catastrophic

Interpretation of RPN = S × O × D

90%	95%	99%	Common scale
Minor risk 1–13	Minor risk 1–6	Minor risk 1–2	Minor risk 1–17
Moderate risk 14–52	Moderate risk 7–24	Moderate risk 3–8	Moderate risk 18–63
Major risk 53–125	Major risk 25–125	Major risk 9–125	Major risk 64–125

Where:

S = Severity O = Occurrence D = Detection

Table F.1 Numerical guidelines for 1–5 scale* in occurrence, detection, and severity.

*All the above numerical values may be changed to suite specific applications.

Ranking	Probability of occurrence or frequency	Degree of severity	Probability of detection	Likelihood of the defect or defective product reaching the customer
1 = very low or none	Rare < 1 per 10^4 to 10^6	Minor nuisance	Detectable before service is released	Very low to none
2 = low or minor	Infrequent 2 to 10 per 10^4 to 10^6	Product operable at reduced performance	Detectable after release but before production	Low or minor
3 = moderate or significant	Moderate 11 to 25 per 10^4 to 10^6	Gradual performance degradation	Detectable before reaching the customer	Moderate or significant
4 = high	Frequent and high 26 to 50 per 10^4 to 10^6	Loss of function	Detectable only by customer and/or during service	High
5 = very high or catastrophic	Very high to catastrophic >50 per 10^4 to 10^6	Safety-related catastrophic failures	Undetectable until catastrophe occurs	Very high

Table F.2 Word description of 1–5 scale for design FMEA.

Note: This guideline is only a sample. It may be changed to suit specific applications.

Ranking	Probability of occurrence or frequency	Degree of severity	Probability of detection	Likelihood of the defect or defective product reaching the customer
1 = very low or none	Rare < 1 per 10^4 to 10^6 or less than once a year	Minor nuisance; almost no effects on products	Detectable before product is released	Very low to none; outstanding control
2 = low or minor	Infrequent 2 to 10 per 10^4 to 10^6 about once a month	Reduced product performance and slow creeping in of inefficiency	Detectable after release to production	Low or minor; very good control. 90–95 percent of the time action taken when process out of control and parts within spec at all times.
3 = moderate or significant	Moderate 11 to 25 per 10^4 to 10^6 or about once every two weeks	Gradual product degradation; moderate inefficiency; reduced productivity; operator starts to be frustrated	Detectable before reaching the customer	Moderate or significant or mediocre control which is not very effective. Action taken only < or = 50 percent of the time. Increased percentage or above parts out of print
4 = high	Frequent and high 26 to 50 per 10^4 to 10^6 or almost every week	More than 50–70% no build condition. Requires high operator efforts. High inefficiency, low productivity. High scrap; loss of function in field	Detectable only by customer and/or during service	High. Very low control. Action taken infrequently. 90 percent or above parts out of specifications
5 = very high or catastrophic	Very high to catastrophic >50 per 10^4 to 10^6 or every other day or more	No build condition. Line shut down; safety-related or catastrophic.	Undetectable until catastrophe occurs	Very high. No controls. No actions. 100 percent wrong parts built

Table F.3 Word description for 1–5 scale for process FMEA.

Note: This guideline is only a sample. It may be changed to suit specific applications.

Ranking	Probability of occurrence or frequency	Degree of severity	Probability of detection	Likelihood of the defect or defective product reaching the customer
1 = very low or none	Rare < 1 per 10^4 to 10^6 or less than once a year	Minor nuisance; almost no effects on service. Great job	Detectable before service is released	Very low to none; outstanding control
2 = low or minor	Infrequent 2 to 10 per 10^4 to 10^6 about once a month	Reduced service performance; no rework. Minor inspection	Detectable after release	Low or minor; very good control. 90–95 percent of the time action taken when process out of control
3 = moderate or significant	Moderate 11 to 25 per 10^4 to 10^6 or about once every two weeks	Moderate inefficiency; reduced productivity; operator starts to be frustrated; aware of problem. May or may not fix	Detectable before reaching the customer	Moderate, significant, or mediocre control which is not very effective. Action taken only 50 percent of the time
4 = high	Frequent and high 26 to 50 per 10^4 to 10^6 or almost every week	Operator frustration. Great dissatisfaction. Needs to fix it now. No possible repeat business	Detectable only by customer and/or during service	High. Very low control. Action taken infrequently. Tight schedules and outside forces.
5 = very high or catastrophic	Very high to catastrophic >50 per 10^4 to 10^6 or every other day or more	No repeat business. Take it back. Very heavy dissatisfaction level	Undetectable until catastrophe occurs	Very high. No controls. No actions. 100 percent bad service

Table F.4 Word description of 1–5 scale for service FMEA.

Note: This guideline is only a sample. It may be changed to suit specific applications.

Effect	Rank	Criteria	Resolution
No effect	1	No effect on product or subsequent processes.	If the numerical value falls between two numbers *always* select the higher number. If the team has a disagreement in the ranking value the following may help. 1. If the disagreement is an adjacent category, average out the difference. For example, if one member says 5 and someone else says 6, the ranking in this case should be 6 (5 and 6 are adjacent categories. Therefore 5 + 6 = 11, 11/2 = 5.5). 2. If the disagreement jumps one category, then consensus must be reached. Even with one person holding out, total consensus must be reached. No average, no majority. Everyone in that team must have ownership of the ranking. They may not agree 100 percent, but they can live with it.
Very slight effect	2	Customer more likely will not notice the failure. Very slight effect on product/process performance. Nonvital fault noticed sometimes.	
Slight effect	3	Customer slightly annoyed. Slight effect on product or process performance. Nonvital fault noticed most of the time.	
Minor effect	4	Customer experiences minor nuisance. Minor effect on product/process performance. Fault does not require repair. Nonvital fault always noticed.	
Moderate effect	5	Customer experiences some dissatisfaction. Moderate effect on product/process performance. Fault on nonvital part requires repair.	
Significant effect	6	Customer experiences discomfort. Product/process performance degraded, but operable and safe. Nonvital part inoperable.	
Major effect	7	Customer dissatisfied. Major effect on process; rework/repairs on part necessary. Product/process performance severely affected but functionable and safe. Subsystem inoperable	
Extreme effect	8	Customer very dissatisfied. Extreme effect on process; equipment damaged. Product inoperable but safe. System inoperable.	
Serious effect	9	Potential hazardous effect. Able to stop product without mishap; safety-related; time-dependent failure. Disruption to subsequent process operations. Compliance with government regulation is in jeopardy.	
Hazardous effect	10	Hazardous effect. Safety-related—sudden failure. Noncompliance with government regulation.	

Table F.5 Severity guideline for process FMEA* (1–10 qualitative scale).

*All the above guidelines and rankings may be changed to reflect specific situations.

Detection	Rank	C_{pK}	Criteria	CNF/1000	Resolution
Almost never	1	>1.67	Failure unlikely. History shows no failures.	<.00058	If the numerical value falls between two numbers *always* select the higher number. If the team has a disagreement in the ranking value the following may help. 1. If the disagreement is an adjacent category, average out the difference. For example, if one member says 5 and someone else says 6, the ranking in this case should be 6 (5 and 6 are adjacent categories. Therefore 5 + 6 = 11, 11/2 = 5.5 ≅ 6). 2. If the disagreement jumps one category, then consensus must be reached. Even with one person holding out, total consensus must be reached. No average, no majority. Everyone in that team must have ownership of the ranking. They may not agree 100 percent, but they can live with it.
Remote	2	>1.50	Rare number of failures likely.	.0068	
Very slight	3	>1.33	Very few failures likely.	.0063	
Slight	4	>1.17	Few failures likely.	.46	
Low	5	>1.00	Occasional number of failures likely.	2.7	
Medium	6	>0.83	Moderate number of failures likely.	12.4	
Moderately high	7	>0.67	Frequent high number of failures likely.	46	
High	8	>0.51	High number of failures likely.	134	
Very high	9	>0.33	Very high number of failures likely.	316	
Almost certain	10	<0.33	Failure almost certain. History of failures exists from previous or similar designs.	>316	

Table F.6 Occurrence guideline for process FMEA (1–10 qualitative scale).*

*All the above guidelines and rankings may be changed to reflect specific situations.

Detection	Rank	Criteria	Resolution
Almost certain	1	Current controls almost always will detect the failure. Reliable detection controls are known and used in similar processes.	If the numerical value falls between two numbers *always* select the higher number. If the team has a disagreement in the ranking value the following may help. 1. If the disagreement is an adjacent category, average out the difference. For example, if one member says 5 and someone else says 6, the ranking in this case should be 6 (5 and 6 are adjacent categories. Therefore $5 + 6 = 11$, $11/2 = 5.5 \cong 6$). 2. If the disagreement jumps one category, then consensus must be reached. Even with one person holding out total consensus must be reached. No average, no majority. Everyone in that team must have ownership of the ranking. They may not agree 100 percent, but they can live with it.
Very high	2	Very high likelihood current controls will detect the failure.	
High	3	Good likelihood current controls will detect the failure.	
Moderately high	4	Moderately high likelihood current controls will detect the failure.	
Medium	5	Medium likelihood current controls will detect the failure.	
Low	6	Low likelihood current controls will detect the failure.	
Slight	7	Slight likelihood current controls will detect the failure.	
Very slight	8	Very slight likelihood current controls will detect the failure.	
Remote	9	Remote likelihood current controls will detect the failure.	
Almost impossible	10	No known controls available to detect the failure.	

Table F.7 Detection guideline for process FMEA (1–10 qualitative scale).*

*All the above guidelines and rankings may be changed to reflect specific situations.

Effect	Rank	Criteria	Resolution
No effect	1	No effect on product or subsequent processes.	If the numerical value falls between two numbers *always* select the higher number. If the team has a disagreement in the ranking value the following may help. 1. If the disagreement is an adjacent category, average out the difference. For example, if one member says 5 and someone else says 6, the ranking in this case should be 6 (5 and 6 are adjacent categories. Therefore 5 + 6 = 11, 11/2 = 5.5 ≅ 6). 2. If the disagreement jumps one category, then consensus must be reached. Even with one person holding out total consensus must be reached. No average, no majority. Everyone in that team must have ownership of the ranking. They may not agree 100 percent, but they can live with it.
Very slight effect	2	Customer more likely will not notice the failure. Very slight effect on product/service performance. Nonvital fault noticed sometimes.	
Slight effect	3	Customer slightly annoyed. Slight effect on product or service performance. Nonvital fault noticed most of the time.	
Minor effect	4	Customer experiences minor nuisance. Minor effect on product/service performance. Fault does not require attention. Nonvital fault always noticed.	
Moderate effect	5	Customer experiences some dissatisfaction. Moderate effect on product/service performance. Fault on nonvital part requires repair.	
Significant effect	6	Customer experiences discomfort. Product/process performance degraded, but operable and safe. Nonvital service incomplete.	
Major effect	7	Customer dissatisfied. Major effect on service; rework on service necessary. Product/service performance severely affected but functionable and safe. Subsystem incomplete.	
Extreme effect	8	Customer very dissatisfied. Extreme effect on process/service; equipment damaged. Product/service incomplete but safe. System incomplete.	
Serious effect	9	Potential hazardous effect. Able to stop product/service without mishap. Safety-related. Time-dependent failure. Disruption to subsequent process operations. Compliance with government regulation is in jeopardy.	
Hazardous effect	10	Hazardous effect. Safety-related—sudden failure. Noncompliance with government regulation.	

Table F.8 Severity guideline for service FMEA* (1–10 qualitative scale).

*All the above guidelines and rankings may be changed to reflect specific situations.

Detection	Rank	C_{pK}	Criteria	CNF/1000	Resolution
Almost never	1	>1.67	Failure unlikely. History shows no failures.	<.00058	If the numerical value falls between two numbers *always* select the higher number.
Remote	2	>1.50	Rare number of failures likely.	.0068	If the team has a disagreement in the ranking value the following may help.
Very slight	3	>1.33	Very few failures likely.	.0063	
Slight	4	>1.17	Few failures likely.	.46	1. If the disagreement is an adjacent category, average out the difference. For example, if one member says 5 and someone else says 6, the ranking in this case should be 6 (5 and 6 are adjacent categories. Therefore 5 + 6 = 11, 11/2 = 5.5 ≅ 6).
Low	5	>1.00	Occasional number of failures likely.	2.7	
Medium	6	>0.83	Moderate number of failures likely.	12.4	
Moderately high	7	>0.67	Frequent high number of failures likely.	46	
High	8	>0.51	High number of failures likely.	134	2. If the disagreement jumps one category, then consensus must be reached. Even with one person holding out, total consensus must be reached. No average, no majority. Everyone in that team must have ownership of the ranking. They may not agree 100 percent, but they can live with it.
Very high	9	>0.33	Very high number of failures likely.	316	
Almost certain	10	<0.33	Failure almost certain. History of failures exists from previous or similar designs.	>316	

Table F.9 Occurrence guideline for service FMEA (1–10 qualitative scale).*

*All the above guidelines and rankings may be changed to reflect specific situations.

Detection	Rank	Criteria	Resolution
Almost certain	1	Current controls almost always will detect the failure. Reliable detection controls are known and used in similar processes.	If the numerical value falls between two numbers *always* select the higher number. If the team has a disagreement in the ranking value the following may help. 1. If the disagreement is an adjacent category, average out the difference. For example, if one member says 5 and someone else says 6, the ranking in this case should be 6 (5 and 6 are adjacent categories. Therefore $5 + 6 = 11$, $11/2 = 5.5 \cong 6$). 2. If the disagreement jumps one category, then consensus must be reached. Even with one person holding out total consensus must be reached. No average, no majority. Everyone in that team must have ownership of the ranking. They may not agree 100 percent, but they can live with it.
Very high	2	Very high likelihood current controls will detect the failure.	
High	3	Good likelihood current controls will detect the failure.	
Moderately high	4	Moderately high likelihood current controls will detect the failure.	
Medium	5	Medium likelihood current controls will detect the failure.	
Low	6	Low likelihood current controls will detect the failure.	
Slight	7	Slight likelihood current controls will detect the failure.	
Very slight	8	Very slight likelihood current controls will detect the failure.	
Remote	9	Remote likelihood current controls will detect the failure.	
Almost impossible	10	No known controls available to detect the failure.	

Table F.10 Detection guideline for service FMEA (1–10 qualitative scale).*

*All the above guidelines and rankings may be changed to reflect specific situations.

APPENDIX G

Guidelines for Designing the Reasonably Safe Product

This appendix provides a summary of guidelines for designing the reasonably safe product. Both design and legal considerations are addressed. All areas identified are affected by the use of an appropriate FMEA.

1. Elements of production defect
   - The identification of the flaw or flaws relative to manufacturing or physical property standards
   - The evidence that the failure or malfunction of the product is directly attributable to the flaws
   - The relationship of the failure or malfunction to the expected performance standards of the product
   - The causal link between the failure or malfunction and the injury
2. Elements of design defect
   - The identification of the design flaw or flaws which occasioned the injury
   - The delineation of alternative design features
   - The evaluation of such alternative design features relative to the expected performance standards of the product as well as
     - –Their effect upon the subsequent usefulness of the product
     - –Their effect upon the subsequent cost of the product

- The comparison of this product with other similar products
- The causal link between the design deficiency and the injury

3. Components of an active system design
   - Foreseeable product elements
     –Assembly
     –Testing
     –Shipping
     –Communications
     –Installation
     –Inspection
     –Maintenance
     –Service
     –Performance
     –Foreseeable product environment
     –Foreseeable product users
     –Foreseeable product uses
4. The product as a system
   - Component integrity
   - Assembly consistency
   - Interface compatibility
   - Performance and safety standards
   - Component specifications
   - Product specifications
   - Testing: performance, environment, failure
5. Procedure for system design safety
   - Identify
     –Product environments
     –Product users
     –Product uses
   - Postulate
     –Hazards and estimate
     –Probability of occurrence
     –Seriousness of harm

- Delineate
  - –Design, production, testing alternatives
  - –Installation, maintenance, service procedures
  - –Effective communications

6. To reduce harm
   - Evaluate
     - –Alternatives relative to performance, utility, and costs of product
   - Incorporate
     - –Appropriate alternatives, procedures, communications
7. Product safety audit
   - The team
     - –Design, production, quality control, testing, service, legal counsel, technical writing, marketing, safety assurance
   - The process
   - Stages
     - –Concept
     - –Prototype
     - –Pilot line
   - Review
     - –Claims
     - –Complaints
     - –Service reports
     - –Injury data
     - –Court decisions
   - Incorporate
     - –External and internal standards
   - Considerations
     - –Product components and features
       a. Human factors
       b. Foreseeable misuses
       c. Warnings and instructions
   - Results
     - –Material and component selection
       a. Production methods
       b. Design features

   c. User communications
   d. Production testing
   e. Field testing
   f. Failure reporting

8. Design and warnings
   - Design out the hazard; if not
   - Guard against the hazard; if not
   - Warn against the hazard

9. Warning design
   - Must communicate
     –Type of hazard
     –Magnitude of risk
     –Action to minimize risk

10. Warnings: intrinsic elements
    - Fundamental
      –Identification of the need
    - Objective
      –Colors
      –Print type
      –Durability
      –Symbols
      –Format
    - Subjective
      –Signal words *(danger, warning, caution)*
      –Content
      –Languages
      –Size
      –Locations

11. Documentation
    - Preparation
      –Considers adverse use
      –Develops and maintains comprehensive product history
      –Responses to unfavorable reports
      –Establishes responsibility for control
      –Ease of access
    - Retention

–Assistance in design review
–Meet legal requirements
a. Statutes of repose
b. Useful safe life
–Guidance in litigation

12. Documenting the reasonably safe product
    - Hazard and risk data
      –Historical
      –Field or laboratory
      –Causation analysis
    - Design safety formulation
      –Fault-tree
      –Failure modes
      –Effects analysis
    - Warnings and instruction formulation
      –Methodology for development and selection
    - Standards
      –In-house
      –Voluntary
      –Mandated
    - Quality assurance program
      –Methodology for procedure selection
    - Performance of product in use
      –Reporting procedures
      –Follow-up data acquisition and analysis
      –Recall
      –Retrofit
      –Instruction and warnings modification
    - Decision-making methodology
      –The "HOW" and "WHO" of the process

13. Communications
    - Warnings/instructions
      –Written for user
      –Communicated directly to user
    - Warranties/disclaimers
      –Legally correct

–Communicated directly to buyer
- Advertising/catalogs/sales talk
  –Consistent with specifications, warranties, contracts
- Basis of the bargain

14. Lessons from the law
    - Design must
      –Account for reasonably foreseeable product misuse
      –Acknowledge human frailties and actual users
      –Function in true environment of product use
      –Eliminate or guard against the hazards
      –Not substitute warnings for effective design
15. Legal bases for liability
    - Designer/engineer—negligence
    - Manufacturer/assembler/seller—negligence
    - Express warranty/misrepresentation
    - Strict liability

Appendix H
A Summary of Some Tools Used in FMEA

Tools

This appendix provides a summary of the most often used tools in the problem-solving process. The problem-solving process was defined as an eight-stage process.

1. Identify
2. Scope
3. Define
4. Analyze
5. Implement
6. Evaluate
7. Follow-up
8. Continually improve

Affinity Diagram. A number of small cards (1" × 3") each inscribed with an idea or solution. The affinity diagram is based on brainstorming and a cause-and-effect diagram.

What it does: Tool that is useful when (1) facts/thoughts are in chaos, (2) a breakthrough in traditional concepts is needed, (3) support for justifying a proposed implementation is needed.

When to use it: Stage 1: Identify
Stage 3: Define
Stage 4: Analyze

Box and Whisker Plots. Alternative to a histogram. Has appearance of a rectangle (the box) with a horizontal and a vertical line passing through its center and extending outside the box (the whisker).

What it does: Displays the main features of a data set and permits simple comparisons of several data sets.

When to use it: Stage 4: Analyze
Stage 5: Implement
Stage 6: Evaluate

Brainstorming. An idea-generating technique that relies on team participation and interaction. All ideas are noted before any less practical ones are discarded.

What it does: Enables a team to create as many ideas as possible in as short a time as possible.

When to use it: Stage 1: Identify
Stage 5: Implement

Cause-and-Effect Diagram. Simple means for finding the causes of an effect (problem) by an individual or a team. Also known as the fishbone diagram because of its shape.

What it does: Graphically shows the relationship of causes and subcauses to an identified effect. Helps reveal potential root causes.

When to use it: Stage 4: Analyze
Stage 6: Evaluate

Computer Simulation. Computer-based technique probably requiring the assistance of operations research to prepare the programs.

What it does: A pictorial representation of an area layout showing the movement of items within that area. A means of solving what-if questions and examining the effects of various related data over long- and short-term periods.

When to use it: Stage 4: Analyze
Stage 6: Evaluate
Stage 7: Follow-up
Stage 8: Continual improvement

Control Chart—*c*. Standard control chart for the total number of nonconformities, based on a constant sample size.

What it does: Graphically displays stability of process. (For example, total number of errors in a batch of 100 forms rather than just the number of faulty forms.)

When to use it: Stage 4: Analyze
Stage 5: Implement
Stage 6: Evaluate

Control Chart—Median and *R*. Standard chart that is an alternative to the *X*-bar and *R* chart for the control of processes. It is less sensitive to trends, however, and, under some circumstances, is considered to be more difficult to construct.

What it does: Graphically displays stability of a process. Yields similar information to *X* bar and *R* charts, but has several advantages: (1) easier to use—daily calculations are not required; (2) individual values and medians are plotted, median chart shows spread of process output and gives an ongoing view of process variation; (3) shows where nonconformities are scattered through a more or less continuous flow of a function; (4) shows where nonconformities from different areas may be evident.

When to use it: Stage 4: Analyze
Stage 5: Implement
Stage 6: Evaluate

Control Chart—*np*. Standard control chart similar to the *c* chart, but must be used if the sample sizes vary.

What it does: Graphically displays stability of process. Measures actual number of nonconforming items rather than total number of faults. (For example, total number of faulty forms in a batch irrespective of faults in any one form.)

When to use it: Stage 4: Analyze
Stage 5: Implement
Stage 6: Evaluate

Control Chart—*p*. Standard control chart requiring a constant sample size. Charts either conforming or nonconforming items.

What it does: Graphically displays stability of process. Measures actual number of conforming and nonconforming items rather than total number of faults. Expresses numbers in either fractional or percentile terms (whether conforming or nonconforming items are used) of total sample. (For example, total number of faulty forms in a batch irrespective of number of faults in any one form.)

When to use it: Stage 4: Analyze
Stage 5: Implement
Stage 6: Evaluate

Control Chart—*u*. Standard control chart that is similar to the *c* chart, but must be used if the sample sizes vary.

What it does: Graphically displays stability of process. (For example, total number of errors in a batch of 100 forms rather than just the number of faulty forms.)

When to use it: Stage 4: Analyze
Stage 5: Implement
Stage 6: Evaluate

Control Chart *X*-bar and *R*. Standard control chart; the most used chart. Requires a number of consecutive units be taken *n* times per work period and analyzed for specific criteria.

What it does: Graphically displays process stability. Shows data in terms of spread (piece-to-piece variability) and its location (process average). *X*-bar covers averages of values in small subgroups (sample taken); known as measure of location. *R* chart deals with range of values within each sample (highest minus lowest); known as measure of spread.

When to use it: Stage 4: Analyze
Stage 5: Implement
Stage 6: Evaluate

Control Chart *X*-bar and *S*. Standard control chart similar to *X*-bar and *R* chart, however the *S* part of chart considers standard deviation and is more complicated to calculate.

What it does: Graphically displays stability of process *S* factor; is more accurate indicator of process variability, especially with larger sample sizes. This chart is less sensitive in detecting special causes of variation that produce only one value in a subgroup as unusual.

When to use it: Stage 4: Analyze
Stage 5: Implement
Stage 6: Evaluate

Cross-Functional Process Map. Shown as a series of columns representing departments across which the flow of a process is mapped.

What it does: Allows a map of the process to be shown, its order of precedence, and which departments it is routed through.

When to use it: Stage 4: Analyze
Stage 5: Implement
Stage 6: Evaluate

Design of Experiments (DOE). Several methods available of which the following are examples: (1) Taguchi method, including S/N ratios, (2) accelerated testing methods, (3) factorial and fractional factorial designs.

What it does: Factors common cause variation into its components in order to optimize process/product variables and reduce variation.

When to use it: Stage 3: Define
Stage 4: Analyze
Stage 5: Implement
Stage 6: Evaluate

Dot Plots. A display somewhat similar to a histogram, but the axis is divided into many more divisions.

What it does: Usually used when there are insufficient criteria to construct a histogram or a box and whisker plot. Used for comparison purposes.

When to use it: Stage 4: Analyze
Stage 5: Implement
Stage 6: Evaluate
Stage 7: Follow-up

Failure Mode and Effect Analysis (FMEA). A what-if approach to evaluating design weaknesses that starts at the component level and proceeds through the complete system.

What it does: Bottom-up approach that identifies potential product/process weaknesses. Begins with study of known failure modes for each component of product or process. By using physical analysis or mathematical models, a determination is made of the effect of failure on a component, subsystem, or complete system.

When to use it: Stage 3: Define
Stage 4: Analyze
Stage 6: Evaluate
Stage 7: Follow-up
Stage 8: Continual improvement

Fault-Tree Analysis. Graphical display similar to the shape of a tree.

What it does: Begins with the definition of an undesirable event and traces that event through the system to identify basic causes—a top-down appraisal.

When to use it: Stage 3: Define
Stage 4: Analyze
Stage 6: Evaluate
Stage 7: Follow-up
Stage 8: Continual improvement

Gauge Repeatability and Reproducibility (Gauge R and R). A measurement of the repeatability and reproducibility of a gauge and the operator, respectively.

What it does: Measures variations in gauges and test equipment to ascertain: (1) bias in accuracy due to improper calibration, (2) variation in precision due to operation of the device, (3) variation in reproducibility when different people use the equipment, (4) variations in stability due to changes in environment, power fluctuations, and so on.

When to use it: Stage 4: Analyze

Graphs—Bar Charts. An *X-Y* type of graph that uses narrow rectangular bars to signify frequencies of occurrence.

What it does: Compares discrete data from a number of sources (For example, absenteeism on specific days in several offices.)

When to use it: Stage 4: Analyze
Stage 6: Evaluate

Graphs—Gantt Charts. An *X-Y* type of graph that uses narrow rectangles or lines, usually parallel to the *X* axis, to represent periods of time on a specific task or tasks.

What it does: Displays, to scale, time to perform a unit of work that occurs at a given point in the process. Allows a comparison of its position in the process with other units of work and how they relate. Useful tool to use with a process flowchart to highlight and quantify information in both pre- and postinvestigation situations.

When to use it: Stage 4: Analyze
Stage 6: Evaluate
Stage 7: Follow-up

Graphs—Pie Charts. Circle divided into sectors, each of which represents a factor and its area is a proportion of the whole—expressed as a percentage.

What it does: Shows all the criteria involved in a process/survey and individual percentages of the total. Area of the circle can be used to demonstrate a change/compare circumstances (for example, a chart showing car market by year and a specific company's share of that market).

When to use it: Stage 4: Analyze
Stage 6: Evaluate

Histogram. An *X-Y* graph that uses narrow rectangles to display frequencies of occurrence of a specific set of data.

What it does: Gives a picture of the frequency of occurrence for a range of specific data and demonstrates its normalcy or lack of it. In other words, if the center point of the top of each column of recorded frequencies were joined by a continuous line (normal distribution curve), the shape produced would be that of a bell, more or less distributed around the median (central point).

When to use it: Stage 4: Analyze
Stage 6: Evaluate
Stage 7: Follow-up

Operational Definitions. Terms necessary for the common understanding of a process.

What it does: Contains three elements: (1) a set of criteria; (2) a test by which criteria are applied; (3) a yes/no result from the test. The result must be accepted by all who use it.

When to use it: Stage 1: Identify
Stage 2: Scope
Stage 3: Define
Stage 4: Analyze
Stage 5: Implement
Stage 6: Evaluate
Stage 7: Follow-up
Stage 8: Continual improvement

Pareto Diagrams. *X-Y*-bar chart with the bars prioritized in descending order (from left to right) and distinguished by a cumulative percentage line. It is based on the 80/20 rule which states that about 80 percent of improvement in an effect can be achieved by acting on 20 percent of the causes.

What it does: The prioritization of the inputs (causes) indicate those that should be considered first (in other words, those on the left of the chart).

When to use it: Stage 1: Identify
Stage 4: Analyze
Stage 6: Evaluate
Stage 8: Continual improvement

PERT or Critical Path Analysis. Road map of interdependent elements within a process and containing criteria indicating critical routes through the elements.

What it does: Illustrates elements within a process and indicates earliest and latest event timing against each element. Clarifies order of sequential priority within process and allows a critical path through the process to be identified.

When to use it: Stage 4: Analyze
Stage 6: Evaluate
Stage 7: Follow-up

Process Flow Chart. A road map of the process from supplier(s) to customer(s).

What it does: Illustrates/clarifies events in a process and the events between them. Assists in highlighting, (1) present situation, (2) differences between what should/is thought to be happening and actual situation, (3) proposed situation, and (4) potential problem areas (gaps, and so on).

When to use it: Stage 1: Identify
Stage 2: Scope
Stage 3: Define
Stage 4: Analyze
Stage 6: Evaluate

Program Decision Process Chart (PDPC). A *tree*-type chart.

What it does: Maps conceivable events/contingencies that occur when moving from problem to statement to possible solutions. Used to plan possible chains of events that need to occur when problem/goal is unfamiliar.

When to use it: Stage 4: Analyze
Stage 6: Evaluate

Pugh Technique. A chart that shows alternatives on the *X* axis and base criteria on the *Y* axis.

What it does: Technique that allows comparisons between current concept/design, criteria required, and a number of alternative solutions. Each alternative is compared with current situation, requirement by requirement, and summarized in form of total +/- points, which indicate the alternative to use.

When to use it: Stage 4: Analyze
Stage 6 Evaluate

Quality Function Deployment (QFD). An array which enables a comparison of customer requirements against a number of design elements. Also allows areas of conflict to be plotted.

What it does: broad management system that assists in translating the voice of the customer into operational definitions that can be used to produce and deliver product/service desired by the customer. Highlights conflicting customer requirements so they can be reconciled in an optimum manner.

When to use it: Stage 1: Identify
Stage 2: Scope
Stage 3: Define
Stage 4: Analyze
Stage 5: Implement
Stage 6: Evaluate
Stage 7: Follow-up
Stage 8: Continual improvement

Regression Analysis. A procedure for fitting a mathematical model (expressed in terms of equations with variables and coefficients; for example, $y = Mx + b$) to a set of data.

What it does: Used to explore factors in a given set of data (for example, barometric and humidity effects on production of CO production from combustion). Also used in instrument calibration, design, and process analysis.

When to use it: Stage 3: Define
Stage 4: Analyze
Stage 6: Evaluate

Reliability Analysis. A series of statistical formulae, tables, and graphs based on probability.

What it does: Broad area of study that is concerned with random occurrences of undesirable events/failures, during the life of a physical system.

When to use it: Stage 4: Analyze
Stage 6: Evaluate

Run Charts. An *X-Y* type of graph that compares a measurement (%, $, and so on) on the *Y* axis with time or sequence (days, order, and so on) on the *X* axis.

What it does: Used to monitor a process to assess whether or not the long-range average is changing. If it is changing is it improving or deteriorating?

When to use it: Stage 4: Analyze
Stage 5: Implement
Stage 6: Evaluate
Stage 7: Follow-up

Scatter Diagrams. An *X-Y* graph that examines the possibility of a relationship between two variables.

What it does: Checks for possible cause-and-effect relationships. Cannot prove one variable causes another, but makes clear whether or not a relationship exists and strength of relationship.

When to use it: Stage 4: Analyze
Stage 6: Evaluate

Shared and Interlocking Objectives Matrix. Chart that lists various departments on both the *X* and *Y* axis.

What it does: Enables department heads to specify their requirements from each of the other departments in order to achieve a certain goal (in other words, each customer can specify his or her requirements from each supplier).

When to use it: Stage 2: Scope

Stem and Leaf Plots. A vertical line with data to the left of the line being known as the *stem* and individual criteria as stem ends. Criteria to right of line is known as the *leaf.* An alternative to the histogram.

What it does: Quicker to produce than histograms and allows data used to be viewed in traditional column format.

When to use it: Stage 4: Analyze
Stage 6: Evaluate

Surveys. Investigative questioning technique.

What it does: Through a programmed questioning of supplier and customer a picture is formed of: (1) problems encountered, (2) customer desires, and (3) shape of the process, and so on.

When to use it: Stage 1: Identify
Stage 2: Scope
Stage 7: Follow-up
Stage 8: Continual improvement

Time Series Forecasting. Series of statistical formulae, tables, and graphs.

What it does: Broad area of study that takes data measured at discrete, equispaced time intervals. Constructs mathematical models for forecasting over a given period of time (lead time).

When to use it: Stage 4: Analyze
Stage 6: Evaluate
Stage 7: Follow-up
Stage 8: Continual improvement

Appendix I

Glossary

Terminology Used in the Construction of a FMEA

The vocabulary used in this appendix is an abbreviated (and paraphrased) version of the most common words used in FMEA based on the ISO 8402 standard and the ASQC definitions. For the exact ISO definition, refer to the ISO 8402(A3) standard. For the exact ASQC definition, refer to the ANSI/ASQC standard A3-1978.

Advanced statistical methods–To analyze and understand the complex relationships between process variables (for example, design of experiments, correlation analyses, and so on).

Attributes–Output characteristics classified into two categories which indicate OK and not OK (for example, characteristics such as the presence of a required label and installation of all required fasteners). Other examples include characteristics that are inherently measurable, but have results recorded in a simple yes/no fashion. For these examples, *p, np,* and *c* charts are used instead of *X*-bar and *R* charts,.

Average–A central tendency. The sum of values divided by the number (sample size) of values. The average is designated by a bar over the symbol for the values being averaged or a tilde-bar over the symbol of subgroup medians.

Awareness–Personal understanding of the interrelationship of quality and productivity, directing attention to requirement for management commitment and statistical thinking to achieve continuous improvement.

Basic statistical methods–Applies methods of collection and organization of sample data through use of statistical process control; includes control chart construction and interpretation (for both variables and attributes data) and capability analysis.

Bimodal distribution–A distribution that has two identifiable curves within it with different averages. Indicates a mixing of two populations, such as different shifts, machines, workers, and so on.

Binomial distribution–A discrete probability distribution for attributes data that applies to conforming and nonconforming units and underlies the *p* and *np* charts.

Box–A schematic showing many of the factors that affect a process—the customer, outputs of the process, inputs of the process, and associated tasks.

Brainstorming–An intentionally uninhibited technique for generating the greatest number of possible solutions to a problem, for later evaluation and development using group dynamics.

Breakthrough–An improvement in process performance that has never previously been attained. The improvement must be a result of human effort, not a result of chance.

Capability–(Can be determined only after the process is in statistical control.) A process is capable when process average plus and minus the 3-sigma spread of the distribution of individuals ($X \pm 3\sigma$) is contained within specification tolerance (variables data), or when at least 99.73 percent of individuals are within specification (attributes data). Efforts to improve capability must continue, however, consistent with the company's philosophy of continuous improvement in quality.

Cause-and-effect diagram–A technique developed to represent the relationship between some effect and all the possible causes influencing it.

Central line–Line on a control chart that represents average or median value of items being plotted.

Characteristic–Distinguishing feature of a process or its output on which variables or attributes data can be collected.

Common cause–Source of variation that is always present; part of random variation inherent in the process itself. Origin usually can be traced to an element of the system that only management can correct. Employees, however, can contribute to identification of causal factors and corrections needed.

Competitive benchmarking–A technique that measures products, services, and business practices against the competition and/or excellent companies to identify opportunities for process improvements. In addition, competitive benchmarking promotes a learning experience to adapt and build upon the practices of excellent companies to enhance process improvement efforts.

Consecutive–Units of output produced in succession; a basis for selecting subgroup samples.

Continuous improvement in quality and productivity–Operational philosophy that makes best use of talents within company to produce products of increasing quality for customers in an increasingly efficient way that protects return on investment to stockholders. A dynamic strategy designed to enhance the strength of the company in face of present and future market conditions. It contrasts with any static strategy that accepts (explicitly or implicitly) some particular level of outgoing defects as inevitable.

Control chart–Graphic representation of a characteristic of a process, showing plotted values of some statistic gathered from that characteristic a central line and one or two control limits. Has two basic uses: a judgment to determine if a process was in control, and an aid in achieving and maintaining statistical control.

Control limit–Line(s) on a control chart used as a basis for judging significance of variation from subgroup to subgroup. Variation beyond a control limit is evidence that special causes are affecting process. Control limits are calculated from process data and are not to be confused with engineering specifications.

Customer–Any person, section, department, plant, or operation, whether (internal or external), that receives or purchases services or goods.

Detection—or inspection–Past-oriented strategy that attempts to identify and separate unacceptable output after it has been produced. (See **Prevention**).

Distribution–Statistical pattern into which observed values fall. This is based on the concept of natural variation that states that anything measured repeatedly in a stable process will arrive at different results. A bell-shaped curve (normal distribution) is an example of a distribution in which the greatest number of observations fall in the center with fewer and fewer observations falling evenly on either side of the average. A process has distribution only if it is stable. (See **Stability**).

Facilitator–Ideally an expert with no vested interest in process under investigation, but with knowledge and ability to guide project leader and the team through the various process improvement steps. They will work with the sponsor to identify the opportunity, develop a structure for the project, contract for the boundaries of the project and timing issues. He or she should be aware of sources for information, expert advice, and practical assistance.

Frequency distribution–Statistical table that graphically presents a large amount of data arranged in order of magnitude and occurrence in such a way that the central tendency (mean, median, mode) and distribution are clearly displayed.

Gap–Used to describe differences between what the customer needs and what the process provides. Objective of process improvement is to define and measure that gap and provide the tools to close it.

Individual–Single unit or measurement of a characteristic.

Location–General concept for denoting placement of typical values or central tendency of a distribution measured by a mean or median.

Mean–The average of values in a group of measurements.

Median–Middle value in a group of measurements, when arranged from lowest to highest. Conventionally if the number of values is even, the average of the middle two values is used as the median. Subgroup medians form basis for simple control charts for process location. Medians are designated by a tilde (~) over the symbol for individual values: $\tilde{X}$ is the median of a subgroup.

Mode–Point in a frequency distribution where the greatest number of observations lie.

Nonconforming units–Units that do not conform to a specification or other inspection standard; sometimes called discrepant or defective units. *p* and *np* control charts are used to analyze systems producing nonconforming units.

Nonconformities–Specific occurrences of a condition that does not conform to specifications or other inspection standards; sometimes called discrepancies or defects. An individual nonconforming unit can have the potential for more than one nonconformity (for example, a door could have several dents; a functional check of a carburetor could reveal any number of discrepancies). *c* and *u* charts are used to analyze systems producing nonconformities.

Normal distribution–The continuous, symmetrical, bell-shaped frequency distribution for variables data that underlies control charts for variables. When measurements have a normal distribution, about 68.26 percent of all individuals lie within ± one standard deviation unit of the mean, about 95.44 percent lie within ± two standard deviation units of the mean, and about 99.73 percent lie within ± three standard deviation units of the mean. These percentages are the basis for control limits and control chart analysis (since subgroup averages tend to be normally distributed even if the output as a whole is not), and for many capability decisions (since output of many industrial processes follows the normal distribution).

Operational definition–Means of clearly communicating quality expectations and performance; consists of (1) a criterion to be applied to an object or a group, (2) a test of the object of the group, (3) a decision: yes or no—object or group did not meet criterion.

Pareto chart–A bar chart with problems prioritized in descending order of importance. The prioritizing helps direct attention and resources to the important problems.

Poisson distribution–Discrete probability distribution for attributes data that applies to nonconformities and underlies the *c* and *u* control charts.

Population–The set of all possible observations about a specific characteristic of interest.

Prevention–Future-oriented strategy that improves quality by directing analysis and action toward correcting the production process. Prevention is consistent with a philosophy of continuous improvement.

Problem solving–Process of moving from symptoms to causes (special or common) to actions that improve performance. Among techniques that can be used are Pareto charts, cause-and-effect diagrams, and statistical process control techniques.

Process–Combination of people, machines/equipment, raw materials, methods, and environment that produces a given product or service.

Process average–Location of the distribution of measured values of a particular process characteristic, usually designated as an overall average *X*-bar or *X* double bar.

Process capability–Measured, built-in reproducibility (consistency) of product turned out by the process. Such a determination is made using statistical methods, not wishful thinking. The statistically determined pattern/distribution can only then be compared to specification limits to determine if a process can consistently deliver product within those parameters. This process capability can be measured by a C_{pK}, C_p, and/or C_r.

Process improvement–A process that identifies work in the form of interrelated processes and then (utilizing improvement techniques), insures that those processes are meeting customer needs and wants, and eliminates negative value operations.

Process map–A process map is a visual display of various stages of the process and a demonstration of the flow of product or service over time. The process map shows how a process operates and focuses on what is done, not only on what is produced.

Process spread–Extent to which distribution of individual values of process characteristic vary about the mean; often shown as the process average ± some number of standard deviations.

Project leader–Person responsible to process sponsor for leading the investigation, selling solution(s), and implementing the revised/new process. The leader also can act as the facilitator.

Project scope–Used to decide study limits, provide a vehicle for stakeholders to understand their involvement, identify team members, and provide a framework for them to work within.

Quality–Defined by customers; customers want products and services that, throughout their lives, meet customers' needs and expectations at a cost that represents value.

Randomness–Condition in which individual values are not predictable, although they may come from a definable distribution.

Range–measure of variation in a set of data. It is calculated by subtracting the lowest value in the data set from the highest value in that same set.

Run chart–Simple graphic representation of a characteristic of a process, showing plotted values of some statistic gathered from the process (often individual values) and a central line (often the median of the values), which can be analyzed for runs.

Runs–Patterns in a run/control chart within which a number of points line up on only one side of the central line. Beyond a certain number of consecutive points (statistically based) the pattern becomes unnatural and worthy of attention.

Sample–One or more individual events/measurements selected from the output of a process for purposes of identifying characteristics and performance of the whole.

Sigma (σ)–The Greek letter used to designate a standard deviation.

Special cause–Source of variation that is intermittent, unpredictable, unexpected, and signalled by a point beyond the control limits.

Specification–The engineering requirement for judging acceptability of a particular characteristic. Chosen with respect to functional or customer requirements for the product, a specification may or may not be consistent with the demonstrated capability of the process (if it is not, out-of-specification parts are certain to be made). A specification should never be confused with a control limit.

Sponsor–Manager who has accepted the responsibility (possibly on behalf of a number of stakeholders) for taking the necessary steps to cause an improvement in a process.

Spread–General concept for extent by which values in a distribution differ from one another; dispersion.

Stability–Absence of special causes of variation; property of being in statistical control; predictable.

Stable process–A process in which variation in outcomes arise only from common causes. A process in statistical control.

Stakeholder–Manager who has a direct interest/responsibility in a process under investigation and would probably assign one (or more) of the staff to the process improvement team.

Standard deviation–Measure of spread of the process output or spread of a sampling statistic from the process (for example, of subgroup averages); denoted by Greek letter σ (sigma).

Statistic–Value calculated from or based upon sample data (for example, subgroup average or range); used to make inferences about the process that produced the output from which sample came.

Statistical control–Condition describing a process from which all special causes have been removed, shown on control charts by absence of points beyond control limits and by lack of nonrandom patterns/trends within control limits.

Statistical process control (SPC)–Use of statistical techniques (such as control charts) to analyze a process or its output in order to take appropriate actions to achieve and maintain a state of statistical control and to improve the capability of the process.

Subgroup–One or more events or measurements used to analyze the performance of a process. Rational subgroups usually are chosen so that variation represented within each subgroup is as small as feasible for the process representing the variation from common causes, and so that any changes in process performance (in other words, special causes) will appear as differences between subgroups. Rational subgroups typically are made up of consecutive pieces, although random samples are sometimes used.

Supplier–Any person, section, department, plant, or operation, (internal or external) that gives or sells services or goods. This giving is based on a win-win relationship between supplier and customer as opposed to win-lose relationship which is the main characteristic of a vendor.

Trends–Patterns in a run chart or control chart that feature continued rise or fall of a series of points. Similar to runs, attention should be paid to such patterns when they exceed the seven points. The difference between a run and a trend is that the run is one or the other side of the average line, where the trend always crosses the average line in either an upward or a downward direction. In either case, a change in the process has occurred.

Trigger–The event or input that starts the process. It may be a document of some sort (invoice, request form, or a vehicle order) that helps define that which starts the process, and therefore, the input boundaries.

Type I (α) **error**–Ascribe a variation or mistake to a special cause, when the cause actually belongs to the system; overcontrol. It is usually referred as the producer's error.

Type II (β) **error**–Ascribe a variation or mistake to the system when the cause actually was special; undercontrol. It is usually referred to as the customer's error.

Variables–Characteristics of a part that can be measured (For example, length in millimeters, resistance in ohms, closing effort of a door in kilograms, and the torque of a nut in foot pounds). (See also **Attributes**)

Variation–The inevitable difference among individual outputs of a process; the sources of variation can be grouped into two major classes: common causes and special causes.

Voice of the customer–Feedback obtained on customers' needs, wants, and expectations.

Voice of the process–Feedback obtained from performance indicators generated within the process (for example, measures of process performance).

Selected Bibliography

Aitchison, J., Jr., and J. A. C. Brown. 1957. *The lognormal distribution.* New York: Cambridge University Press.

Akao, Yoji, ed. 1990. *Quality function deployment.* Cambridge, Mass.: Productivity Press.

Automotive Industry Action Group. 1993. *Failure mode and Eeffect analysis.* Southfield, Mich.: AIAG.

Baldwin, S., F. H. Hare, Jr., and F. E. McGovern, eds. 1992. *The preparation of a product liability case,* 2d ed. Boston: Little Brown and Company.

Bass, L. March 1993. Cumulative supplement to *Products liability: design and manufacturing defects.* Colorado Springs, Colo.: Shepard's/McGraw-Hill.

Bechtel Power Corporation. 1978. *Reliability engineering methods: No. 2.1 failure mode and effects analysis.* Ann Arbor, Mich.: Ann Arbor Power Division.

Blanchard, B. S., and E. E. Lowery. 1969. *Maintainability: Principles and practices.* New York: McGraw-Hill.

Blanchard, B. S., and W. I. Fabrycky. 1981. *Systems engineering and analysis.* Englewood Cliffs, N.J.: Prentice Hall.

Box, G. E. P., W. G. Hunter, and J. S. Hunter. 1978. *Statistics for experimenters.* New York: John Wiley and Sons.

Bralia, J. 1986. *Product design for manufacturing.* New York: McGraw-Hill.

Brush, G. G. 1988. *How to choose the proper sample size.* Vol. 12. Milwaukee: ASQC Statistics Division.

Ciery, J. 1993. Design technology: Providing fault tolerant control systems." *Technology* (Engineering Society of Detroit) (July).

Crook, D. L. 1979. "Method of Determining Reliability Screens for the Time Dependent Dielectric Breakdown." *Proceedings 1979 Int. Rel. Phys. Symp.* 1.

Davich, B. 1993. Reliability statistics: An introduction. *ASQC Statistics: Division Newsletter* (September).

Davis, D. J. 1952. An analysis of some failure data." *Journal of the American Statistical Association.*

DeGreene, K. G. 1970. Human factors. In *Systems psychology.* New York: McGraw-Hill.

Dhillon, B. S. 1981. Network reliability evaluation—application of bathtub failure rate curve. *IEEE Transactions on Reliability.* R. 21.

Drenick, R. F. 1960. The failure law of complex equipment." *J. Society Ind. Appl. Math.* 8.

Duncan, A. J. 1986. *Quality control and industrial statistics,* 5th ed. Homewood, Ill.: Richard D. Irwin.

Eades, R. W. 1993. *Jury instructions on product liability,* 2d ed. Charlottesville, Va.: The Michie Company.

Esaklul, K. A., ed. 1992. *Handbook of case histories in failure analysis.* Vol. 1. Materials Park, Ohio: ASM International.

Feigenbaum, A. V. 1983. *Total quality control,* 3d. ed. New York: McGraw-Hill.

Ford Motor Co. 1972. *Reliability methods: design verification and production validation. module IX.* Dearborn, Mich.: Reliability Office, North American Automotive Operations.

———. 1972. *Reliability methods: failure mode and effect analysis for processes. module XIV-A.* Dearborn, Mich.: Reliability Office, North American Automotive Operations.

———. 1972. *Reliability methods: design reviews. Module XV.* Dearborn, Mich.: Reliability Office, North American Automotive Operations.

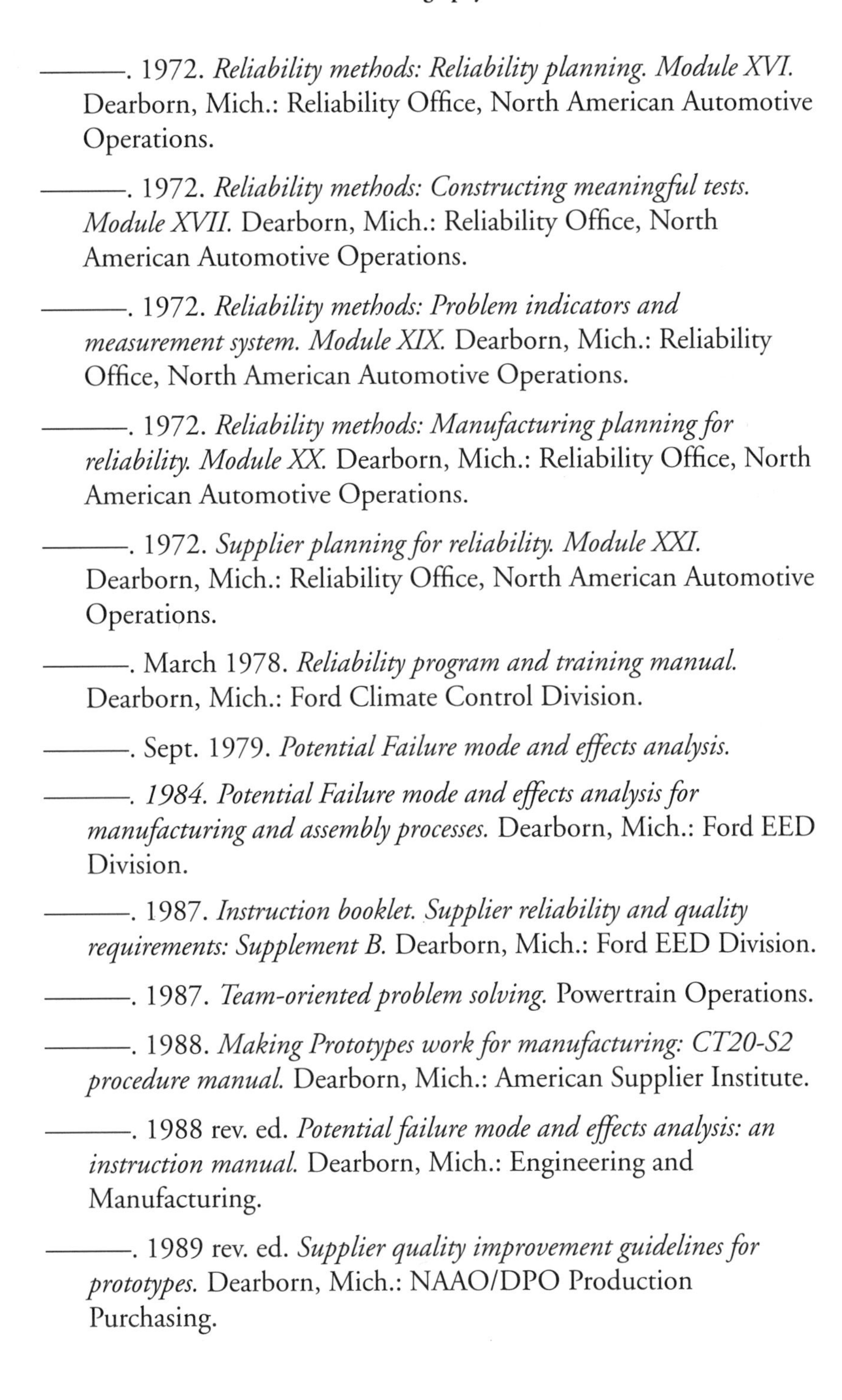

———. 1972. *Reliability methods: Reliability planning. Module XVI.* Dearborn, Mich.: Reliability Office, North American Automotive Operations.

———. 1972. *Reliability methods: Constructing meaningful tests. Module XVII.* Dearborn, Mich.: Reliability Office, North American Automotive Operations.

———. 1972. *Reliability methods: Problem indicators and measurement system. Module XIX.* Dearborn, Mich.: Reliability Office, North American Automotive Operations.

———. 1972. *Reliability methods: Manufacturing planning for reliability. Module XX.* Dearborn, Mich.: Reliability Office, North American Automotive Operations.

———. 1972. *Supplier planning for reliability. Module XXI.* Dearborn, Mich.: Reliability Office, North American Automotive Operations.

———. March 1978. *Reliability program and training manual.* Dearborn, Mich.: Ford Climate Control Division.

———. Sept. 1979. *Potential Failure mode and effects analysis.*

———. *1984. Potential Failure mode and effects analysis for manufacturing and assembly processes.* Dearborn, Mich.: Ford EED Division.

———. 1987. *Instruction booklet. Supplier reliability and quality requirements: Supplement B.* Dearborn, Mich.: Ford EED Division.

———. 1987. *Team-oriented problem solving.* Powertrain Operations.

———. 1988. *Making Prototypes work for manufacturing: CT20-S2 procedure manual.* Dearborn, Mich.: American Supplier Institute.

———. 1988 rev. ed. *Potential failure mode and effects analysis: an instruction manual.* Dearborn, Mich.: Engineering and Manufacturing.

———. 1989 rev. ed. *Supplier quality improvement guidelines for prototypes.* Dearborn, Mich.: NAAO/DPO Production Purchasing.

———. April 1989. *Supplier quality improvement guidelines for production parts.* Dearborn, Mich.: NAAO/DPO Production Purchasing.

Grant, E. L., and R. S. Leavenworth. 1980. *Statistical Quality Control,* 5th ed. New York: McGraw-Hill Book.

Green, A. E., and A. J. Bourne. 1972. *Reliability technology.* New York: Wiley-Interscience.

Green, P. E. 1973. On the analysis of interactions in marketing research data. *Marketing Research* 10: 410–420.

Gumbel, E. J.1958. *Statistics of extremes.* New York: Columbia University.

Hahn, G. J., and S. S. Shapiro. 1967. *Statistical models in engineering.* New York: John Wiley and Sons.

Hall, M. A. 1993. *Formation and regulation.* Boston: Little, Brown and Company.

Hammer, W. 1980. *Product safety management and engineering.* Englewood Cliffs, N.J.: Prentice Hall.

Harry, M. J., and R. Stewart. 1988. *Six sigma mechanical design tolerancing.* Schaumburg, Ill.: Motorola.

Hjorth, U. 1980. "A reliability distribution with increasing, decreasing, constant and bath-tub shaped failure rates. *Technometrics* 22, 1.

Hollenbrook, J. J. 1977. *Failure mode and effect analysis.* Society of Automotive Engineers. No. 770740.

IEEE STD-352-1975. *IEE guide for general principles of reliability analysis of nuclear power generating station protection systems.*

Ireson, W. G. 1966. *Reliability handbook.* New York: McGraw-Hill.

Juran, J. M., ed. 1979. *Quality control handbook,* 3d ed. New York: McGraw-Hill.

Juran, J. M., and F. M. Gryna. 1980. *Quality planning and analysis.* New York: McGraw-Hill.

Kapur, K. C., and L. R. Lamberson. 1977. *Reliability in engineering design.* New York: John Wiley and Sons.

Knack, K. 1993. Prototyping with FPGAs. *ASIC & EDA* (Dec.) Los Altos, Calif.

Lloyd, D. K. 1986. Forecasting reliability growth." *Quality and reliability engineering international* 2.

Lowewenstein, P. 1994. A Formal approach. *ASIC & EDA.* (Jan.) Los Altos, Calif.

McClain, J. O., and V. R. Rao. 1974. Trade-offs and conflicts in evaluation of health systems alternatives: a methodology for analysis. *Health Services Research* 9: 35–52.

McCormick, E. J., and M. S. Sanders. 1982. *Human factors in engineering and design,* 5th ed. New York: McGraw-Hill.

Meeker, W. Q., and G. G. Hahn. *How to plan an accelerated life test.* Vol. 10. Milwaukee: ASQC Statistics Division.

MIL-HDBK-727. April 1986. *Design guidance for producibility.* Washington, D.C.: U.S. Army Material Command.

MIL-STD-471A. 1973. *Maintainability verification, demonstration, evaluation.* Washington, D.C.: Department of Defense.

MIL-STD-781C. 1981. *Reliability design qualification and production acceptance tests: exponential distribution.* Washington, D.C.: Department of Defense.

MIL-STD-1472. 1974. *Human engineering design criteria for military systems, equipment, and facilities.* Washington, D.C.: Department of Defense.

MIL-STD-2070 (AS). *Procedures for performing a failure modes, effects and criticality analysis for aeronautical dquipment.* Washington, D.C.: Department of Defense.

MIL-STD-9858A. 1963. *Quality program requirements.* Washington, D.C.: Department of Defense.

Montgomery, D. C. 1985. *Introduction to statistical quality control.* New York: John Wiley and Sons.

Moura, E. C. 1991. *How to Determine sample size and estimate failure rate in life testing,* Vol. 15. Milwaukee: ASQC Statistics Division.

Nelson, W. 1983. *How to analyze reliability data.* Vol. 6. Milwaukee: ASQC Statistics Division.

Peck, D. S. 1962. Uses of semiconductor life distributions. *Semiconductor Reliability* 2.

Phillips, J. J., and R. E. Pryor 1993. *Products liability.* Vol. 1, 2d ed., Vols. 2 and 3. Charlottesville, Va.: The Michie Company.

Pollock, S. R. 1993. Aiming Toward Flexibility." *ASIC & EDA.* (Nov.) Los Altos, Calif.

Rao, V. R., and G. N. Soutar. 1975. Subjective evaluation for product design decisions." *Decision Sciences* 6: 120–134.

Ross, P. J. 1988. *Taguchi techniques for quality engineering.* New York: McGraw-Hill.

Roy, R. 1990. *A primer on the Taguchi method.* New York: Van Ostrand Reinhold.

Scherkenbach, W. W. 1988. *The Deming route to quality and productivity.* Washington, D.C: Creep Press Books, and Milwaukee: ASQC Quality Press.

Shapiro, S. S. 1990. *How to test normality and other distributional assumptions.* Vol. 3. Milwaukee: ASQC Statistics Division.

Shingo, S. 1986. *Zero quality control: Source inspection and the poka-yoke system.* Translated by Andrew P. Dillon. Cambridge, Mass.: Productivity Press.

Vick, C. R., and C. V. Ramamoorthy. 1984. *Handbook of software engineering.* New York: Van Nostrand Reinhold.

Williams, R. 1984. Corporate policies for creation and retention of documents and their application to the defense of a product liability case. In *Product liability of manufacturers prevention and defence.* Colorado Springs, Colo.: Practicing Law Institute.

Index

–D–

–E–

–F–